LECTURES ON
PSYCHOANALYTIC PSYCHIATRY

LECTURES ON

PSYCHOANALYTIC

PSYCHIATRY

A. A. BRILL, Ph.B., M.D.

ALFRED A. KNOPF · NEW YORK 1947

THIS IS A BORZOI BOOK

PUBLISHED BY ALFRED A. KNOPF, INC.

Copyright 1946 by Alfred A. Knopf, Inc.

PUBLISHED JULY 11, 1946

SECOND PRINTING, FEBRUARY, 1947

Published simultaneously in Canada by The Ryerson Press

TO THE STATE HOSPITAL PHYSICIANS

who bear the brunt of curing
and alleviating mental ailments;
in whose ranks I served and to
whom these lectures were first
addressed.

INTRODUCTION

THESE LECTURES were first given in 1924 in the old
Pathological Institute (Ward's Island) and were then repeated
annually, from 1929 to 1943 in the New York State Psychiatric
Institute as part of the postgraduate courses in Neurology and
Psychiatry at the College of Physicians and Surgeons, Columbia
University. The object of this course was to show how Freud's
new concepts were developed from 1893 [1] to 1939 [2] and how
they were successively applied to clinical psychiatry.

For the first fourteen years of his psychoanalytic career,
Freud stood alone surrounded by a skeptical and hostile world.
His theories of the neuroses which he formulated during this
period of "splendid isolation" were rejected and derided by the
neurologists and psychiatrists of his time. However, "In 1907,"
he states, "the situation changed at one stroke, contrary to all
expectations. It appeared that psychoanalysis had unobtru-
sively awakened interest and had gained some friends, and that
there were even some scientific workers who were ready to
admit their allegiance to it. A communication from Bleuler had
already acquainted me with the fact that my works were
studied and applied in Burghölzli." [3]

In 1907 I joined the group of Bleuler's assistants which was
later known as the Zurich School of Psychiatry, and which in
my opinion was mainly responsible for changing the old descriptive psychiatry into the dynamic science of today. Having amply described these changes elsewhere, [4] I will merely

[1] Breuer and Freud: "The Psychic Mechanisms of Hysterical Phenomena," *Studies in Hysteria,* translated by A. A. Brill, p. 1, Monograph
Series.

[2] Freud: *Moses and Monotheism,* translated by Katherine Jones, Alfred
A. Knopf, New York.

[3] Freud: *Basic Writings,* "History of Psychoanalytic Movement," p.
947, translated by A. A. Brill, Modern Library, 1939.

[4] For a description of the Zurich School and the application of psychoanalysis to psychiatry see Brill: *Freud's Contribution to Psychiatry,*
W. W. Norton, 1944.

repeat that the study and treatment of the mind have been completely revolutionized since Bleuler opened the portals of his clinic to psychoanalysis.

We are now in the midst of a new psychiatric era, psychic anomalies are no longer shrouded in horror and mystery. Terms like "lunatic" and "insane asylum" have as completely disappeared from psychiatric parlance as the outmoded theories and institutions of the past centuries. The younger psychiatrists no longer consider mental ailments as puzzling and awe-inspiring phenomena, but rather as new books on the problems of psychic adjustment.

By virtue of their sensitiveness, neurotics and psychotics succumb to the same trials and tribulations that are part and parcel of every person's struggle for existence, and studied psychoanalytically, no sharp distinction between them and so-called normals can be discerned. Only in extreme cases can normal be distinctly separated from abnormal. Indeed it has been charged that our case histories read more like novels, like romances, than psychiatric anamneses. This is quite true, but it must not be forgotten that the structure of a neurosis or psychosis represents pathetic human documents of the struggle for supremacy between the most primitive and most ideal components of mankind, and that in recording such conflicts even briefly, one must give at least some of the tragicomic fluctuations of mental adjustment. It is hoped, however, that these case histories will serve to remove the stigmata that still adhere to mental maladies.

A. A. BRILL

February 1946

LECTURES ON
PSYCHOANALYTIC PSYCHIATRY

LECTURE I

TOPICS :

LADIES and gentlemen:

I am not going to try to make psychoanalysts out of you. You are supposed to be psychiatrists of experience, and the fact is that you do not need to be psychoanalysts in order to be good psychiatrists.

But, as you will presently hear, psychoanalysis has markedly influenced the course of psychiatry during the last fifty-five years or so, just as it has modified and "rewritten" all the other branches of the mental sciences. Psychoanalysis took the pure descriptive psychiatry of the German school—which was practiced when I first entered the service in this state—and changed it into our modern interpretative psychiatry. Nowadays every patient is like a new fascinating book: if you are interested in present-day psychiatry, you will want to turn over the chapters; you will love to sit down and talk to the patient.

But formerly that was impossible. Before psychoanalysis injected life into it, psychiatry was a dry, monotonous subject. I feel that you, as psychiatrists, should have a good knowledge of how psychoanalysis effected that change. You do not need to go through all the abstruse stuff that you will find in psychoanalytic literature. In the first place, you will not understand it; and in the second place, it is absolutely useless in your work. In this course I intend to give you a sort of orientation in the relation between interpretative psychiatry and psychoanalysis.

I am presumptuous enough to feel that I can present such a course to you because I grew up, as it were, with this whole movement. It is now over forty-four years since Dr. Adolf Meyer became director of the New York Psychiatric Institute, then called the New York Pathological Institute, and located on Ward's Island. I was trained by Dr. Meyer for the position of pathologist—or perhaps better, neuropathologist—and I served in that capacity for about two years before turning to clinical psychiatry. Then, in the fall of 1907, I became interested in psychoanalysis—accidentally, as probably everything in life is accidental. In that year I went to Bleuler's clinic, where I first became acquainted with Freud's work. Bleuler is dead and Freud is dead, but their works and their influence have been left with us. Whatever happens to psychiatry in the future, the Bleuler-Freud epoch will always be recalled as momentous. Certainly it will take a long time before psychiatry will again experience the impetus and the evaluation to which it was subjected during the scientific lives of these two men.

I watched the evolution of psychiatry during all that period. When you read psychiatric textbooks written within the last two decades, you find that many of them do not even mention psychoanalysis. Yet, if you know the subject, you will discover that they nevertheless contain a lot of material taken from Freud. Of course, there are a number of reasons for this.

Psychoanalytic Psychiatry

Some people do not like to acknowledge that they have gotten anything from anyone. (That is particularly true of scientists!) Others feel that there will be prejudices against their works if they mention psychoanalysis. Well, it does not make any difference to us. After all, we are not interested in putting this or that word or personality on the map. We want to enable those who are interested in mental diseases to study the nature and origin of mental diseases. It is enough that psychoanalysis is the best instrument for that purpose. From my own experience, I feel that up to its advent only a few very gifted people were really studying the mind in any way that could be called adequate.

When I began to study psychiatry in 1903, the most advanced work was that of the descriptive German school—notably Kraepelin. I always like to talk about the status of psychiatry in New York State during those years because I believe that modern American psychiatry started right here and gradually spread to the rest of the country. At that time, Kraepelin's name shone resplendently throughout the world. It was soon after he had given us his two great entities—dementia praecox and manic-depressive psychosis. If you read the earlier English, American, German, Italian, French, or any other literature before him you will find many interesting writers; some of them had brilliant ideas, but most of them still groped in the dark. They still talked of masturbation insanity and many other disturbances that were later found to be merely symptoms. Kraepelin's two entities represented a distinct step forward. They were more or less combatted in his time and since; yet there is no doubt that they do exist. In developing them, Kraepelin justly earned the right to be called the "father of modern psychiatry."

Dr. Adolf Meyer, who had only recently come to the New York Institute, began to acquaint us with everything that was new in psychiatry at that time. He taught us mainly what I would call Kraepelinian psychiatry, into which he injected many of his own modifications. He started by giving us abstracts of Kraepelin, Ziehen, Wernicke, and the other psychiatrists active at that time. He distributed the abstracts to all the members of the hospital staffs and urged us to write case histories according to that scheme.

The younger members (including myself) took easily to Meyer's new plan. Those few of us who could read German got the works in the original; and we were all pleased by the fact that at last we could describe a case properly, follow its psychological attributes, and come to some conclusions about the prognosis. Meyer, like Kraepelin (who was a pupil of Wundt) looked at the patient from a normal psychological viewpoint. We were taught to describe the patient's attitude and manner, his anthropological make-up; we examined all phases of his orientation, memory, judgment, insight, etc. Last, but not least, the psychiatric examination was always preceded by a thorough physical and neurological examination.

To realize what a radical departure this was, you must go back to the files of your hospitals around 1900 or earlier, and look at the case records. As a rule they were very simple, and a typical history would read something like this: "Patient admitted in June 1885. He is dull, stupid, and demented." A few years later a new doctor happened to come on the scene, and his entry read: "Patient is stupid, dull, and demented." A note written a few years later read: "Patient continues as above," or "Patient is stupid, demented and dull." (It is remarkable how many permutations and combinations they made of those three words!) The whole record, sometimes covering a period of thirty years, would occupy no more than three quarters of a page. It would usually end up: "Patient died suddenly. Diagnosis: Chronic dementia." If you think I am joking, please refer back to some of those case histories; with a few variations like "excited, agitated, and noisy," but with the same ingenious combinations, you will find just that.

The younger men, as I said, were glad to follow Dr. Meyer's new scheme. But most of the hospital doctors were old-timers, and they were very much upset by it. For years they had been used to getting up not before eight o'clock, breakfasting leisurely, and sitting around with their feet up on the desks until the mail came in. They would then read the morning papers and do a few necessary things. At around eleven they would walk through the wards, "make the rounds," and then wait for lunch. After lunch they would take a snooze, and those who had the vigor then spent most of the afternoon playing tennis. It was a mighty easy life until Meyer appeared, and naturally they felt outraged about all those innovations. How they hated Meyer! That he survived destroyed the little confidence I had in the efficacy of maledictions. But the older men were gradually eliminated. The younger generation recognized the value of what Meyer taught them and has followed him since—even though a mental examination is now quite a different thing from what it was then.

Meyer inaugurated several other wholesome practices which have been followed by all the directors who succeeded him. He visited every hospital himself, gave talks, became acquainted with the members of the staffs, and discussed cases presented by them. He also started the custom of asking all the state hospitals to send selected members for courses in the Pathological Institute. I believe that I was in the first group to take these courses, and I can tell you that they were very valuable in many ways. Dr. Meyer not only interested us in the mental aspects of the patient, but also in the organic factors of psychiatry. To that end we were asked to read and abstract the literature of this or that psychic or organic topic, and then read it to the class. The discussions were very fruitful and at times inspiring. Later, when it was decided that each hospital should have a pathologist, I was also selected for that course. After three months' intensive training in laboratory technique, I returned to the Central Islip State Hospital and organized the pathological laboratory.

That experience was valuable for me. I did many autopsies and often used to take interesting specimens to the Institute for further examination and study. But after about two years I got tired of that kind of work, and I turned to clinical psychiatry. I was first a junior assistant in the reception service and later had full charge of it. Here I followed in every way Meyer's scheme of examination. It so happened that the metropolitan hospitals were all filled to capacity, so we received all the Manhattan and the Bronx patients for over a year.

There was plenty of material and I was very interested; and, if I say it myself, I worked hard. I had a stenographer who took notes while I gave every newly admitted patient a thorough neurological and mental examination. The average case history ran from twelve to sixteen typewritten pages, and as psychiatric histories go, they were quite complete. Whenever possible, I went into the *vita anteacta* of the patient, laying stress on the normal and abnormal psychic development; and the examination, as well as the subsequent observations of those cases that I kept in my service, left little to be desired. The treatment was purely symptomatic. It was before Dr. Cotton came out with his focal infection surgery, and before Dr. Dennison claimed to cure tabes and paresis by injecting a three per cent solution of boric acid into the patient's urethra. Indeed it was before all the wonderful panaceas which have come into vogue since then.

After a few years as clinical psychiatrist I got tired of this work too. For what could one do with this mode of procedure? We classified and made a diagnosis, and then there was nothing to be done except watchful waiting. It was the same everywhere. At the Vanderbilt Clinic, where I began to work while I was still in the hospital, we had mixtures designated as tonics and sedatives which we gave to the patients—the former if the patient felt "dopey," a sedative if he felt "nervous." Later, after I returned from Bleuler's clinic and became a regular assistant at the Vanderbilt Clinic, I appreciated how illogical such treatment was.

At all events I became discouraged after a few years of routine work in the reception service of the hospital. I said to myself: "It is all very well to write, or rather, to dictate these case histories while you are in the hospital. But if you want to get married and leave, that will be of no avail. You will not be able to start in with your own secretary; you won't be able to reel off a long history and then send the patient to Ward G or D. You will have to do something tangible for the patient." But—there was nothing to be done with the techniques at my disposal.

As I have always been an avid reader of the literature of

other countries, I found that in France, especially in Paris, much attention was given to what we called the borderline cases of mental diseases—namely, hysterias and psychasthenias. I said to myself: "Those are the kind of cases you will get in private practice, and you had better learn something about them."

I began to study them. Hypnotism and the Dubois method of persuasion were then much talked about as forms of treatment. I read Forel's book on hypnotism and Dubois's book (which was translated into English in 1905 by White and Jelliffe) and I began to hypnotize some of my hospital patients. It was not a very encouraging beginning. To study new methods from books is not easy, and there was no one near me to direct me. Hypnotism, you know, is always fascinating to a young man, and it fits in especially well with the temperament of those who select psychiatry as their specialty. Hypnotism is the highest expression of the omnipotence of thought: like a god, you can make everyone do what you want! Most doctors like it; it certainly appealed to me. But there were very few borderline cases in the hospitals. Occasionally I would run across mild praecoxes who were through their acute episode and became accessible to treatment; or I would find mild depressive patients, or some who were in the stage of recovery from a manic or depressive attack. These were accessible, and some could be hypnotized. Few, if any, psychoneurotics were to be found in the hospital at that time. As a matter of fact, I think it is no different today, even though you sometimes diagnose them that way. I am speaking, of course, of real psychoneurotics, of persons who suffer from hysteria, compulsions, or anxieties, but who nevertheless carry on. Such patients do not wish to go to hospitals, and they never stay there, even if they are prevailed upon to try it. Early in my experience I concluded that anyone who wanted to remain in a state hospital, or even in the best private institution, was schizophrenic. I am still of the same opinion.

Be that as it may, I practiced hypnotism on as many patients as I could select. On some it worked well, but on others it did not. I tried once to hypnotize a young woman. I went through

[7

the usual formula. "You are beginning to be drowsy. Your eyelids are drooping. You are falling asleep. You are asleep." But the young woman looked up quickly and said: "No, doctor, I am not asleep." Well, you feel like five cents when that happens to you. Being an egotist, I decided I could not stand such unpleasant contradiction. Nevertheless, the poor girl refused to fall asleep!

In my dilemma I went to see a well-known hypnotist named Dr. Quackenbos. This man was connected with Columbia University, and the daily papers at the time were full of the wonderful cures he effected by means of hypnotism. He was a nice, gentlemanly fellow, and he quickly showed me where my trouble was. "Of course, your patients do not want to fall asleep," he said; "you are following the wrong methods." He picked up a couple of small, familiar-looking bottles. "Just give them a stiff dose of chloral or paraldehyde—they will sleep." He had a number of little cubicles in his office where patients were snoring away; and, as demonstration, he walked from one to the other making the proper suggestions. Dr. Quackenbos assured me that it worked perfectly.

Well, I did not try Dr. Quackenbos's method. All our patients in the hospitals at that time used to get chloral and paraldehyde by the bucket; and since the drugs left distinct after-effects, the patients would refuse to take them. At the time I thought the doctor's method was sheer quackery, and I could see why people looked upon him with a certain amount of suspicion. But this was not justified. Dr. Quackenbos did the best he could, and in fact, was something of a pioneer. Like Boris Sidis, Morton Prince, and other men of that period, he was groping for some means of helping the patient. Hypnotism had its good and bad results but effected no cures of a permanent nature—we shall see why, later. But it was at least an interesting attempt in an otherwise barren field.

In June 1907, I finally decided to go to Paris, which, I believed, was the center of psychotherapy. I was sure that everything relating to the treatment of borderline cases would be revealed to me there. At someone's suggestion, I entered one of the big hospitals, Bicêtre, under Pierre Marie. To my great surprise, I discovered that hypnotism and suggestion were already outmoded there. "If you remove one symptom," they told me, "another takes its place."

They were enthusiastic, instead, about a new treatment called the "isolation method." This was nothing more than a modified form of the rest cure originated in this country by Dr. Weir-Mitchell. It consisted simply of isolating the patient in a little room and allowing no one—not even the doctors—to talk to him. The patient was well fed, and usually received no medication—but was kept, as it were, incommunicado. After a few weeks of this, the patient was supposed to get well.

I watched some of those patients until I could speak French fluently enough; then I broke the rules and engaged one of them, a young woman, in conversation. She had already been in the hospital for several weeks, she told me and added: "I am going home soon." I discovered that this was her fourth or fifth visit. She liked being away in a nice, comfortable place, free of all household duties. Each time she would remain until she got tired of being alone. Then, after informing the doctor that she was well, she would go home.

I could not see the rationale of such treatment. From this and other cases, I felt that the isolation method was no better than hypnotism, which had been given up. I was terribly disappointed, moreover, in the whole attitude of French psychiatry, which was very backward in comparison with what we had in New York. The French were extremely chauvinistic. They still classified according to Pinel, and refused to have anything to do with anything that came from the German school. One or two of the men whom I met did read Kraepelin; but these were exceptional, and they read him only in secret. Pierre Marie himself was a brilliant, charming man and an excellent neurologist who was especially interested in aphasia. The first problem he suggested was that I study epileptoid attacks in a case of acromegaly. When I told him that I had come to Paris to study borderline cases, he said something to the effect that I could learn that any time.

I was utterly discouraged, and believe it or not, I thought seriously of becoming a nose and throat specialist. I wrote to my former teacher, Dr. Frederick Peterson, and told him of my disappointments. He came to Paris shortly after and urged me not to give up psychiatry, which he knew I liked. "Why don't you go to Zurich—to Bleuler and Jung?" he said. "They are doing that Freud stuff over there. I think that you would like it." His surmise proved correct; I did like it in Zurich. I remained there for about a year, and then returned to New York. From that time dates the beginning of psychoanalysis in the United States.

It was early in August 1907, that I made my first visit to Bleuler's clinic in Burghölzli. Before then, I had run across Freud's name only once, as far as I remembered. During a visit to Europe in 1905, chance threw me into the company of a young man, an Austrian army officer. I met him in Liège, and we became quite friendly, traveling around together for a while. When we separated, I mentioned that I might return to Europe in a year or two for some special work. "Well," he said, "why don't you come to Vienna, to Freud?" When I asked him who Freud was, he said: "I don't know anything about him; but he must be somebody because he has so many opponents!" Mind you—this was a lieutenant of artillery in the Austrian army!

Well, I was not much impressed by the physical aspects of Burghölzli. It was so different from our own new and well-equipped institutions. But after attending the first staff meeting, I felt inspired. The way they looked at the patient, the way they examined him, was almost like a revelation. They did not simply classify the patient. They took his hallucinations, one by one, and tried to determine what each meant, and just why the patient had these particular delusions. In other words, instead of registering phenomena, they went into the dynamic elements which produce those phenomena. To me, that was altogether new and revealing.

I had to return to Paris to finish my report on the acromegaly case at Bicêtre, and I did not begin my work at Burghölzli until a month later, when I joined the group of men—Jung, Abraham, Meier, Riklin, Binswanger and others—who were working with Bleuler. Jung was the first assistant and at that time a very ardent and pugnacious Freudian. You could not express any doubt about Freud's views without arousing his ire. Riklin had just resigned. After I had been there about six weeks, Abraham resigned, and I was appointed in his place. During my stay there, Kraepelin came once or twice and spent a week end in the clinic. All of this was very interesting and very exciting.

The importance of the work done there cannot be overestimated. Bleuler was the first psychiatrist to recognize the validity of Freud's claims, and to open his clinic to psychoanalytic experimentation. Bleuler did not accept all of Freud's teachings at first—not by a long shot! Jung, as I have said, gave the impression that he was fully convinced of everything at that time. But Bleuler, while he agreed with Freud on psychogenesis, was still loath to accept the infantile sexuality. It was not until later that he changed his mind about it, becoming convinced, as he told me, by observing his own children. I believe that is the best way: everyone should investigate for himself. I do not ask anyone to accept Freud right off; those who do so are not doing justice to him. What you accept on faith you can also drop on faith.

Bleuler went about it in a strictly scientific manner. "There is more psychology in one page of Freud," he said, "than in some voluminous textbooks. It is easy enough to make fun of him; but what we should do is to examine Freud's concepts and either confirm or disprove them scientifically."

When I joined his group, they had already been working for about a year on their investigations. The object was to determine whether there really was an unconscious, as Freud claimed, and whether Freud's views on sex in the neuroses were true. To do this, Bleuler and Jung devised their famous association experiments. Now, psychiatrists had delved into association work before this. Wundt, Kraepelin, Sommers, Bonhoeffer, and others followed Wundt's experiments, but in a relatively superficial and entirely different way. They discovered merely that certain types of patients gave certain types of responses. Thus they found that a catatonic will either not answer or will perseverate in his associations, while other patients either responded this way or that way. That was interesting, but it got nowhere.

The Zurich investigators did it quite differently. They were not interested in what the patient said, but in what the patient *meant*. Those of you who would like a fuller account of this work should read Jung's *Diagnostic Association Studies*, which appeared also in English, and his Worcester Lectures, which I translated.[1] Here, I shall give you only a brief summary of the method.

We had a list of one hundred words, which had been carefully selected to touch upon all the ordinary objects of life, and we used this list on every person tested. We told the test person to answer as quickly as possible, and to say anything he pleased, whether it seemed to be an intelligent answer or not. We all worked with stop watches registering one fifth of a second (I still have mine) and we timed the response. The tests were printed on a chart something like this:

Stimulus	Reaction	Time	Repetition
Bread	Butter	2.3	Light
Sun	Elephant	4.5	. . .

We had found, after long investigation, that the average person took 2.4 seconds to respond to a word that was indifferent to him. If it took the test person longer to react, it showed that some emotional factor had been aroused by the stimulus word and impeded the reaction or response to it. In that case, we would underline it as a *complex indicator*. Then, after going through the list, we would repeat the process without registering the reaction time, but asking the test person to give the same answers as before. If an answer was different on this second trial, it showed another emotional disturbance, and again we marked it as a complex indicator.

The test, thus, was made with the object of finding the complex. The word "complex" originated in Burghölzli, and it simply means a past, repressed, emotional experience. As I

[1] Carl C. Jung: "The Association Method." the *American Journal of Psychology*, April 1910.

frequently hear it, the word is now greatly misused, and you get a lot of nonsense like: "He has a money-complex," or a "father-complex." The populace always uses things wrongly; they broaden terms to such an extent that all meaning is lost. A few years ago, one of our leading dictionaries sent me a long definition of a *complex*. It took up more than half a page, and I was asked to give my opinion of it. Well, I was there when the term was devised, but I assure you I did not know what that long definition was all about. In my reply, therefore, I suggested that they should also put in my definition—namely, a complex is a *past, repressed, emotional experience*. That is all there is to it. To be sure, I have not yet discussed the meaning of repression, and so you may not know that anything repressed is unconscious. We shall return to this later.

At the end of our test, then, we would have five, or ten, or any other number of complex indicators. We would take these words and ask the test person what this word or complex brought to his mind. We tried to do, in other words, what Freud did with his continuous or "free" associations. The whole thing was very remarkable. Invariably we would find that the complex indicator uncovered something unconscious —something which went way back to an experience long forgotten by the test person. At first he might say: "Nothing comes to my mind." But after repeated urging, he would recall some event which he had not thought of for years.

We actually discovered all kinds of situations which our test persons begged us not to reveal. You see, we did not confine ourselves to patients, but tested anyone and everyone we could get. For instance, we often used one of the hospital attendants as a test person, paying him about a dollar to go through each experiment. One day, through the associations, he revealed that he had once been charged with murder, and had served a long prison term. He was a very good attendant, and no one had ever known this about him.

We found scores of things like this, and they convinced us that Freud was right—that there is an unconscious, that things are repressed, that they can be evoked sometimes by a chance association without apparent rhyme or reason. To cite a more recent example: I had a patient who commuted from West-chester on the train. One morning he arrived at my office in a very irritable mood. He had had a quarrel, it seems, with his good friend, Jim. They were accustomed to coming in to-gether every morning, and the first one to get on the train would save a seat for the other. Jim had arrived last and had asked my patient to hang up his coat for him. "What do you mean—hang up your coat!" my patient replied in a sudden outburst of anger. More words followed, and the quarrel ended with Jim saying: "You can go to Hell!"

In telling me this, my patient said that he had objected to Jim's request because it had not been framed: "*Please* hang up my coat." Of course he added that he knew it was all nonsense and could not understand why he had become so angry over a triviality.

I could have let it go. But, as it turned out, my patient also brought me a dream for analysis that morning, and in the dream he told me that one of his uncles had committed suicide by hanging. Well, the patient came of a manic-depressive family, and he did not attach much importance to what he was telling me. But, to me it became clear at once why he had quar-reled with his friend. He was a sensitive man, and the moment he heard the word "hang" in "Hang up my coat," he became extremely angry, without knowing why. The word had aroused the unconscious complex. In the association experi-ments, "hang" would have been a complex indicator. Further-more, there was what Bleuler called a *complexbereitschaft*, a complex readiness or sensitiveness, for the hanging episode was contained in the dream, which he was to report to me later. Many an unexplained emotional explosion is caused by such complex-sensitiveness.

I regret very much that so little attention is paid nowadays to the subject of associations in mental medicine. The laws of association gave us the greatest sort of conviction about the hidden meaning of mental processes, and they were also ex-tremely useful in diagnosis. We learned, for example, that epileptic reactions were different from those of normals and other neurotics, and with our association tests we could discern an epileptic type even though the patient had never had epilepsy. Mental deficiency of the mildest type can also be shown by the association experiment. Such tests are very definite and very characteristic, and I am convinced that if you would do associations with patients as a routine, you would learn more about mental processes than by ordinary examinations. I feel that the present generation of psychiatrists is not sufficiently versed in psychopathology, just because they do not give enough time to the patient. But if you want to be a clinician, if you want to understand your patients, you will have to know the law of normal and abnormal associations.

In any case, the work of the Zurich investigators gave clinical demonstration of the fact that Freud was correct in his assumptions. It proved that, as in the neurosis, there is a psychogenesis in the psychoses: that every hallucination and delusion is based on something in the life of the patient. But long before, in 1896, Freud had reported a case of what he called "paranoid-dementia" (the patient undoubtedly was a paranoid type of praecox) in which he analyzed her delusions and hallucinations.[2] Jung then took a chronic case of dementia praecox, a certain Fräulein Staub, who had been in the hospital at Burghölzli for many years. (I knew the case very well.) After spending a lot of time with her, Jung fully corroborated Freud's discoveries, and embodied the results in his book, *The Psychology of Dementia Praecox*, which was translated by me.[3] It was, I might say, the first translation that I made in the field of psychoanalysis, and it was the first English book on psychoanalysis to be published here. In this work Jung showed that the Freudian mechanisms are all found in dementia praecox just as they are found in hysteria. *The Psychology of Dementia Praecox* is the best psychiatric work Jung ever did in his life; it is a classic which you should all read. I say this not only because Jung corroborated Freud's views, but because the book gives all the literature on dementia praecox up to 1907 and contains everything worth knowing about dementia praecox that had been written up to that time.

[2] *Neurologisches Zentralblatt*, 1896, No. 10.

[3] Monograph Series, Journal of Nervous & Mental Diseases Publishing Co.

[15

I say, without much fear of contradiction, that since then little has been done on the elucidation of this subject. Lately we have heard a lot about the new efforts made to stifle dementia praecox by shocking the patient out of it. Now, I am interested in anything that seems to offer help in the psychoses, but I believe the recent shock therapies, except for the new techniques, offer very little that is new. If you read the old psychiatric literature you will find that insane patients were subjected to shock therapy long ago by means of beating, violent swinging, operations and other procedures; and its votaries have reported cures and improvements through each and every one of these methods. Moreover, we always knew that a shock of any kind would influence even the most recalcitrant patient and bring about some modification of the symptoms and behavior. Long ago it was found that chronic patients would often improve simply by transferring them from one ward to another.

In my own experience, long before I ever heard the name Freud, I reported the case of a patient, a chronic paranoiac, who suddenly developed peritonitis, with a temperature of 104. When we operated on him (I was the anesthetist, by the way) he miraculously became well. During all the period from the beginning of this illness until some time after the operation, he seemed perfectly well. It was the most amazing thing I had ever seen: this man—who for years had been there as a chronic, inaccessible paranoid schizophrenic—now talked sensibly. I explained it by saying that when it was a matter of life or death, he gave up his delusions and returned to reality. We were so encouraged that after presenting him to the staff meeting we decided to send him home as cured. But when it came to the day of his scheduled departure, I found him standing there in the same place, in the same attitude, and acting as peculiarly as he had before the operation. I believe that the effect of insulin and the other shock therapies is the same as the results claimed for the other treatments. That I am not the only one holding this view is attested by the report of a Swiss committee of psychiatric experts, who thoroughly examined the results of insulin and metrazol therapy in schizophrenia for a period of six years. They maintain that whereas the duration of the attack may sometimes be shortened—which is also possible by other means—a real curative effect on the schizophrenic process from these medications cannot be established.[4]

I cannot imagine how a drug like metrazol or insulin, or any other shock therapy, can throw much light on the nature and origin of schizophrenia—except to cover it up. Moreover, so far I have not seen a single case that was *cured* by shock therapy. You may tell me that some patients improve and leave the hospital. But do not forget—we have seen that before, and anyone who speaks of a real "cure" in this connection is just talking through his hat.

My feeling is that schizophrenia is a peculiar mental evolution which develops in our patients long before we see them in the hospital or in private practice. We see the patients after they have fully developed the disease, when they are usually unmanageable, when even the parents admit that there is something wrong with them. What produces it is a question. Kraepelin at first thought dementia praecox develops as a result of the stress of civilization at the pubescent period of life. He reasoned that people who live in primitive, more simple environments are probably immune to this malady. After traveling in the Orient and finding the same disease, with the same symptoms, as prevalent there as in Europe, he changed his mind. He then concluded that dementia praecox must be a very old, constitutionally determined malady which cannot be produced by the stress of modern life. But if you examine those patients who are more accessible, you will always find that for a long time they have suffered from many mental and emotional conflicts of some sort. They invariably suffer shipwreck when they begin to struggle with sex problems. (We do not mean just sexual intercourse; we mean adjustment to the love life in general.)

Recently I saw a young man of twenty-five who, after having done well for three years in college, suddenly began

[4] "Schizophrenie und Militärdienst," Schweiz, *Arch. f. Neur. u. Psychiat.*, Bd. XLIV, 2 (Zurich, 1939).

to act strangely. Thus, when taking his chemistry examination he answered none of the questions, but instead tore out a page of the textbook and sent it in an envelope to the professor. For some time it was noticed that he became increasingly indifferent and finally stopped attending classes altogether, and that he sat in his room for days without saying a word. The parents at first thought it was all due to laziness, and upbraided him for it, and it was not until he became pugnacious that they sought psychiatric help. According to the parents, the patient began to show this strange behavior after he went through an abortive love affair which they strenuously opposed.

Another case: I saw a young man of twenty-three, who had been a brilliant student in college. He was about to receive his Phi Beta Kappa, when all of a sudden he refused to take the final examination. He told his parents, who were very anxious for his success, that he did this to spite them. He later entered his father's business, but he merely sat in the office, did what he was told, and showed no interest in anything. He never wished to go out or to meet anyone. About a year later, when I saw him, he said that he resented his mother's ambition for his success. Any young man might have had such feelings, but only a schizophrenic would react to it in this manner. In neither of these cases could I find any hallucinations or delusions. They both showed a general emotional deterioration in the form of indifference to the world around them. Here, I learned that the patient had always been very guarded by his mother, but despite this he began to make coarse advances to an elderly servant. The latter not only discouraged it but reported the matter to his mother, who scolded the patient for it.

This apathy was considered by Kraepelin as the most characteristic symptom of dementia praecox, and everyone who wrote about this malady dwelt particularly on this emotional deterioration. But, as time went on, many psychiatrists found that not all cases of dementia praecox showed this central symptom in the manner described by Kraepelin. Dr. Meyer was one of the first psychiatrists who, while stressing the emotional factors, nevertheless modified Kraepelin's classifications. In his abstracts of Kraepelin and in his lectures, Meyer maintained that not every case is either a clean-cut dementia praecox or a manic-depressive psychosis, and that some cases have something of both entities. He therefore added two sub-groups—"allied to dementia praecox," and "allied to manic-depressive psychosis." I believe that this was a happy modification, for every psychiatrist soon finds out that there are hardly two cases which run true to type. By the diagnosis "allied to dementia praecox," Dr. Meyer meant that the patient, besides being manic, also showed some of the secondary phenomena of the disease—namely, delusions and hallucinations; and by "allied to manic-depressive psychosis," he meant a schizophrenic who, instead of being dull and indifferent, showed a good affect. At least this was my understanding of Meyer's classifications.

Bleuler, who devoted more study to schizophrenia than any other psychiatrist, thoroughly elucidates the emotional factors of this disease in his book, *Affectivity, Suggestibility, Paranoia*.[5] You will learn a lot from this small, but very interesting work, and I would suggest that you read it. Bleuler, like Meyer, realized that Kraepelin's two entities often more or less merged; and he designated some of these cases as *schizoidmanics*—that is, schizophrenics with good affects. Here the prognosis is quite favorable in comparison with those whose affect is dull. The schizoid-manic patient has attacks which subside as in ordinary manics, and for a time he may be quite adjustable. Ultimately, of course, the schizophrenic process gets the upper hand, and the patient must be left in a hospital. But I have seen quite a number of such cases that maintained themselves extramurally for as long as thirty years and did quite well. On the other hand, if the affect is poor to start with, there is very little hope for any social adjustment.

Now, while men like Kraepelin, Meyer, Bleuler, and others emphasized the importance of classification and of the affectivity in diagnosis, it was not until Freud appeared that any attempt was made to understand the nature of the apathy and indifference. Every experienced psychiatrist knows that no

[5] Translated by Charles Ricksher, State Hospital Press, 1912. Cf. also Bleuler: *Dementia Praecox oder Gruppe der Schizophrenien*, Deuticke, (Wien, 1911).

matter how long a schizophrenic remains in a state of indifference, sooner or later he shows that he is far from apathetic. During my first day in the hospital my senior showed me a catatonic patient whom I was to tube-feed, and he told me a few things about him. The patient was absolutely mute, never attended to his natural needs, and rarely kept his eyes open. A few years later this patient suddenly became normal; he then reminded me of the statements made by Dr. Magness when I first saw him, and disputed some of them. In other words, the patient was not really indifferent when we thought he was; he simply had something more important within himself to think of, at that time, than participating in our conversation. Schizophrenic apathy is nothing but a temporary turning away from the outer world, as we shall show later.

In other words, not until Breuer and Freud showed the meaning of hysteria, and not until Freud then demonstrated the same in the psychoses, did we have any inkling about the meaning of symptoms. In 1893 we learned the psychogenesis of hysteria. Three years later Freud showed that the difference between hysteria and dementia praecox was only one of degree; soon thereafter he demonstrated the same thing between the neurotic and the so-called normal. In his *The Psychopathology of Everyday Life*, he showed that our ordinary faulty actions—mistakes in talking and writing, forgetting, misplacing, and other common errors—are all due to unconscious emotional disturbances, and as such show the same distortions as neurotic and psychotic symptoms. We usually dismiss such things as trivial mistakes, but Freud showed that there is no such thing as a trivial mistake without an underlying reason for it. I hope all of you will read this interesting and valuable work,[6] for here Freud demonstrates fully that the unconscious mechanisms found in the neuroses are of the same nature as those found in lapses of talking, reading, writing, and in faulty everyday acts; in other words, that there is a psychogenesis to every normal and abnormal expression.

[6] *The Basic Writings of Sigmund Freud*, edited and translated with introduction by A. A. Brill, p. 35, the Modern Library (New York, 1938).

As I said, I was fascinated by what I saw in Burghölzli. Under Jung's direction I studied *The Interpretation of Dreams*, and at the same time he taught me the technique of interpretation by analyzing my own dreams.

At that time, Freud had published only five of his books. Besides the *Studies in Hysteria*, which he wrote with Breuer — and which I hope you will all read, since it is the foundation of psychoanalysis — there was the first series of his collection of papers on the neuroses (1893–1906). Then there were *The Interpretation of Dreams* (1900), *The Psychopathology of Everyday Life* (1904), *Three Contributions to the Theory of Sex* (1905), and the book on *Wit*,[7] (1905). It was while I translated Jung's book that I also made arrangements by correspondence with Freud to be his translator. Several factors were responsible for my doing Jung's book first: I was in daily contact with him, the German edition of his work had only recently appeared, and I was then primarily interested in psychiatry — particularly in dementia praecox. When I met Freud a few months later, we arranged that I translate the works just listed. Little did I appreciate the task before me. It did not seem very difficult or very long at that time. But Freud, as you know, was very prolific. In every letter to me he would announce a new work, and the more I translated, the more books continued to appear. I could not keep up with him because I had many other things to do. And so, after translating and editing the previously-mentioned works, and a number of others — a task to which I devoted most of my leisure time during a period of more than ten years — I gave up my job as translator. In all, Freud left about fifteen large volumes. Not all of these works belong strictly to medicine or psychopathology. The book on sex is as interesting to the biologist as to the psychiatrist. The book on *Wit* and *Totem and Taboo* are of more interest to the student of culture and ethnology than to the average psychopathologist. Freud's works ranged over the field of religion, anthropology, and other non-medical subjects; yet it is literally true that through his works Freud

[7] These works form part of Freud's *Basic Writings*, etc.

rewrote the mental sciences. Before him, psychiatry meant the study and treatment of abnormal mental processes. Now psychiatry is the science which treats of the origin and development of the mind, both ontogenetically and phylogenetically; it is all-embracing. You cannot now just examine an individual and send him to a hospital. If you are interested you can find in every case the whole evolution of the human mind. That would have been impossible without Freud, and that is why psychoanalysis is so important.

I am naturally prejudiced in Freud's favor: I have been his translator and expositor since 1907. But every psychiatrist who has seriously studied his works will agree with me. Even those who still talk against him, or who are accustomed to laughing at the idea of dreams in psychiatry, are paying attention to the mechanisms of dreams and sex in their patients. As to the influence of psychoanalysis in other fields, one could talk for hours about it. In the same year that I brought psychoanalysis over here, the mental hygiene movement was launched. It was in that year that Clifford Beers published his *The Mind That Found Itself,* which I assume you have all read. From then on, all the mental hygienists became alive to the new discoveries of Freud, and without them I am sure their subsequent work could never have carried the weight it did so well. Take, for example, the child guidance movement or the field of psychiatric social work. These very important movements could not have existed if psychoanalysis had not been injected into psychiatry. Psychoanalysis has also had an enormous influence upon sociology and pedagogics. If you stop to think about it, even such a thing as the modern "personality study" would have been impossible without it. And, of course, we are wholly responsible, in a way, for the broader aspects of the modern views on sex. To show you the enormous change that has occurred over the years, I will cite an experience I had in 1908. In that year, I wrote up a case of dementia praecox that I analyzed in Zurich, and I mentioned the word "homosexual" without in any way discussing the subject itself. I sent this case record for publication to Dr. Morton Prince, the editor of *The*

Journal of Abnormal Psychology. Prince was very enthusiastic about my work, but he wrote: "There is only one word I would like you to change—the word 'homosexual.'"

Now Dr. Prince was an outstanding psychopathologist, a pioneer in this field; nevertheless, he asked me to leave out that word, which must have offended his aesthetic sense. Since then, of course, I have talked about the subject everywhere. I have even talked in churches about homosexuality, and no one seemed to be offended. You can see what tremendous changes have taken place. I think it is not incorrect, in fact, to say that we stirred up this whole continent—by "we," I mean to include such men as Ernest Jones, who brought psychoanalysis to Canada and later to England. Today Freud's works are read and studied in all the important centers of South America as well.

I do not want you to think, of course, that psychoanalysis can do everything. It has its limited application as far as therapy is concerned. But as far as study is concerned, I know of no other method that can approximate it. And in this course, I will try to show you more in detail how it changed psychiatry from a narrow, limited study into a broad science which takes in the whole gamut of human psychic development. That psychiatry is now interpretative rather than descriptive is due primarily to Bleuler, and, in this country, to Adolf Meyer, August Hoch, George H. Kirby, and others.

It is my practice at the end of each lecture to save a short period for questions and answers. I find it does a lot of good: it clears up many points, it crystallizes many impressions. There is only one difficulty about this procedure. No one wants to talk until it is almost time for me to leave, and then everyone at once tries to say something. I know that most people hate to speak up unless they think they have an intelligent question to ask. But remember, it does not have to be an intelligent question; I will make it intelligent! Just ask anything you please. As psychiatrists, you ought to know by this time that whatever the patient has to say has a meaning. So, do not waste time, and if you have anything to ask—ask!

QUESTIONS AND ANSWERS

Question : How did you get that young man, the one who went into his father's business, to come back to you?

Answer : Knowing what affectivity is, and having had psychiatric experience for thirty-eight years, I just *knew* how to manage him. I was not sure he would come; and if you think I can do that with every case, you are mistaken. It is impossible to give you the *modus operandi*, but if you get to know more about emotional "give and take" and will be willing to exert yourself, you, too, will be able to do it.

When I was in Zurich, Bleuler used to tell us that we could influence even the worst catatonics by suggestion. He gave his own sister as an example. She lived in his home in the hospital, and from my room across the hall I could see her walking to and fro monotonously all day long. Bleuler's children were all quite young, and they seemed to pay no attention to her presence. When they wanted to climb anywhere, they would use her as though she were an inanimate object, like a chair. She emanated no affect, and the children had no affective relationship with her.

Bleuler once had occasion to move her when she was in an acute state of excitement. He did not want to use force, and he thought he would try suggestion. He told us that he worked on her hour after hour, talking to her and urging her, and at last she dressed and went along with him. Bleuler cited that as evidence that you *can* do it.

I felt that I would like to make such an experiment. I was advised to try it on a female patient, but as I was in charge of the male service, Jung suggested that I could try it on one of the young women patients—a typical catatonic who had been in the hospital for about ten years. She was selected not only because she was a typical catatonic, but because she had been born and brought up in Kentucky until she was about eighteen, when she became schizophrenic. Her Swiss parents then brought her to Burghölzli, where she had remained as a semi-private patient.

It took me about three hours to succeed with that patient. I addressed her in English. I cajoled her, urged her, commanded her for hours without getting any response—always remembering Bleuler's experience. After hours of labor, she looked at me and whispered a word or two; and finally she obeyed and got up, took a shower and dressed. She remained normal for three days. During that period I spent an hour with her every morning and I did an association experiment with her. But on the fourth morning the nurse reported to me that the patient had lapsed into her former state.

I made no effort to get her out of her catatonic state again, for, I assure you, it was a great effort in the first place, and I did not care to repeat that experience. After all, we are only human beings. We have only a certain amount of affect, which we can willingly offer only to certain persons at certain times. The experience with Fräulein Liebknecht was very difficult but well worth the effort. It showed me that I could do what I always imagined was impossible—namely, change a chronic catatonic into a normally behaved human being. To be sure, it lasted only a short time, but it showed where the wind blows. I am sure that you can do the same if you have the interest, the knowledge, and the real desire to do it.

LECTURE II

TOPICS :

LAST week I did what I always do in the beginning: I just kept on advancing; and that is a good method if you wish to cover ground. But, after you have advanced for some distance, you must stop and consolidate your position. I told you, among other things, that Freud's concept of psychogenesis was first applied to psychiatry by Bleuler and Jung; and now I want to discuss a little more fully how Freud originally developed his views.

If you think back upon the status of psychiatry around, let us say, 1880, you will see that Charcot was already experimenting with hypnotism. But up to that time no one except quacks and philosophers paid any attention to the psychic factors of man. Physicians certainly did not consider the mind in terms of psyche. Thus, Mesmer, who was a physician, was dubbed a quack because of his interest in hypnotism. The philosophers, of course, talked about the "I think" (Kant) and *Cogito ergo sum* (Descartes), but one only becomes more confused by reading their works. Plato, in his Timaeus, correctly described hysteria in the famous passage where he compares the matrix to a little animal which likes to generate children. But, right up to Charcot's time, hysteria was still looked upon as an exclusively female disease because its name came from the Greek *hysteron*, meaning "womb."

Charcot, as you know, was fascinated by hysteria, and he did a number of things which were most important for the future of psychiatry. He showed that hysteria was really a disease—that the hysteric was not a deceiver, but was really sick—and that males could also suffer from it. Even more important, he demonstrated that hysterical symptoms such as paralyses could be both removed *and* produced by hypnotism. Charcot was still under the spell of his times however, and he maintained that hysteria was due to an ineradicable heredity. He called it a *famille névropathique* and hence a form of degeneration. Nevertheless, his work laid the foundation for a scientific psychopathology, for it demonstrated the influence of the psyche as a causative factor in disease.

Freud spent a year in Paris studying with Charcot and was deeply impressed by what he saw. Freud, of course, had begun as a student of medicine. He did neurological research for several years in Brücke's physiological laboratory, and his early writings on such subjects as aphasia and diplegia are still considered classics. But Freud tells us that he was primarily interested in psychiatry, but the psychiatry of his time was quite different from the psychiatry of today. After a good grounding in neurological research and cerebral anatomy, he went to Paris to study with Charcot, who made hypnotism respectable. But, long before hearing Charcot, Freud had met Dr. Josef Breuer, an older colleague in Brücke's laboratory and a pupil of the famous physiologist, Ewald Hering—of whom you will hear later, when we discuss memory. On one occasion, Breuer told Freud about an interesting case of hysteria which he had been treating—the famous case of Anna O.[1] This young woman had paralyses and anesthesias and many other hysterical symptoms. She had been seen by specialists, but none had been able to help her. Breuer started treating her by hypnotism, and once during such a seance she began to talk about the origin of one of her symptoms. Gradually Breuer discovered that whenever the young woman exhausted all the episodes dealing with the origin of a particular symptom, that symptom would disappear. He let his patient talk for hundreds of hours, and at last the young woman recovered. She herself called the treatment the "talking cure." The whole thing, of course, required extraordinary patience on Breuer's part. But, ladies and gentlemen, in psychiatry—in mental work—you will get nowhere unless you have such patience. Those of you who do not have it should not go into the work.

Freud, who was fascinated by this case, tried unsuccessfully to interest Charcot in it. But the case remained in his thoughts; and after returning from Paris, he began treating his patients by Breuer's method—that is, by hypnotism and questioning. As his results agreed with those reported by Breuer, he finally convinced him that they should publish their findings; and in 1893 they issued a preliminary paper under the title: "On the Psychic Mechanisms of Hysterical Phenomena." This paper was repeated as the first chapter of the *Studies in Hysteria*, which came out two years later, and which, as I have said, formed the foundation of psychoanalysis.

The essential points brought out by Breuer and Freud were these. Hysteria, they said, is a disease of the past. The symptom originated as a result of some very disagreeable or painful experience to which the patient could not adequately react at the time of its occurrence. And because of his inability to give vent to it or assimilate it, he tried to push it away from his consciousness. But in doing this, he merely "repressed" the episode, with its accompanying feelings, into the unconscious. The situation, to describe it in another way, was this: the

[1] Josef Breuer and Sigmund Freud: *Studies in Hysteria*, Translated by Brill, Nervous & Mental Disease Publishing Co. (New York, 1936).

patient had an impulse to do something, but another impulse worked against that act. Because of the conflict between these two antagonistic forces, the act was not carried out; it was repressed and in its place came the symptom.

Now the symptom, as such, would not have been formed if the person had succeeded in keeping his impulses repressed—as he originally wished. The act, with its accompanying feelings or emotions, did not, however, remain repressed; instead, it persisted, like a ghost, in coming up, and finally worked its way back to consciousness—not openly and directly—but by a devious path. The feelings or affects which were connected with the original act then lodged in some part of the body. If they lodged in the head, they gave the patient headaches; if in the arm, they gave him neuritis. Such transformations of psychic feelings into physical symptoms were designated by Breuer and Freud as *hysterical conversion symptoms*.

The process is well illustrated by the case of a man who had been grossly insulted one day by his boss. Now the man hated his boss and many times would have liked to kill him. But, among other things, his bread and butter depended on his position, and naturally he never carried out this act. Shortly after the occasion just mentioned, the man developed a neuralgic pain in his face. He was treated for a long time without relief and finally was sent to a psychoanalyst. Eventually, the insulting episode came up in the analysis and was discussed with the patient—whereupon the pain disappeared. "He made me so mad when he said those things," the patient told the analyst, "that I would rather he had slapped me in the face a thousand times." In other words, the patient had converted the feeling of insult into a definite, physical feeling of pain. Of course, since the pain was around the region of the fifth nerve, it had originally been diagnosed as facial neuralgia.

You know, in the old days we were told that you could diagnose hysteria only if certain symptoms were present. For example, in major hysteria you were supposed to find what Charcot called the *arc de cercle*—that is, the patient would assume the attitude of an arc of a circle: she would lie in a convex position, with only the head and feet touching the bed.

I have not seen such a case for years and years, but the old textbooks always talked about this as a characteristic symptom of major hysteria. Psychoanalytically, the *arc de cercle* represents an unconscious resistance to coitus, in which the feminine position, of course, is concave and receptive rather than convex and rigid, as in the *arc de cercle*.

There were other symptoms which were supposed to be characteristic of hysteria. The older neurologists always had to find pharyngeal or corneal anesthesia or both, in order to diagnose a case of hysteria. It did not matter that the patient might complain of many other kinds of hysterical symptoms; as long as she reacted with gagging or wincing it was concluded that she was not hysterical. But, sooner or later, the patient would notice that the doctor showed disappointment at the normal reaction to such stimulation of the pharynx and cornea. Sensing what he expected of her, she would then gradually stop gagging or closing her eyes when these organs were tickled—and the picture of hysteria was perfect!

Now you probably are familiar with Babinski's explanation of hysteria. He called it a disease of suggestion—"pithiatism." He said that every hysterical symptom was originally suggested and hence can be removed by suggestion. He was right—but not altogether right, for there is more to hysteria than suggestion. Babinski ignored what Breuer and Freud showed us— that hysteria was based on past experiences which had been repressed into the unconscious but eventually manifested themselves consciously as symptoms. I once reported a case in which I succeeded in removing a paralysis of an arm after the symptom had existed for more than twenty years. It took some massaging and coaxing before the patient would actually use the arm; but the paralysis was removed mainly by recalling the repressed episode underlying it—by bringing the forgotten and painful experiences back to consciousness and demonstrating them to the patient.

It was Breuer and Freud who originated this technique of treatment. They found that if the patient was led back to the original situation and allowed to give vent to his feelings by talking, the symptom in question would disappear. They called this the "cathartic" method of treatment (recalling Aristotle's characterization of the drama as a mental catharsis) because it involved a mental purging on the part of the patient. To use their own term, the patient *abreacted* his original, repressed feelings. (It amuses me whenever I hear people criticize this and that term in psychoanalysis. They do not know the situations that confronted me in the beginning. When I finally used the term *abreaction* in my translation, I knew of no other English word to use for it. The German term, *Abreagierung*, was itself coined by Freud. It means "to act off" or "to work off" something by reliving it in speech and feeling. I consulted philologists and thought about this word for a long time, and in the end I had no choice but to coin an English equivalent.)

Now Breuer and Freud, in laying great stress upon the patient's repressed experiences with their impulses and feelings, were following a line of thought which has run all through psychiatry from early Greek times down to our own. I told you last week about the emphasis which Bleuler placed on "affectivity;" and you already know that Kraepelin stressed dullness of emotion as the characteristic element in dementia praecox. The man who gave much thought to these factors is Dr. Erwin Stransky of Vienna, who coined the two words, *noöpsyche* and *thymopsyche,* about thirty-five years ago. The words are Greek, of course, and you will find them discussed in textbooks on psychiatry.[2] I believe Stransky was the first to claim that in dementia praecox there is a marked disproportion between the *noöpsyche* and the *thymopsyche*—that is, between the intellect and the emotions. Normally, he said, there is a definite proportion between them; in the psychoses this balance is markedly upset. A dementia praecox patient, for example, will cry over something which should normally provoke laughter, or he will pay no attention to something which would ordinarily arouse great excitement. There is a disproportion, to repeat, between the *noö-* and the *thymopsyche.*

It remained for Bleuler, who strove constantly to solve the

---

[2] *Noö* means "the mind," *thymo* means "the emotions." *Noöpsyche* thus refers to the mental or intellectual factor, and *thymopsyche* to the emotional part.

problem of dementia praecox, to go more deeply into this question. In one of his papers Bleuler tells us that when you examine the elementary mechanisms of our psyche, you will find two systems. The first is the system of individual experiences upon which reason depends. All reason, all thought, is based on one's past experiences. As you have undoubtedly seen time and again, defectives have little or no capacity to utilize the experiences they themselves have had. In this connection I always think of a patient we had in Central Islip. He was not, strictly speaking, a psychotic, but a sort of low-grade imbecile with transient psychotic episodes. He had the job of driving a wagon from one center of the hospital to another—a distance of about a mile and a half—and I used to see him every morning from my window as he went past. One day I noticed that our driver was in trouble. A new building was being put up, and the workmen had left a large pile of sand on the road, blocking about half of it. Our patient was trying to drive his horse straight ahead, but of course the animal could not get through the pile of sand. One of the workmen then came over and simply led the horse around the pile. I remember saying to myself: "The poor fellow is used to driving on a road without any obstructions, and he hasn't enough reasoning power to go to the right or left around the pile of sand."

Reason, then, depends entirely on your past experiences, on the combinations and permutations which you are able to make of those experiences. In other words, thinking is nothing but a form of comparison. You compare a present situation with all the similar situations that are aroused by it, and in this way you make your decision. A good diagnostician is one who has seen so many cases that he is able, when confronted by a new one, to make immediate comparisons and thus come to a quick conclusion. Naturally, his deductions are much better than the comparisons made, say, by a very bright young man who has not had equally long experience.

The second of Bleuler's two systems is the one based on the ergies. You will now find that term in psychiatric literature, although it has been used for years by German and French writers. "Ergie" comes from the Greek, *ergon,* which means a piece of work, a unit of energy. It refers to what we call emotions, feelings, strivings, affects, impulses, and instincts. The ergies represent the dynamics of thought. The feelings or the ergies are older than thought and may have started in the unicellular organism. They developed gradually through all the former generations and have become adapted to the special needs of the particular species. In other words, they go back much further than reason and intellect. You can see this clearly if you watch the development of any animal or child. The emotions appear long before the child can express his feelings in verbal concepts.

For all these ergies Bleuler preferred to use the term, *affects*. Why? Well, when you stop to think about it, you will find that these ergies cannot be separated from each other. Strictly speaking, you cannot separate an instinct from an impulse or make a definite distinction between a striving and a feeling. You can, however, determine that all our acts are accompanied by a definite feeling tone, by a certain affect, which is either pleasant or unpleasant. An act has a pleasant affect if it corresponds to our impulses. It is unpleasantly accentuated when it contradicts or is opposed to our impulses or instincts. Thus, if you are hungry and get food, you feel well. But if you continued to be hungry and starving, the affect would naturally be unpleasant. Similarly, if sex is gratified, tension is removed and the individual again feels well. Anything which opposes the gratification of hunger or love makes the patient (I say "the patient"—we are all patients) irritable, morose, and pugnacious. And since every act has either a pleasant or unpleasant feeling-tone, Bleuler thought that instead of emotion, feeling, striving, or impulse it would be best to use the term, *affect*, or affectivity—using it in the sense of a part for the whole.

You will have to be alive to the concept of these two systems when you consider any psychic behavior. In evaluating cases, particularly psychoanalytically, that question must be uppermost in your mind. I told you last week about the brilliant young man who went into his father's business. His intellect was excellent; he could reason with you on the highest level. Yet his ergies seemed to be absent. They were paralyzed, inhibited, blocked—or whatever name you may use in psychiatry. Because of the young man's general apathy, I called him a schizophrenic. The average man, when he finds himself in a situation which he does not like, usually gathers enough energy to change it. He does not just sit down, like the chronic catatonic, and let time pass. Our young man, however, did virtually that very thing, even though he was not a catatonic as yet. To use Stransky's terms, there was a marked disproportion between his *noöpsyche* and *thymopsyche*. Or, as Bleuler would have said, the young man showed a blurred affectivity.

The importance of affectivity is clearly shown in the symptoms as described by Breuer and Freud. People who are untrained in analysis (I have in mind a doctor who consulted me recently) often argue that they have read analytic literature, have recognized the meaning of the symptoms, and have explained it to the patient—and yet, the patient's illness remains just the same. I usually answer that probably ninety per cent of the patients who come to me show very soon what, in a way, caused their maladies. I could tell them what the cause is—but it would do no good. You must go back and trace everything to the original source. You must let the patient abreact the whole thing: the idea with the original affect. The patient will do so only if you will find the real facts underlying the symptoms. It is not what you yourself think about it, but what the patient himself will elaborate in the long course of the treatment. Remember that the symptoms are invariably products of distortion; thus, the affects may be displaced. When a dementia praecox becomes agitated over what you may regard as a trifle, you are likely to note merely that "the patient suddenly became excited." But if you investigate, you will find that the excitement can be traced to something definite, to something logical, which emanated from a definite unconscious association, and was displaced to some trifle. Such displacement you will note also in dream analysis. A patient, in reporting anxiety during a dream, will tell you: "I cannot see why I should have been so terrified about this particular thing. There was no reason for it; yet when I woke up I was still in a cold shiver." When you investigate, you find that the affect was justified, but that it had been displaced. The affect is the only true thing you can find in a symptom, in a hallucination, or in a dream, but you must find where it belongs. It is almost always displaced to something trifling in order to mask the situation and thus protect the individual from pain. You will discover the true source only if you succeed in tracing the original situation and let the patient live through the repressed material.

Breuer and Freud collaborated for a number of years while developing their cathartic method of treatment, and then they separated. There were a number of reasons for this. One was the mounting criticism against their views on the role of sex in the neuroses. Breuer had reported that in the case of Anna O., the sexual element was hardly noticeable. Naturally Breuer thought of sex as being limited to genital activity, for that was the view universally held at that time. Yet, as he and Freud went into the deeper recesses of hysteria they discovered the sexual element in abundance everywhere, and of course they said so in print. Well, there is nothing that will excite people so much as the problem of sex. Those who opposed Breuer and Freud all harped on this one question, and Breuer became uneasy at all the unfavorable criticism—especially from the "big bugs" who formerly respected him.

But that was not all. Remember, Breuer was fifteen years older than Freud. I knew him personally, and I can tell you that, in a sense, he was just like Freud—very individualistic, and absolutely determined, once he had made up his mind. The two men had differences of opinion right from the start. Breuer was a general practitioner; unlike Freud, he had not trained himself with the idea of becoming a psychiatrist. When they began to formulate the meaning of the repressed pathogenic ideas, it was quite natural that the two should differ in their interpretations. Breuer, whose experience had been confined to hypnotism, said that those ideas became repressed in a hypnoid state. Freud, on the other hand, imagined that the situation followed more the normal state: he said that the ideas were repressed because the patient defended himself against them in the way that any ordinary person would defend himself against something disagreeable or painful. To say that the process occurred in a "hypnoid state" is to bring up an entirely new problem—namely, "What is a hypnoid state?"

Freud, from the very beginning, adhered to the simple processes that are common to everyone's life. He always went from the abnormal back to the normal. No matter how complicated a process at first appears, you will find, upon tracing it, that it is quite simple and always goes back to everyday life. To be sure, these processes are, for the most part, unconscious, and hence the average person is not aware of them. It is true that poets and writers have always sensed these things and hinted at them in their works, but these references are isolated ones without much scientific value. What Freud did was to discover the key to mental processes and to work it out into a cohesive system of thought.

There was another and perhaps even more conclusive reason for Breuer's ultimate retreat. His famous patient, Anna O., kept coming to see him for advice and assistance with her problems; and Breuer, following his custom, used to hypnotize her. One day the young woman came to him in a hysterical state, and while he was going through the hypnotizing formulas she suddenly grabbed him, kissed him, and announced that she had become pregnant by him. Of course the old man was shocked. He decided that the girl must be crazy, or, at all events, that the treatment had its dangers. The experience was too much for Breuer. He had not been able to brave the world of prudery to begin with, and this final incident was the climax. There and then he decided to separate from Freud.

Working alone, the first thing Freud did was to drop hypnotism. He found, in the first place, that not everybody could be hypnotized. He took one such recalcitrant patient to Bernheim, who had the reputation of being able to hypnotize ninety per cent of the patients brought to him. But Bernheim, too, failed to hypnotize her, and Freud concluded that if this were so, nothing further could be done by following this method.

Moreover Freud never liked hypnotism. It was uncertain as a therapy: when one symptom was removed, another would usually appear instead. Or, if the relationship between doctor and patient was disturbed, all the symptoms would return. I

remember my experiences with it in the neurological department of the Vanderbilt Clinic. Dr. M. Allen Starr, professor of
nervous and mental diseases at P. & S., frequently said that he
did not know much about psychiatry although he lectured annually four times on the subject to the seniors. His chief-of-
clinic, Dr. Cunningham, once asked me to prepare cases for his
clinic on neurasthenia, and when I would ask what kind of
cases he wanted, he said: "Any case that hasn't too many hallucinations or delusions." That was his idea of neurasthenia.
Well, one day I suggested that we show hypnotism. "Can you
do it?" asked Starr. "Sure," I replied. (At that time I could do
anything!) And so I brought in a patient who had a loud,
crowing tic, a sort of belch, which could be heard blocks
away. I had already hypnotized this patient at my other clinic
in Bellevue, and I knew I had a cinch. Of course the demonstration was very impressive: on command, that raucous, bel-
lowing tic immediately vanished. The students were fascinated,
for everyone is impressed by such uncanny power. The students were even more impressed when I subsequently hypnotized a case of astasia-abasia and made the patient walk. Yet
both patients were brought back the following week! I asked
Starr whether we should show them again. "Oh, no," he replied, "that would spoil the show." The students remained in
their ignorance, and my reputation with them as a superman
who could cure everything by command remained untarnished.

Freud was aware of all these deficiencies. Nor did he like
the brutality and violence that were perpetrated on the patients when they were hypnotized. One had to yell at them like
a drill sergeant: "Here, you do this!" In addition, some patients became addicts of hypnosis and could not get along
without it. Many years ago I had a striking instance of this in
the case of a Buenos Aires business man who appeared at my
office one day while on a professional trip to New York. As a
boy of fourteen or fifteen while living in Vienna, this patient
had suffered from severe headaches. No one could help him
until he went to see Krafft-Ebing. (You all know his *Psychopathia Sexualis;* but do not forget that he was also a very excellent psychiatrist.) Krafft-Ebing hypnotized the boy and re-

moved his headaches. Subsequently the boy's family emigrated to Buenos Aires, and when he came to see me he was a man of about fifty. His headaches, he told me, had persisted throughout his life, and nothing could remove them except hypnosis. He did not dare go anywhere without making sure in advance that a competent hypnotist would be available. When he found that he had to visit New York, he wrote to Bellevue, and the hospital gave him my name. After listening to this story, I said: "Have you got a headache?" "No," he replied. He had had none, in fact, for three weeks. But, he added, if he had not made sure that I was there to hypnotize him, he would have gotten one immediately!

Well, that is not a good situation to be in. We discovered later, particularly through the work of Ferenczi,[3] what the nature of that situation really is. It is the relation between father and child, between the omnipotent parent and the helpless infant. (It is not accidental that hypnotists are often Svengalis with big beards.) In psychoanalytic therapy we are anxious to make the child independent so that he will not have to lean on the omnipotent parent. Hypnotism does just the opposite, and for that reason alone it is not good as a form of therapy. Your influence may work for a while. But one loses one's respect even for the greatest people once you know them well, and the influence inevitably wears off. Hypnotism thus works as long as you keep people dependent. Our object however is to make them independent.

Freud was readily able to give up hypnotism because he discovered a much more effective substitute. At Bernheim's clinic he had witnessed an impressive experiment. You know that following hypnosis, the patient usually has a complete amnesia regarding what has occurred. In this experiment however, it was shown that you could bring back the forgotten material just by urging. The patient at first would say: "I do not remember; I did not even know that I was hypnotized." But after repeated urging, the patient would finally recall everything.

Freud thought of that experiment and said to himself: "If I

[3] "Introjektion und Übertragung," *Jahrbuch für Psychoanalytische und Psychopathologische Forschungen*, Bd. I.

cannot hypnotize or do not wish to do so, why can't I bring back the forgotten experiences simply by urging?" He tried this technique. It worked—but not precisely in the way he expected, and he soon got into a terrible maze. The patient would talk and talk, yet Freud was none the wiser regarding the symptoms. After many months had gone by, he finally realized that the patient had revealed long ago the very things he sought; he had simply not known how to interpret what the patient had told him. He then realized that one could not just listen and accept everything literally. Each person, to begin with, has his own mode of expression—his own "free masonry"—and these symbolisms have to be interpreted. For example, women always have their own special terms for menstruation. That is true among all races and nationalities. I once collected more than three hundred such terms, and most of them had a disagreeable connotation—such as "to be ill," or "to have the curse."

Among primitive peoples menstruation has always been surrounded by the strongest taboos. My explanation of this superstitious attitude goes back to the time when the human animal was still governed by the sense of smell. A menstruous female always attracts the male—as you still find in the animal kingdom —and the most difficult time for primitive humans to control themselves was just during this period of menstruation. But the penalty for violating the taboo was death, and so, to aid in exerting that control, the menstruating woman came to be looked upon as "unclean," and therefore undesirable. Something of this attitude still persists among civilized people. The modern woman not only uses disagreeable terms, but may actually get sick during menstruation. There is usually no reason for this whatsoever. It is simply a negative expression used by the modern woman to conceal from herself the true nature of her sexual periodicity. That is why menstruation is designated by secret names indigenous only to that home or family.

But this is only one function which modern man must conceal; there are also a great many important experiences in the patient's life which occurred in childhood, long before he could describe them in words. The patient then can express those experiences only by displaced feelings, or, as we often say, by acting them out in terms of expressions of today. These expressions must therefore be interpreted to the patient himself; otherwise, they continue to remain unconscious. Moreover, many of our early experiences are later expressed in abstractions, although the original concrete images are still retained in the unconscious.

I once asked my class of about forty students, for example, to imagine that they were artists—painters or poets—and to make a drawing or to describe in concrete imagery what is meant by the term, "charity." I did not call for a definition, but simply for a concrete representation of the idea. There were not two among them who had the same concept of charity. They all understood the term as do you, but each one had a different form of representing it. When I investigated, I found that the expressions differed because in each case the concept of the abstract term "charity" was based on some personal experience. Thus, one man made a drawing of a rather stately American woman giving a coin to a decrepit, bent old woman. At first he did not know why he had used this image. By associations he eventually recalled a trip to Italy, during which he had seen one of the women tourists in his group give coins to the native beggars with just such a haughty gesture. Now this man knew the meaning of charity long before that trip. But for some reason or other, the sum total of all his impressions concerning charity became fused, so to speak, under the image of that particular picture. When we went a little deeper, we found that there was an infantile erotic reason for this—one which is not usually associated with the abstract concept of charity.

To discover the meanings of all these hidden and unconscious things, Freud developed what he called the "continuous, or free association" method, with its technique of interpretation. Instead of hypnotizing and questioning, as was done in the cathartic treatment, he followed the patient's free associations and interpreted their meaning, and this method of procedure he called "psychoanalysis." With hypnotism you do not need to know a thing about the patient's history. You proceed just like a surgeon when he operates on a person whose face is covered. The surgeon does not care what the person looks like. Similarly, the hypnotist does not care what kind of mind or character the person has—he simply imposes his will on the patient in front of him. The situation is quite different in analysis when the patient and the doctor are equally interested in the forces behind the symptoms. By discarding hypnotism, Freud discovered the forces behind the symptoms—the forces which hypnotism hitherto had covered up. He discovered, for example, why people really forget and thus came to understand the true mechanisms of repression.

As I have already told you Breuer and Freud found, through their cathartic method, that the hysterical symptom was not due to the process of repression but to a failure in the repression. Please note that it is not repression, but the *failure* of it, which produces the symptom. People constantly misinterpret Freud as having said that one gets sick because of repression, and, *ergo*, they deduce that the best way to remain healthy is never to repress. Now only a complete fool could believe or say such a thing. No one—not even an animal—can do just what he pleases; and certainly Freud and his school never advocated such nonsense. Every living being must and does control his impulses. Suppression or control, however, has nothing to do with repression. Repression is an unconscious process from the very beginning. A thing is usually repressed in *statu nascendi*—while it is being born. As illustration, let me give you the case of a man who came to see me many years ago. He was a professional man of about forty-eight, refined and cultured. He had all kinds of symptoms, particularly sexual impotence. His physician had sent him to me because he could find nothing organically wrong.

Briefly, the patient's history was this: He was already advanced in years when he married his wife. She had been married before and had three children, two sons and a daughter. The patient had been a classmate and friend of her husband. He managed the divorce and later married the lady. The three children were then small and were brought up by him as his own. The wife soon became chronically ill, however, and for many years used to spend the summers abroad at different European spas. During one of these absences, the father and daughter went off on a camping trip together. They would spend the whole day fishing and at night slept in the same tent. Everything went well up to a certain evening. (The patient at the time attributed no importance to that evening; it was only three years later, when I analyzed him, that special significance was attached to it.) That evening the guide cooked the fish they had caught, and after satiating their hunger, they went to sleep. As the father and daughter kissed each other the habitual "good-night," their lips somehow met and clung together, probably a few seconds longer than ordinarily. That was all. Nothing else happened, and nothing was said. But the next day they both agreed that the camping trip should be terminated, and they went home a week earlier than they had originally planned. In the fall the young woman, apparently for no particular reason, decided not to live at home any longer, and she moved to an apartment of her own. Three years later, when I saw the father, he had developed all sorts of hypochondriacal symptoms, notably that of impotence.

Now, what had happened? The patient was a nice, gentlemanly fellow who, so far as I could discover, had never indulged in any sexual irregularities prior to his marriage. He was an unassuming, though public-spirited citizen, until he became somewhat incapacitated by his hypochondriacal symptoms. He had been much attached to his mother, and upon marriage had transferred his whole libido to his wife. Men of this type are always monogamous; they stick to one woman. But the state of affairs prior to the evening in question had not been a satisfactory one. His wife evidently had little craving for sexual relations, so that throughout his marital years he had led almost a life of abstinence. Here he was, then, alone in a tent with a pretty young woman of twenty. She was a healthy, human animal who herself had lived a life of abstinence for almost ten years after nature intended her to mate. They were both in need of sex, and there was nothing in the way except the moral code. The father, as the analysis revealed, had often admired his step-daughter's physical charm. Ordinarily, admiration means wish strangulation; we admire what we cannot get. If she had been a stranger, the stimulation which she exerted on him would have followed the way of all flesh. Because of the parental relationship, however, the desire was suppressed and he merely admired her. When their lips clung together those extra few seconds, they both must have sensed what was happening. But the father's sexual tension was instantly repressed; it was strangulated in *statu nascendi*, and the whole episode vanished completely. In the unconscious, however, the repressed material remained active and finally emerged in disguised form. When his wife returned later, and he attempted coitus with her, he found that it did not work. After several more unsuccessful attempts, he decided that he was impotent. But impotence is usually a reaction to incestuous desires, and it was so in this case. The meaning of the symptom was: "If you are impotent, you cannot have any temptation toward your step-daughter."

You see that the repression was an entirely unconscious process. If the patient had become consciously aware of his sexual craving, he could have said to himself: "I am a man, and here is a young, healthy girl. I would like to have sexual relations with her. But I had better control myself because there would be too many complications." He would then have controlled his desire, and he would not have developed the neurosis. But he was not an average person. He was a neurotic, a hyper-sensitive being. Instead of settling the problem or the conflict, he repressed it along with its affects. The result was a neurosis.

I am often asked why some people are neurotic, and others not. Freud placed great stress on "constitution" as the factor which makes certain people particularly predisposed to neurotic illness. Each of us, Freud held, is a product of constitution and fate. By constitution, of course, we mean the individual's entire make-up as it is inherited from countless generations back. You bring this constitution along with you into the world; the rest is accidental, environmental—that is, fate. Constitution alone does not produce neurotic illness. But if an individual starts, say with a hyper-sensitive constitution, and if the environmental experiences are unfavorable ones, the constitution will then provide a fertile ground for the breeding of neurotic conflicts.

One sees this all the time in the reactions of different people to the same external experience. Most girls, for example, have "necking" experiences with men. Usually, the man wants love —he wants sex. The girl, too, has the same impulses: She is a healthy young woman, a virgin who should perhaps have mated years before. (Sex is nothing but the mating instinct as even the severest moralists will have to admit.) She naturally craves sexual gratification; but the moral standards of her up-bringing oppose it, and as a result a struggle follows. Considering it biologically, we know that nature does not care a bit about moral standards. The sexes simply appeal to each other's instinctive needs. But civilization has changed them; they are no longer a natural male and female. Before they can mate, certain legal and moral prerequisites must now be satisfied. Yet, fundamentally the natural instinct still is there and hence the inevitable inner battle. Virtually all girls have such struggles, and all settle the problem somehow. They think about it and generate an affect; but after a few days or weeks the thing is decided one way or another, and the cathexis [4] disappears.

The average person, then, settles the problem in one way or another. In the neurotic, however, the issue is different. For example, I once treated a young woman who had been sent to me with the diagnosis of hystero-epilepsy. She had attacks which at first looked like epilepsy, but when I analyzed her an entirely different picture emerged. The history of the case was this: The young woman had been brought up in a conventional middle-class family, and she was "a nice, respectable girl." (Only nice girls get neuroses.) During a trip to Europe she met a titled foreigner with whom she came to spend a great deal of time. After some weeks, however, the girl's mother

[4] *Cathexis* means the sum of energy or affect that an act engenders. Freud used the word "*Besetzung*" when he talked about certain feelings occupying the mind. The German word means literally "to occupy" or "to invest with something," but it was rather difficult to translate it by one word. The London analysts finally decided to turn it into Greek and gave *cathexis* a definite but broad meaning.

discovered that the man was a fraud and his title a bogus one. Although she had at first encouraged the relationship, she now forbade her daughter to see the foreigner again. But by that time the girl was in love with the man, and she continued meeting him in secret. One night, when they were alone in an inn, the man tried to have intercourse with her. The girl, as I have said, was a respectable young virgin with conventional views and ideals, and the man's attack was a tremendous shock to her. She struggled violently, fought him off, and walked home alone.

Naturally, since she had been warned against this man, she did not tell her mother anything about the episode. She tried to forget it—with what success we shall see in a moment. Three years later she was brought to me with the diagnosis of hystero-epilepsy. In order to see just what she was suffering from, I ordered her to have one of her attacks. (In my office I have a lounge on which my analytic patients lie down; and in this case I used hypnotism to bring on the attack.) I noted everything—her every gesture and the words she mumbled. It was apparent to me that she was "acting out" something; and it later turned out that she was repeating every element of the episode which occurred in the inn. She imitated every detail: The rigidly extended arm, for example, represented the erect penis which she had warded off that night.

Now this girl, being a neurotic person, had obviously failed to dismiss the situation as an average girl would do. She had repressed the whole thing, with its accompanying cathexis. Had it remained so, she would have been just another respectable girl who had resisted temptation. But it did not stay repressed. She would sometimes reflect upon it and say to herself: "What an idiot I was! Why didn't I have sexual relations? I know that Jane and other girls do it, and no harm comes to them." In time, it is true, she did forget the experience; but then it came to the surface again by a different path. She began to show symptoms which were merely displacements from below to above. In other words, her hysteria was a substitutive gratification for what she should have experienced at the inn.

[45

The difference between the average and the neurotic re-action to traumas is perhaps most concisely illustrated by a story I like to tell in this connection. It concerns a man who, with his young daughter, was reading the papers one Sunday afternoon. The daughter suddenly turned to him and said: "Dad, what does the word, 'to assault,' mean?" The father looked up in surprise and said: "Why do you ask?" "Well," said the daughter, "I just read about a girl who was assaulted and she committed suicide." The father hesitated a moment and then said: "To assault means to be spat upon." "Why, what an idiot that girl was!" the daughter replied. "If I were assaulted I would just wipe it off!"

There you have the difference. Faced with such situations, the normal person "just wipes it off;" the neurotic may attempt or actually commit suicide. The constitution of the average person is not so sensitive as to remain fixed on an experience, no matter how affective it may have been. On the other hand, in the neurotic, the constitution is extremely impressionable and adhesive; here the ego runs away from the bad situation at the first encounter and thus closes to it any normal exit. The repressed energy then makes its way to some organ or part of the body, and, through a process of distortion, the symptom results.

According to Breuer and Freud, then, the hysteric suffers from forgotten reminiscences. The symptom originated in situations in which an impulse to do something was opposed by another impulse. As a result of this conflict, the desired act was repressed and in its place there appeared the symptom. The symptom is thus a distorted expression of something that actually happened. It is a "monument of the past," as Freud expressed it. But one usually does not know what most monuments stand for; a foreigner certainly would not know what the Washington Monument signified unless he were enlight-ened on American history. Similarly, the meaning of the hys-terical symptom cannot be understood without finding its psychogenesis—without revealing the mechanisms of repres-sion and of the unconscious. The therapy, as I said, consisted at first of hypnotizing the patient and, through questioning,

46]

leading him back to the forgotten trauma—that is, to the same psychic state in which the symptom appeared. By recalling the forgotten episode or impulse, with its affects, and by imparting the same verbally to the physician, the symptom disappeared. In theory, the symptom was due to an abnormal utilization of an undischarged sum of excitement which, though at first repressed, later worked its way to the surface on some false path (hysterical conversion). To sum up, we can say that the most important part of Breuer and Freud's work was the discovery that the hysterical symptom was based on psychogenesis and that it can be removed by abreaction, or by mental catharsis.

I have already stated why Breuer and Freud gave up their scientific partnership. Working alone, Freud soon reconstructed the pathogenic process in the following manner: In normal life, if some impulse arises which is strongly opposed by another force, a conflict ensues between the opposing forces, and the struggle continues consciously until the impulse is rejected and its cathexis withdrawn. In the neurosis, the ego withdraws from the disagreeable impulse at the first encounter and in this way closes to it the access to consciousness and to direct motor discharge; but the impulse retains its full cathexis. According to Freud, this process constitutes what he calls *repression*. I have already shown that this repression fails in time and gives origin to the symptom, which is a substitutive gratification for the repressed situation. The process of repression may be compared to a primary defense reaction to an attempted flight. This is well illustrated by the cases cited above.

There are a number of other factors connected with repression which we must not fail to mention. In the first place, the ego, which has brought about the repression through its flight, must henceforth use a great deal of energy, or *counter-cathexis*, to keep it down. For everything that recalls the original situation or that might in any way refer to it openly must immediately be held down. The ego thus becomes impoverished. Moreover, the repressed material, which is now unconscious, can still find an outlet or substitutive gratification on some by-path and thus cause a failure of the primary repression. In conversion hysteria, this by-path leads to some physical innervation, and the repressed material then breaks through somewhere in the body, forming a symptom. The latter, as you can see, is a compromise formation; although it is a substitutive gratification for what the patient missed, it is nevertheless distorted and deflected from its aim through the resistance of the ego.

The girl in question showed these mechanisms in her attacks. To be sure, she was sick—but her neurosis was a good compromise between what she originally missed and the repression. In other words, the patient really gained something through her malady. It was, to be sure, a *morbid gain*, but she did profit something. Of course, she had to be treated by doctors, but at least no one need be ashamed of being sick. Do not forget, besides, that doctors are pretty nice fellows, and, if one has the money, it is not so unpleasant to visit them. Some patients of this type often hate to get well, particularly after they have been ill for many years; they are extremely loath to give up this "morbid gain." In his interesting book, *Roaming Through the West Indies*, Harry A. Franck tells the story of a blind beggar who had apparently been incapacitated for many years.[5] An American medical missionary noticed that the mendicant's blindness was due to cataracts and offered to remove them free of charge. One might think that the beggar would have been overjoyed to have his sight restored—but, no, he declined the offer on the grounds that it would cut off his means of livelihood.

Undoubtedly, this beggar felt very miserable when he first became blind—when he had to give up his work and take up begging as a profession. But he had become "used to it," and in time it became easier than the hard labor which had formerly been his daily lot. His blindness, which was at first a misfortune, soon turned out to be a profit to him: it was a "morbid gain." In the neurosis, the same thing prevails. The girl of our case got used to her attacks and thus solved her problem. Through those attacks she unconsciously relived the original episode; and that was her outlet. Of course, judging by normal

[5] p. 299, Century Co., 1920.

standards, it was a very inadequate outlet—but it was an outlet, nevertheless.

Freud's view of the symptom as a substitutive gratification for the repression did not develop until after he became aware of the important role which sex plays in our lives. Freud's concept of sex, of course, was much different from that held by the average person or even by the psychiatrists and neurologists of his day. Freud found sex, for example, in the relationships between parents and children, or between friends. Such relationships play as great a part in the individual's actual disturbances and in the formation of symptoms as do real sexual situations in the ordinary sense. Freud felt, therefore, that the word, sex, was not an adequate term to describe the true situation. His meaning of "sex" was what the Germans call "*das Liebesleben*"—the "love life" of a person. In this sense, of course, the term need not necessarily be restricted only to matters concerning genital union. Thus, a child may suffer from a sexual disturbance if he is neglected by a parent or maltreated by someone in authority over him. The loss of a parent may make a child nervous: it is a disturbance in the latter's love life.

Thus, as he investigated more deeply, Freud broadened the term sex by using the word, *libido*, which he defined as a quantitative love energy directed to an object. Under this view, some part of the libido, or sexual energy, is directed to the definite aim of sexual union. But not all of a person's libido is so directed. We say of many people, for example, that they are "wedded to their professions." Such people often direct almost all of their libido to their work. They may be happy in this sphere, but in most cases they do not get along very smoothly in other aspects of their lives. I have had such people come to consult me. They were aware of no sexual disturbances, and they came to me for entirely different reasons. Yet I could readily see that their real problem was an emotional one which had arisen because they had no adequate outlet for their libido.

Thus, I was once consulted by a young writer who suddenly developed difficulties in his work. "I have been doing very well for a number of years," he said to me, "but now I simply cannot go on. I cannot finish anything I write. I always stop. I don't know why." Then he added: "Is there anything wrong with my mind, doctor?" Well, I could have told him right off that there was nothing wrong with his mind. But he insisted that something might be organically wrong, and so I had to go through all the rigmarole of examining him. I found nothing, of course, and finally I told him that there was something wrong with his psychosexual life.

After a few talks, that young writer brought me a host of material. He had been unable to finish his book because he could not put the hero on the spot. But the hero could not be "put" because he represented the author himself, who, as it turned out, had a very strong homosexual component. I could talk at length about this case, but I will say only that it did not help to give him the end of the plot. I might have told him how to finish the book, and still he would not have been able to do it. After he was analyzed, however, he finished the story. By that time he had recognized his sexual difficulties and had begun to take a healthy interest in life. His real disturbance, in other words, had been the lack of a proper adjustment in his libido or love life.

When Freud first presented this enlarged concept of the sexual life, everyone became uneasy. Until then Freud had been hailed as a great discoverer. If you refer back to the contemporary literature, you will find that everyone spoke well of Freud's neurological works and of the earlier works on hysteria which he and Breuer published in 1895. But this attitude changed with Freud's increasing emphasis on the sexual factors. I have already told you how Breuer had to part with Freud because of this change. Later, when Freud made the famous statement that, "No neurosis is possible in a normal sexual life," there was an almost universal reaction against him. Everyone was shocked; and from that time on until he died, Freud was reviled for it. Critics who were only superficially acquainted with his work could always reproach him for calling attention to the sexual factors observable everywhere in life. On the other hand, of course, Freud has been compared to Aristotle and to Darwin—the latter comparison I think is very apt. Most of Darwin's critics, in his own day, thought only of one thing: that he tried to make monkeys out of men. Of all the wonderful discoveries which Darwin gave to the world, that was the one element which the theologians (and even some scientists) harped on. And of all the wonderful discoveries which Freud gave us, sex is what his critics still continue to rant about. Of late, to be sure, the criticisms have varied somewhat: one scientist recently criticized Freud because he did not use the statistical method.

It has always seemed strange to me that people should object to some of the ideas which Freud brought to our attention. Take, for example, the Œdipus complex, a concept which he developed later when he began to trace back experiences into early childhood. Freud said, in essence, that the little boy loves his mother so much that he will not brook any rivalry, even from his own father, and consequently wishes that his father should die, which to the boy means to be away from home. Now, any superficial observation will demonstrate that this is true. Perhaps Freud should not have used mythological names, as was his habit. The term "Œdipus" of course recalls the myth which tells how Œdipus unwittingly married his mother and killed his father. Some people were shocked by this reference; yet if they had really read what Freud said, they need not have been so upset. For it is only natural that little boys should be more attached to their mothers than to their fathers. Everything that the child needs, everything that he considers good, comes from his mother; while the father he can only perceive as an intruder whose position in the home is annoying to him, to say the least. Every normal boy shows such feelings; and we have always considered this natural. Freud wanted to convey, simply, that between the little boy and his father there is a natural rivalry which shows itself unconsciously even after the boy has become adjusted to his father.

Of course, one who is not versed in psychoanalytic literature is often unable to grasp the importance of parental influences on the development of the mind. But let us not forget that Freud was the first scientist to trace human behavior back to early childhood. No one before had had the ingenuity, or rather, the audacity, to venture into this undiscovered region. What he found there was new, especially to psychiatrists, who still believed that hysterical symptoms were due to circumscribed irritation in some part of the brain. But in his desire to clarify his new findings, Freud naturally tried to elucidate them in terms of analogous situations which were known to him. Frankly, I do not know of anything which explains the early family situation better than the play of Sophocles based on the Œdipus myth.

The case of the hysterical girl contains all the basic elements of the Freudian psychology. For the present, however, I have given only a very small fragment of it. The thing to remember, at this point, is that Freud's formulations were essentially different from what he and Breuer originally described.

QUESTIONS AND ANSWERS

Question : Was Mesmer a qualified physician?

Answer : He was a physician, but he took up hypnotism, which until then was used only by quacks. Mesmer was fascinated by it but knew nothing about its nature and quality. He attributed its effects to animal magnetism. The other physicians were dead against him and his views. The French Academy finally appointed a committee to investigate the genuineness of his cures. Our own Benjamin Franklin was on that committee, and he is supposed to have written the report. The committee agreed there was no doubt about the cures being genuine, but they decided that these cures were due merely to the patients' imagination—and hence hardly worth considering.

The main point is that doctors, or, I might say all people who have had long experience in a special field, are very conservative when it comes to any innovation in that field. You may call this good or bad; in any case, this phenomenon results in a struggle between the generations. In Mesmer's time, *Mens sana in corpore sano*—"a healthy mind in a healthy body"—was considered absolutely proven, so that no one would for a minute entertain the belief that emotional things could produce hysterical symptoms.

Charcot, who demonstrated the genuineness of hysterical

52

phenomena by means of hypnotism, still believed that everything had some organic basis. But he was followed by men like Forel, Haidenhein, Janet, and others who differed from him insofar as they looked for psychological explanations. They believed that there must be a psychological reason for the symptoms, and Janet, when he later wrote the *Major Symptoms of Hysteria,* showed that the psychological element does play a part. But all of Charcot's early pupils were groping in the dark. It was not until Breuer and Freud came on the scene that the situation was changed.

Question : Referring to the case of the hysterical girl, do you regard a girl who would act in such a way as normal—as suitable for marriage?

Answer : Neurotics, as a rule, are at least of average mentality, and as a class, they constitute what one may call "the salt of the earth." But they are all very sensitive and may develop neuroses. When they are well, they never ask us whether they should marry or not. When they suffer from a psychoneurosis, they are sick, and left to themselves, they usually do not marry. Some of them marry on the advice of a physician who, though disagreeing with Freud, nevertheless believes that sex cures everything. Such marriages usually end in separations and divorces. Concerning the girl in question, I can tell you that she has been married for a number of years and is getting along nicely. But she could not have married before she was analyzed.

The following case may help to elucidate your question: Not long ago, a single woman of 32 came to see me because she was depressed and complained of all sorts of difficulties. She was a college graduate with degrees from Columbia and from the Sorbonne. She told me that a very fine position had only recently been offered to her, but her illness prevented her from taking it. Her ignorance of sex was really remarkable; she seemingly knew nothing about it. If you can imagine that a woman who was a college graduate and who had lived in Paris could be that ignorant, you will understand why she was sick.

She had been treated for years by various doctors. In our

first interview she told me that for years she had been obsessed by the thought of naked men, particularly of their genitals, and this, she thought, was the cause of all her suffering. Well, it is not unusual for a mature woman to think of male genitals. The unusual part of the case was that she had to think of it all the time—that she was obsessed by it. "I did not dare speak of it," she explained. For some reason, I was the first one who inspired her with sufficient courage to talk about it. Now, that woman could have married a dozen times. Many men, ever since her girlhood, had proposed to her, and she was still an attractive woman. But she just could not think of marriage. She was incapable of accepting the sexual situation to which the average woman adjusts herself at an early age. There are men and women, to be sure, whom I call sexual idiots or imbeciles; but in this case the woman's upbringing was chiefly responsible.

Of course, it is somewhat remarkable that one should see such cases today. In 1908, when I started in private practice, I saw such cases galore; but now there is more sophistication. Only the other day, a girl of sixteen asked me what homosexual men and women do. She said her schoolmates had been discussing homosexuality, and she asked me that question as a simple matter of information. Naturally, she will grow up to be quite different from the college graduate I just mentioned. I might add, however, that doctors, too, have asked me the same question.

Question: Whatever happened to Breuer?

Answer: I saw him in 1907, when I had to get his permission to include the first paper he had published with Freud into my first translation of Freud's works.[6] He continued to be a very highly regarded general practitioner in Vienna. He worked scientifically until he died some ten years ago. Breuer did not do anything more in psychopathology. He was not a psychiatrist or a neurologist, and he did not really want to be one. If not for Freud's urging, he would not have published his famous case of Anna O. Although the two were not on speak-

---

[6] *Selected Papers on Hysteria and Other Psychoneuroses* Monograph Series.

ing terms in later years, Breuer always defended Freud when it came to an argument.

Question : There is another question we are concerned about. It has to do with the treatment in the state hospitals and the ability to use a modified form of psychoanalysis. It is also a question of whether one—I mean a psychiatrist—should be analyzed.

Answer : Do what you please about it. It all depends on what you want to accomplish. I wish everyone could be psychoanalyzed. If every psychiatrist could be analyzed, we would have an ideal condition. But if you cannot or do not wish to be analyzed, then you should orient yourself in the fundamentals of psychoanalysis, for through it you will be able to see the roots of a problem which might otherwise remain hidden.

Many of the younger hospital psychiatrists have been analyzed, and many of them are under analysis now; but the number is hardly a drop in the ocean. To be sure, I know that lots of men who do not believe in psychoanalysis are nevertheless doing good work, and I do not want you to think that psychoanalysis is a "cure-all." We say that psychoanalysis is to the mental sciences what bacteriology is to the physical sciences. When I was a medical student, we had many cases of typhoid in every hospital. Today we hardly have any—yet, once a man has typhoid today, I do not think he has any more chance of recovery than he had at that time. The disappearance of typhoid epidemics followed the discovery of the Eber's bacillus and its mode of transmission. We cannot cure the psychoses, or even all the neuroses, but we hope to develop in time a prophylaxis against mental diseases. We say that psychoanalysis has given us the microscope to mental diseases. If you wish to devote yourself to psychoanalysis, you will have to be analyzed. Otherwise, you can do what so many others do. You can accomplish much, as long as you know that all mental and nervous illnesses are not due to a local irritation of the cortex or to some other organic lesion.

LECTURE III

TOPICS :

THOSE of you who are familiar with psychoanalysis may have noticed that so far I have touched on some of its high spots without troubling to go into them thoroughly. I take for granted that you are more or less familiar with most of them; and if not, that you will read Freud's *Basic Writings* to which I referred in my first lecture. My purpose here is to help you understand those things which you read and may pass over. I want you, as psychiatrists, to know how psychoanalysis is applied to your work; and with that end in view, I have tried to point out the part played by Bleuler in the application of the Freudian mechanisms to the study of the patient. Bleuler, the greatest psychiatrist who ever lived, accepted a large part of everything Freud said. He did not follow Freud completely, as I have told you. But I think he accepted all of his basic views; and he definitely felt that without psychoanalysis, psychopathology would not have progressed.

Like Freud, Bleuler stressed the biological part of psychiatry, devoting much of his later work to bridging the gap between the individual and the race. Freud's first approach to biology, following his contributions to sex, was in his book, *Beyond the Pleasure Principle*. In this work he starts with the phenomena that can be observed in the playing of children and elaborates from it the theory of repetition-compulsion; and, leaning on the works of many American biologists, he then laid the foundation for the concept of the life and death instincts, which he completed in his *Ego and the Id*. Here he deals with the instinct as "a tendency innate in living organic matter, impelling it towards the reinstatement of an earlier condition." [1] Bleuler, too, devoted decades of his life to biology but started from a different angle. The objective of both men, however, was to gain further insight into the phenomena of memory as it manifests itself in psychic processes—as you will presently see.

You recall that last week the question arose as to why some people show a tendency to repressing while others do not. I said that Freud ascribed this to a difference in the constitution of so-called normals and neurotics. Now, whether Freudians or not, we all speak of predisposition and constitution, and we often hear of such diagnoses as "constitutional psychopathic inferiority." It is not, however, so easy to tell what is meant by constitution, except that it has something to do with the past or with the patient's ancestry. Of course, even the older psychiatrists always laid stress on heredity. When I first came to the state hospital, we invariably noted: "Heredity denied,"

[1] Cf. *Beyond the Pleasure Principle*, translated by Hurback, p. 44, International Psychoanalytic Press; 1922.

if the patient's relatives failed to give a history of insanity in the family. We simply took for granted that any patient in such a hospital must have had at least one insane relative.

But as a matter of fact, constitution involves more than direct heredity. I remember talking to Freud about this a few years after I took up analysis. Freud, you know, originally thought that the neurotic constitution could be confirmed by the existence of lues in one of the parents. When I told Freud that I did not agree with him, he replied that he had dropped that idea long before and that he had come to believe that constitution involves the individual's total heredity—not the parents, grandparents and great-grandparents, but something that goes back to remote generations.

Obviously, this viewpoint at once brings in the moot question: "Are acquired characteristics inherited?" Biologists have fought over this question for centuries, and they are still arguing about it. As you know, Lamarck was the first to assert that this was true. He was followed later by Darwin,[2] Haeckel, and many other prominent biologists. Of course, anyone who looks at anything in life can see—whether he is a biologist or not— that one brings along much from our ancestry. Biologists tell us that the embryo goes through the same stages of evolution, from the fertilization of the ovum until birth, that the whole race has gone through from the beginning of existence; in other words, that ontogeny repeats phylogeny. But the quarrel among biologists concerns something much more specific. It deals with the question whether traits directly acquired can be transmitted to the offspring. Now, those who support this view do not say that a child whose parents played Beethoven and Tchaikovsky on the piano, for example, will directly inherit the ability to play those specific musical compositions. They do claim, however, that children born of a long line of musical families will tend to be more musical—they will be more likely to absorb music—than those who come from ordinary families. It is not merely that they may inherit long fingers, for ex-

---

[2] *Descent of Man*, Volume III, p. 714, Collier & Son (N. Y., 1901). Also, Bölsche: *Das Liebesleben in der Natur*, p. 220, Diderich (Jena, 1922).

ample, and thus be better pianists than those with short fingers, or that they will tend to musical expression as an emotional outlet simply because they are accustomed to hearing their parents play all the time. It is something deeper than that: it is an innate ability which enables them to be better musicians than those without such a heredity. That fact really seems to have been demonstrated. Books have been written to prove it— particularly as regards musicians.[3] You may find that the same is true in regard to other talents.

Not long ago I reported the case of a lightning calculator [4] —a boy of five, who was able to add long columns of numbers instantly. I have known this case for some twenty years. I first saw him when he was about six, after he had been exhibited in public and before scientific societies. Naturally, a case like this is very fascinating. That boy could neither read nor write. The only written number that he knew at that time was the number "3," and he had learned this number months after he had already manifested his strange talent. I tested him by writing down about a dozen numbers each of five or six digits. I would call them out as I wrote them, and at the end the boy would immediately blurt out the answer. It took me some time to add them, and when I made a mistake, as sometimes happened, the boy noticed it and corrected me at once. He was always right.

Such phenomena are not as rare as you may think. Cases like this have been reported many times, but this was the only one I saw myself. It came to my attention because the father, a poor man, was exhibiting the boy in an effort to make some money. A charity organization worker brought the boy to me and asked what should be done about him. Now, all lightning calculators of whom we have histories lost their talent early in life. Besides, most individuals of this type, at the age of fourteen or a little later, either become praecoxes or just peter out into nothing. The mere fact that such a boy is exhibited and made

[3] Feis: *Studien über die Geneologie und Psychologie der Musiker*, Bergman, (Wiesbaden, 1910).
[4] "Some Peculiar Manifestations of Memory with Special Reference to Lightning Calculators," *Journal of Nervous and Mental Diseases*, Vol. XCII, No. 6 (December 1940).

the object of so much fuss is in itself a bad thing for him. I therefore advised the boy's parents to stop exhibiting him, to ignore his talent, and to give him the same environment as the average boy—that is, to let him acquire an education at school in the usual way.

My suggestions were followed, as I learned later, but I heard nothing more about the boy until about eighteen years later, when I was asked whether I would be interested in seeing him again. I naturally assented and in due course was confronted by the lightning calculator, now a group-up man. I naturally wanted to know whether he was still a lightning calculator. He replied that he had lost this talent at the age of eight or nine, and was now no better in calculating than any average person.

As I have said, prodigies of this type in any field, with very few exceptions, peter out at an early age. Usually, too, their ability is extremely one-sided. They are often what the French call *idio-savant*—idiots in everything else, but savants in one particular specialty. They themselves, moreover, are unable to explain their talent. That little calculator, for example, had no idea of how he did those amazing feats. His talent was discovered accidentally when he was about five years old. His older brother, then ten, was doing his homework one day with some schoolmates. The little fellow kept annoying them by giving the answers to their problems in addition. At first they did not believe him, but then they discovered that he was really giving the correct answers.

The most remarkable thing about these prodigies is in every case the memory. They can remember so much! Yet, while this kind of talent fascinates us when it appears in human beings, we seem quite oblivious to similar phenomena in animals. For example, take the chick that is brought to life in an incubator. Soon after it comes out of the egg it begins to scratch in the straw and will catch grain thrown to it. Just think what co-ordination and knowledge such actions require! One cannot dismiss the thought that such spontaneous acts must have something behind them.

Butler who believes in the inheritance of acquired characteristics says that this chick while still in the egg (which is just a

cell) remembers everything that happened before to its an-
cestors—that it remembers how to do every act necessary as
each stage of its development unfolds. It remembers these
stages in the way that a little child memorizes a poem even
though he cannot read or write. The child can do this in
French or German or any other language that it does not know,
and yet repeat the poem correctly. But if the child makes a
mistake—say, in the third stanza—he won't be able to correct
it without starting the whole poem over again.[5] Like a chick, in
other words, he is able to recite the poem only if he starts
from the beginning.

What we may thus call the "automatic" character of memory is again strikingly shown when a Menuhin or a Heifetz
performs a concerto—a work that may take a half hour or more
to play through. Think of all they must do during this period!
Millions of acts must be memorized and carried out: it is not
only the notes, but the finger positions, the accents, the cre-
scendos, and what not. When you listen to this you must say
to yourself that here is something very prodigious indeed,
that such a performance requires a truly astonishing memory.

You need not even take such relatively unusual feats. Just
think of all the things that you yourself remember in everyday
life. You may make up your mind, for example, to do something in a week from today at five o'clock. You do not have to
think of it throughout the week, but you are reminded of it
and you do it. This same operation can be set in motion
through hypnotism. You tell the hypnotized person that he
will do a certain thing on such a day at such a time. When
awakened, he is absolutely unconscious of what he has been
told, yet at the precise time on the exact day he will do what
the hypnotist had suggested. If you try to prevent him from
doing it, he will show a feeling of displeasure, he will argue
and insist upon it, showing the same thwarted feelings that any
person will normally show when prevented from doing something he wants very much to do. In other words, what can be
demonstrated through post-hypnotic suggestion happens normally every day. Millions of things take place in our minds as

[5] The same is true of grown-ups.

the result of previous impressions that have been put into us throughout our life. If we are thwarted when we try to carry out these operations, we feel uncomfortable. We do not know why we feel this way because the whole process is unconscious.

I am coming back to the point, of course, that memory is an unconscious process. In 1870 Ewald Hering (who, as I told you, was a professor of physiology and the teacher of Breuer) delivered his classical lecture, *On Memory as a General Function of Organized Matter*. Hering said at that time that *heredity*, *memory*, and *habit* seemed to resemble each other insofar as their reproductive powers are concerned; and he claimed that this reproductive power is a function of both animals and plants. The same question was investigated, shortly after, by other men, one of whom was Samuel Butler, author of *The Way of All Flesh*. Butler became fascinated by the problem of memory, and he wrote several works on the subject.[6] Butler concluded that we remember best those things of which we are entirely unconscious. He pointed out, for example, that no musician plays well if his performance is accompanied by consciousness of what he is actively doing. But it was not until the work of Richard Semon that this subject was elaborated upon in a scientific manner. Semon, a great student of Haeckel, was a physician who devoted himself mainly to biology. In 1904,[7] he pointed out that Hering's statement represented more than an analogy, and he wrote a number of books on what he called *Mnemism*, which is defined in Bleuler's *Textbook of Psychiatry* as "memory without consciousness." Semon claimed that heredity, habit, and memory are virtually one and the same thing. They can be observed in all organized matter and are not only acquired but inherited. Semon illustrates his concept of mnemism by citing the experience of a young pup that was kindly treated at home where he was liked and where he had perfect confidence in all the human beings of his own little world. One day, while he was out in the street, some boys threw stones at him. That stimulus, that impact on his body, gave him pain and produced certain ef-

[6] *Unconscious Memory* and *Life and Habit*.
[7] Cf. *Die Mneme*, Engelmann, Leipzig.

fects on his organism. The dog never forgot that experience. He reacted in the same way not only when a stone was again thrown at him, but even when he saw people bend down to pick up any object from the ground. The whole thing—the stimulus with its reactions—was reproduced. In other words, the susceptible organism of the dog was never the same as before. You might say that the situation was similar to what Pavloff later showed as the conditioned reflexes or what we have always called "habit."

Now, such an experience or stimulus leaves an impression which Semon called an *engram*—which means an imprint. This imprint is engraved, as it were, in the susceptible organism; and any organic substance, be it a plant or human being, never loses this engram once it has been made. Later, by association of ideas, this engram will come up and reproduce the same effect as the original stimulus. That process of reproduction Semon called *ecphoria*, which may be defined as a bringing up or a reproducing. Stated more concisely, the associations cause the engrams to be "ecphoriated."

Those terms, like so many in medicine, are Greek, of course. They used to make me angry, but I am beginning to think that their use is justified. They are symbols, as it were, for things whose meaning it would otherwise be difficult to convey. Besides, we cannot take the whole populace into our confidence. Lacking our training and experience, they would distort things beyond recognition. On the other hand, you must not think that designating something in Greek is enough. When I worked in the Vanderbilt Clinic, for example, patients used to come in with all kinds of phobias. It was not sufficient to note that they suffered from anxiety neuroses or compulsion neurosis; we had to write the names of the phobias in Greek, despite the fact that most of us had only a year or two of it in college. To be sure, textbooks give the Greek names of the most common phobias, and the great psychologist, Stanley Hall, compiled a long list of them in one of his works. Even so, we would meet with exceptional cases, and I often found it very hard to recall the Latin and Greek words that would give the name to this particular phobia. Thus, one day a patient in the clinic told me that he was afraid to go out alone. That was easy: I told him he suffered from *agoraphobia*. But after I talked with him a while he said that he was not afraid simply of going out alone; what he feared was that some particular thing would happen when he did go out alone. "You will think I am crazy, doctor," he said, "but I am afraid that when I walk along the street I might see or hear some woman blow her nose."

Well, I was hard put to it to translate that into Greek! In the end I sent that man as a voluntary patient to the St. Lawrence State Hospital. But the main lesson to be learned from this story is that human feelings do not always express themselves in the same way, and that psychiatric or psychoanalytic terms must be comprehended in the broadest sense. Nevertheless, all our expressions are based on something we have known or experienced before. It may be entirely unconscious, and based on something that took place in the individual or in the race. As Semon would say, every person possesses a sum of engrams, some acquired and some inherited, which can be ecphoriated by some association. If you will read his book on mnemism,[8] you will find this ingeniously demonstrated with clinical material from human beings and plants. Bleuler not only accepted Semon's terminology, but his whole trend of thought.[9] For the last twenty years of his life, in fact, Bleuler occupied himself intensively with the problem of mnemism.

Bleuler, as mentioned above, defined Mnemism as memory without consciousness—which is not quite the same as the Freudian unconscious, although the latter also embraces mnemisms. For in his last book, *Moses and Monotheism*, Freud definitely avows that memory is inherited. To give a few examples, I will mention Bleuler's term, *psychoid* ("like the psyche"), which expresses the fact that any organ like the stomach, heart, or liver has its own psyche. That is, the organ acts independently in accordance with its past experiences of

[8] Cf. *The Mneme*, translated by Louis Simon, the Macmillan Co., New York, 1921.
[9] Cf. *Bleuler's Textbook of Psychiatry*, translated by Brill, the Macmillan Co., New York, 1924; and also Bleuler's *Naturgeschichte der Seele*, Springer, (Berlin, 1932).

hundreds of thousands of years. Thus, when a stomach is upset, it is because some unfamiliar thing happened to confront
it: The stomach then acts like a child who cries because it sees
a stranger. That every organ has a memory and a guiding force
is shown in many other ways. Thus, if you strike your finger
with a hammer, it will become elongated or broadened and
swollen; but in time all the traumatized material is removed by
the phagocytes, and the new cells form the finger into exactly
the same size and shape as it was before. There must be some
sort of "information bureau," says Bleuler, which guides the
cells so that they know exactly what to do to restore the finger
to its original form. Another example is furnished by the
amœba which, as is known, makes a stomach of itself when it
wants to digest food. Experiments show that if you put little
granules of sand into its food, the amœba at first will absorb
the whole thing throwing the sand out later. But if this is repeated several times, the amœbic cillia will eliminate the sand
before it absorbs the particle of food. Now, when a human being does something similar, you say that he is reasoning, that
experience has taught him that sand is indigestible. But the
amœba has no nervous system, no brain. Other experiments
have been made with animal embryos which seem to demonstrate Bleuler's psychoid theory. According to the theory of
mnemism, this can be understood only by assuming an unconscious, phyletic memory.

Let me add an example from my own observations, which,
more than anything read, convinced me of the principles of
mnemism. I once brought up a young starling that had been
thrown out of its nest. Since he had hardly any feathers, he
must have been only a few weeks old. My wife and I fed him
by hand for at least two weeks before he could grasp his food.
I finally put two cups in his cage—one filled with food, and
the other with water—and watched to see whether he would
feed himself. Presently he went to the food cup and devoured
as much as he could. Then he went to the other cup, stuck his
mandible into the water, and drank to his heart's content. What
was most remarkable, however, was this: after he had finished

[65

drinking, he began to shake his wings and to take a bath just like an old bird. By what means did he know how to do this—how to go through the motions just like any other free bird? I concluded that this little bird, who had no possible chance of imitating his parents, remembered from his past existence the whole process—that putting his mandible into the water, in other words, acted as a stimulus which caused him to ecphoriate the inherited engrams constituting the process of bathing.

Such observations are quite common. We do not see them so glaringly in human children for two reasons. In the first place, the human being—unlike the starling or the chick—is not born with a completely developed brain. His brain must still grow and mature. Secondly, the human child is surrounded by a totally artificial environment from the moment he comes into life. We do not allow free play to his natural endowments. We invest him with all sorts of artificialities; or to put it another way, we impress too many engrams upon him that are unnatural to his organism. He must abide by them in order to learn how to use them. He is very much in the position of the musician when he first learns to play. The musical beginner must watch the individual notes carefully, and it takes many years before he can play a sonata, for example, and at the same time listen to conversation. The child functions similarly in all his behavior. You impose consciousness on the child with every act that you teach him; and, by our standards, he does not know how to behave naturally until those engrams are so deeply impressed that he is no longer conscious of them. Stated the other way around, as long as the child follows his unconscious impulses, you cannot take him into the parlor; until the acquired engrams become, so to say, a part of his second nature, he has to be made conscious of what he is doing. We prevent him, in other words, from making free use of whatever phyletic inheritance he may possess.

I am very much tempted to go on with these thoughts, but they will lead us too far afield. I brought them up in order to show why Bleuler and Freud believed in the inheritance of acquired characteristics and how they applied these theories to the neuroses. When Freud first published his views on the life and death instincts,[10] many critics asserted that his work savored of mysticism. Of course it was nothing of the sort. It was simply an extension of his investigations into phylogeny; and a moment's reflection will show you that there is really nothing peculiar about these views. We are a product of everything that has happened from the time we and our ancestry were unicellular organisms; and no matter how concealed and unnatural our present expressions are, the phyletic unconscious still influences our behavior. For you, this view is especially important since you will often find amazing mechanisms that cannot be explained by ontogeny alone. But if you will consider "constitution" in the mnemenistic or phyletic sense, you may be able to solve problems which otherwise have no meaning.

Freud naturally went only occasionally into phylogeny. His conclusions were drawn chiefly through observation of patients; and I have already told you, in discussing his theory of pathogenic processes, how he traced the neurotic symptom back to the individual's past experiences, which had been repressed into the unconscious. You will notice when you read Freud that he never talks about a subconscious or a co-conscious—but always about an *unconscious*. To Freud, the *unconscious* is something of which the individual is completely unaware. When a neurotic patient has a pain, paralysis, contraction, or some other symptom, he himself is unable to fathom its meaning. Unless you interpret the unconscious material for him, he will never know what it is—and even then, he will often reject your explanation. Do not forget: what is unconscious is entirely unknown to the patient. His symptom is a distorted expression, and often enough you yourself can judge only by his emotional display what the unconscious meaning may be.

Thus, a woman was once sent to me by the New York Police Department because for years she had been a great nuisance to them. She was a nice sort of person, but she constantly imagined that fiendish men were injecting electricity into her body during the night. She had only the vaguest idea of who these

[10] *Das Ich und Das Es*, International Psychoanalytic Verlag, (Wien, 1923).

[67

fiendish men might be, but she was certain that they injected the electricity into her eyes, her nose, her ears, and her mouth. She would frequently visit police headquarters to appeal for help. Since she otherwise conducted herself properly, the police department wanted to know whether there was any help for her.

This woman was about fifty years old and single. The descriptive psychiatrist would have diagnosed her as a paranoid praecox—which she undoubtedly was, since she had delusions of persecution based on hallucinations of a somato-psychic nature—and let it go at that. But I was interested in this woman from a psychoanalytic view, and I saw her several times. From the way she recited her story, I was impressed by the fact that these fiendish men, while they injected the electricity into her upper bodily cavities, never did so into the openings below the waistline. She told me that they injected the electricity into her legs but never into the vagina or rectum. In telling me these facts, too, she always added: "I cannot understand why a pure woman like me, who has always led a good life, should be treated in that way."

Now, the whole thing became clear to me soon enough. Here was an unmarried woman of fifty who seemed physically normal; she claimed that she was being annoyed by fiendish men who injected something into her which she called electricity, and she protested that she had always led a "pure" life. "This woman," I said to myself, "expresses, in indirect and distorted form, the last gasps of unfulfilled maternity. Under natural conditions, she would have gone the way of all females, but as a result of civilization she was deprived of this." Her unconscious wish, of course, was that some man would inseminate her; but the disguised outward expression was that many fiendish men tortured her by injecting "electricity" into most of the openings of her body. The fact that there were many "fiendish" men indicated the force of the wish for one man; and the fact that she failed to enumerate those openings which relate to the sexual functions, while mentioning all the others, definitely showed the unconscious censorship at work for the purpose of masking the real situation. In other words, instead of saying frankly that she wanted a man to impregnate her, she unconsciously disguised her wish and then projected it to the outside in the form of hallucinations and delusions. To the ordinary psychiatrist, a hallucination is based on nothing and is merely a false perception; but psychoanalytically, a hallucination is an outward projection of the patient's own feeling. This woman's hallucinations, moreover, expressed a negative feeling as well as the positive one: in the language of the unconscious she was also saying, in effect: "I have never had any sexual relationship because I consider it fiendish and shocking. I feared men, and hence I have led a pure life." May we not further assume that her somato-psychic delusions also had a phyletic background?

Of course, a patient like this arouses your sympathy, and you say to yourself: "Poor victim!" When you ask, further, of what she is a victim, the answer is, "civilization." We say that in nature every healthy female finds a mate and reproduces herself. But civilization—the forces we have developed for ourselves in order to regulate our unnatural mode of existence—insists that we control our instincts and especially the mating impulse. If we did not control it, civilization could not endure very long. We have animal instincts, but can no longer function like animals. The animal is still more or less periodic in its mating: it has to get food first, and because the struggle for existence is so hard, it can mate only at certain times. Among primitive peoples the same conditions still prevail; self-preservation comes first. But civilization has changed all that. By controlling the forces of nature, by being able to obtain food whenever he is hungry, modern man's mating impulses are always active. Women still show a periodicity not only physically, but also psychically. Thus, many women experience an orgasm only at certain times and for the rest simply accommodate their husbands in order to hold them. But the average man is *semper paratus*, as someone once put it. It seems that he was phyletically destined to impregnate any œstrous female.

But you can imagine what chaos would result if these instincts were not controlled. Freedom of sex, the dream of some misguided crack-pots, never existed in nature; the struggle for

[69

existence and for mates makes that impossible. In civilization, where stern reality is ordinarily controlled, and where there is a constant striving, therefore, for the pleasure principle, man has to exert additional control by means of a highly developed morality. But morality is nothing but a set of customs which, after long trial and error, the majority believed good for the community. These customs, or mores, were then accepted as abiding principles which all have to follow. Yet people differ. What is best for the majority may be unacceptable to the individual, and hence conflicts arise. The average person, as I have said, comes through these conflicts without serious harm. Others, whose constitutions are too sensitive, cannot always assimilate the restrictions imposed upon them. They cannot reconcile their primitive impulses with the moral standards of the community. Every day, for example, I see young people who begin to act neurotically or psychotically when they reach puberty. They cannot properly dispose of the new wave of emotion which suddenly threatens to inundate them; they cannot assimilate the new situation and develop conflicts which result in pains, doubts, phobias, and obsessions or in hallucinations and delusions.

The woman with the delusions of electrical injections unconsciously expressed such a situation. She tried to repress her whole sex instinct; and she succeeded fairly well until the approach of her menopause, when the last efforts at maternity enabled the repressed material to break through and come to the surface in distorted form. Her symptoms represented a failure in the repression; her ego no longer could hold down the repressed material, so that it worked its way to the surface by devious and inappropriate paths. Had I been able to change her, she would have said, frankly: "I have always had sexual feelings, and I wanted to love a man." But unfortunately she was always completely unconscious of this, and she will never know it. Once paranoiacs develop these distorted mechanisms they are lost to the outer world.

According to the Freudian meaning, then, what is unconscious is entirely unknown to the individual. I mentioned last week, in passing, that a good part of this unconscious material goes back to early childhood before the individual has learned to use words. All parents know that babies show remarkable understanding, and they will tell you admiringly about the many clever and fascinating things their little ones do at the age of a few months or later. But the average person hardly remembers anything of the first four or five years of life. The admiration and amazement which grown-ups express on such occasions is due to the repression of their own childhood. No one likes to recall the time when he was helpless and dependent, and nothing is so disconcerting to a grown-up as to be told by an old mother that he did or said this or that when he was a child. The old mother, on the other hand, loves to recall these things because it takes her back to a time when she was still young; but many a man or woman dreads the weekly parental dinner because they hate to be told how childish they once were.

One must not forget, however, that a child does not start with Locke's *tabula rasa*, with a blank slate upon which nothing is as yet written. As I have repeated, the child brings along an old racial inheritance; and, like any baby animal, it is equipped with a perfect mechanism for self-preservation, of which the parents are seemingly unconscious. As psychiatrists, we are frequently asked to diagnose whether this or that child is normal. I do not mean defective children—it needs no expert to tell that the child is an idiot—but children whose mothers have valid or neurotic reasons for consulting you. I have had dozens of them come to me for such diagnoses. If you think I was always the first one consulted, you are mistaken; most of them had visited several other neurologists and psychiatrists before me. In a recent case of this kind, I was called in to see a little child who was about a year old. The mother, who had some heredity burden in the family—and who had read a lot besides—wanted to know whether there was something wrong with the child. Knowing that every animal feels best, most secure, in its home environment, I advised against bringing the child to my office. As I came into the apartment, I was greeted by the mother, who carried her child, a lovely little girl, in her arms. It did not take nearly as long to get on friendly terms with little Sally as it did with the above-mentioned Fräulein Liebknecht. After I had observed her for a while, I said: "I cannot see anything wrong with the child." But the mother was loath to accept my verdict. She had expected me to "examine" the child—perhaps to open the child's skull or look inside with instruments—and she could not understand how I could otherwise reach any decision.

Well, I was charging her a good fee for my visit, and I had to give her something for value received. In my dilemma, I noticed a photograph on the mantle. It happened to be that of a grandparent. I picked up the picture and put it down in another part of the room. Little Sally followed my movements closely. Then, as I had hoped, she actually pulled the mother to the picture, and made known to her that she wanted the photograph to go back where it belonged. The mother finally had to take the picture and restore it to its original position. Only then did the child stop fussing about it.

This behavior convinced the mother that her child was normal. I naturally had to explain what this experiment meant, and the mother was satisfied I had proved that the child knew its environment well and had immediately noticed a slight change in it. I explained that every animal must have a thorough knowledge of its environment if it is to survive. If a change has been made in one's home during his absence, he will notice it immediately upon his return. And whereas this may not be so necessary in civilization, a child still lives close to nature. I explained that every healthy animal is endowed with the sense of curiosity and that the animal from the start would be in great danger if it did not have it. Inquisitiveness, I said, works for security, and I pointed out that Sally possessed this necessary attribute. I told her that primitive people, like animals and children, rarely leave their own environment, because they are in danger of being killed if they do so. One way of committing suicide in New Guinea is to paddle one's canoe into waters that do not belong to the clan. A native who does this is immediately killed. All primitive people, in fact, do not trust themselves to the outside world. But we, who have been so well and so long protected by civilization, do not use our senses to their natural extent. The child, like the animal, still does; Sally, I pointed out, was suspicious of me when she first saw me—a reaction that was quite natural. But she soon concluded that I was harmless, because she noticed that there was a good rapport between her mother and me.

In brief, my diagnosis was based on the existence of the instincts which every animal brings along when it is born. I first removed her suspicions of the unfamiliar elements that I brought into her environment, and then presented her with a lollipop (furnished by the mother) which appeased her hunger. You know that hunger and love control everything, especially little girls. And last, but not least, I ascertained that she had good perceptive faculties which she used normally.

While we are on the subject of primitive modes of perception, I might add that in civilization all our senses, except sight, become dulled and, as it were, atrophied from disuse; but they are sometimes revived in unusual situations. During the last wars, soldiers discovered that their senses of hearing and of smell became astonishingly keen. One colonel told me that when driving in the dark at the front he always sensed when he was coming to a shell-hole. He would stop, get out, and feel around; and invariably he would find a shell-hole in front of him. The colonel, in telling me the story, added that this premonition must have been an act of Providence. Actually, a shell-hole means a break in the continuity of the ground; this in turn caused a change in the vibrations of the ground as the car approached. Forced back into a primitive mode of behavior, such as moving in the dark, the colonel's senses reverted to their original alertness: his sense of hearing (perhaps also of sight) detected the change, where ordinarily he would not have perceived it. In peace times, of course, he had no need for such acute hearing or sight.

Yet primitive people in the jungle notice the slightest change in their environment—such as changes in leaves after an animal has passed through. Similarly, paranoiacs show extreme awareness of the most trivial changes in their surroundings. The paranoiac will tell you that he saw a man walking on the other side of Fifth Avenue, that the man moved his cane in a special way, and that this signified something definite to him. When we listen to the paranoiac who lays stress on such trifles, we decide that this is delusional; we say the patient is over-suspicious and imagines things. That is probably true; but what the paranoiac does is to revert to an archaic mode of behavior. He acts, in other words, just like primitive man or like animals. In children, these senses and feelings are still very keen and are based on inherited engrams. If the little year-old baby had been deficient, she would not have had such control of her inherited engrams, and she would not have objected to the change in the location of the photograph.

When we analyze patients, we find that the unconscious contains an enormous mass of such material. Some of this material is based on experiences which are of a pre-verbal period, and hence cannot be expressed in words. Virtually all of these early experiences are completely forgotten in the adult; they all merge into the infantile amnesia. In the analysis, patients often "act out" these things, giving expression to them in symbolic or distorted form. They themselves do not know the meaning of what they are doing. You have to interpret it to them; and you, yourself, can frequently judge what it is by the displaced affects. Once in a great while, however, you find ample confirmation for your assumptions. On a number of occasions I had experiences like the following: I analyzed an intelligent man of about thirty-five, and, as always happens in analysis, we came upon many things that went back to his early life. From over-accentuated, obsessive episodes in the patient's later life, I judged that similar things must have occurred much earlier. When I made these interpretations, however, the patient failed to recall them, and frequently was loath to accept them as true. One day, the patient received a letter from his father, a former newspaper editor who was then past eighty. The father, it seems, had kept a diary of the patient's life from birth up to the age of thirty; and he now informed the son that he was sending it by registered mail. The patient had not known of this diary, and we were both curious to see what it contained. To our great surprise, many of my assumptions were confirmed by actual incidents which had occurred in the patient's early childhood. They were recorded in the diary as having taken place before the patient learned to express himself in words. The unconscious, as you see, is really unconscious.

But there is another state of mind—called by Freud the *fore-conscious*, or the *pre-conscious*—which is an intermediate stage between consciousness and unconsciousness. In the Freudian psychology, consciousness is simply an organ of perception. You are conscious t the present moment of what you perceive from your environment, and you are unaware of millions of past memories which you have stored in your mind. Most of these memories are unconscious; they are utterly unknown to you at the present time. But some of them you can recall after a certain amount of effort. They are midway between the conscious and the unconscious, and belong to the fore-conscious part of the mind. The most typical example of this occurs when you try to recall a name that is "on the tip of your tongue." You know the name well, but you have to go through deep thinking before it comes back to you. Very often it is impossible to tell why it returned.

As illustration, I will cite my own experience with a fore-conscious forgotten name—an experience which occurred when I was at Bleuler's clinic in Zurich and which converted me to the belief in the Freudian psychology. Everyone in the hospital, of course, had already accepted the exactness of the Freudian mechanisms; but I was just a novice and was still very skeptical about it. Well, one Sunday on my afternoon off, I sat down after dinner and began reading the German Journal of Neurology and Psychiatry. My interest was drawn to a case that reminded me of one of my own previously reported cases. I started to make a marginal note to that effect, but to my surprise I could not remember the name of my patient. Here— I said to myself—was a fine opportunity to test the Freudian free association method: I would try to recall the name by using the method as described by Freud in *The Psychopathology of Everyday Life*.[11]

I had a long, yellow pad before me, and I began to write

[11] Cf. Freud's *Basic Writings*, p. 35.

whatever came to my mind. This case of mine was a very interesting one concerning a patient in the Central Islip State Hospital. It had furnished the material for the very first paper that I wrote as a psychiatrist, and had given me, as it were, my psychiatric spurs. My first association now was of this patient, and then came numerous engrams and pictures from Central Islip where I had been for about five years. I wrote them down as quickly as I could. I wrote and wrote until it got dark. A colleague, noticing the light in my room, asked me to make rounds for him if I were going to stay in that night. I did so. But I was so absorbed in the problem of testing the Freudian mechanisms that I went right back to my yellow pad. I wrote some more, until finally I said to myself: "If this is the way the method works, it is not for me." The process was entirely too slow for my temperament, and I thought it silly to tarry so long on a little thing like this.

Yet, I could not drop it. I was not hungry for supper. I continued writing until about one o'clock in the morning but was still no better off than before. Disgusted with the whole thing, I finally went to sleep. Yet at about 4:30 I was again awake. As I lay in bed, the same associations began coming back to me—and all of a sudden I knew the name of my patient. It had come to me as if by inspiration.

Now, Freud tells us that we forget because we do not wish to remember, or because we do not consider the forgotten material important. For example, most of us who study algebra and differential calculus in college forget the rules very soon afterward. We forget because most of us never really cared for mathematics and have no reason for retaining it. But I have a friend, a professor of mathematics, with whom I used to do my school homework. He did not forget; he remembers all he learned as well as hundreds of other rules that I do not know. Again, I doubt whether a brain surgeon ever forgets his anatomy of the brain. But many of the psychiatrists I meet do not know a thing about it; they feel that they have no need for remembering it. In brief, we forget a thing because we do not wish to remember it, because we are not interested in it, or because of an unpleasant affect that goes with it.

You will find that this holds true for all your reactions. At Burghölzli, we used to investigate these mechanisms at every opportunity. Everyone at the hospital was steeped in them, and you could not make the slightest mistake without being forced by someone to explain it. If you made a slip in talking, you had to have a reason for it. If you made a mistake in your case records, and someone happened to notice it, you had to explain it in the presence of everybody. We learned in this way not to be afraid to tell things and to face the truth.

But, why did I forget that name? I forgot it because the case was connected with a painful situation as you will presently hear. This patient of mine had tried to set fire to St. Patrick's Cathedral in broad daylight. He had collected a lot of newspapers and set them afire; he had been arrested, taken to Bellevue, and later sent to us at Central Islip. I was then a junior physician. My senior was Dr. Fowler. He made the examination on admission, and I continued the observation of the patient after he had finished. Fowler's notes showed a diagnosis of dementia praecox, but something about the patient made me disagree. "What is he, then?" asked Fowler when I voiced my dissent. Now the patient had been perfectly willing to talk; he seemed confused, but he showed no such affectivity as you would find in the praecox "It looks to me," I finally said, "like some form of epilepsy—some dreamy state following a pre- or post-epileptic episode." "Oh," said Fowler skeptically, "you must have read that in one of those Dutch books." He was referring to the fact, of course, that I read Kraepelin and everything else of German psychiatry that I could get hold of.

Well, the patient cleared up in about ten days. He then told me that he had had five similar attacks. He came from Montreal where he was an editor of a French journal. When he got these attacks, he said, he would run away from home (poriomania), go on drinking bouts (dypsomania), and set fire to buildings (pyromania). He had set fire to a church in Canada and to a railway station. On his last attack he had run away from Montreal and gone to London where he joined the army for the Boer War. A few months later he woke up to find himself a sergeant—which in ordinary life was the last thing he wanted to be.

The case was, of course, very fascinating, and everyone complimented me on my unusual diagnosis. I then looked up all the available literature on psychic epilepsy and prepared the material for publication. Everyone in the hospital was anxious to see the case, and my ego rose to great heights. The superintendent, who ordinarily paid no attention to the scientific part of the hospital, now visited us, discussed the case, and then said that he would like to report this case before the Suffolk County Medical Society. Naturally I did not like this new development, especially since my colleagues began to tease me about it. I finally finished writing up the case, however, and brought the material to the superintendent. As it happened, I had quoted a lot from German, French, and Italian sources. The superintendent, who did not know these languages, assumed that I had used English references. When I told him that I had read everything in the original, he decided that I had better go and read the paper myself. But by that time the program was already printed, with "Dr. Z." as the announced speaker. When I appeared at the meeting, everyone in the audience assumed that I was merely sent to read the paper for him. They were all greatly interested in the case, but the confusion about the paper's authorship spoiled the triumph for me.

In other words, there was a strong ambivalence about the whole episode. I was pleased but also very displeased. We always like to impress our fellow beings with what we can do. If you know a good joke, you like to tell it to an audience, and when they laugh, you laugh with them. In this case, I felt that I did not get proper credit for my achievement. Moreover, Dr. Z. sort of ordered me to let the Long Island Medical Journal have my paper. But I wanted to publish it in the Journal of Nervous and Mental Diseases and had already talked to the editor about it. Thus, the whole thing left a bad impression upon me. It was because of this unpleasant association that I could not remember the patient's name.

How did it come back to me? As I kept on writing my associations (I covered almost thirty pages), one scene always reappeared. The Central Islip State Hospital in those days was an undeveloped region of about 1200 acres. It was full of woods, mainly scrub oak which harbored rabbits, quail, and other small animals. We often had brush fires, and these were always great events. Squads of patients would be lined up to transport pails of water which had to be brought from some distance; and altogether it was quite exciting. This recurring scene centered on one such occasion when attendants brought guns to shoot the rabbits which had been driven from the brush by the fire. I was standing on one side of the superintendent with Dr. Murray on his other side. Dr. Z. was militaristically inclined, and we all had to parade regularly and wear naval uniforms with bars on our collars designating our rank. (I found out later why, despite being a "land force," we nevertheless wore naval uniforms. Z. confided to me, one afternoon, that he had once taken the navy examinations and flunked. He had then unconsciously made a little navy, so to speak, of his own!) Well, in this scene I saw the picture of an actual occurrence. I saw Z. in admiral's attire, and heard him say to one of the attendants: "Let me have that gun. I want to see if I can get that rabbit." He aimed, fired, and missed; and the rabbit continued on its way. Murray and I glanced at each other with a pleased look.

When I afterwards examined my associations, I found that this scene had come up twenty-eight more times than any other association—this picture of Dr. Z. aiming and saying: "Let's see whether I can get this rabbit." When I awoke that morning and heard those words again, I suddenly knew the name of the patient. It was *Lapin*. Those of you who know French, of course, know that *lapin* means "rabbit." [12]

Had I been more skilled in psychoanalysis, I would have found the name after the first three pages. But I had not yet learned that you must interpret. The whole thing was really in this one association. Z. was trying to get that case away from me (Lapin), and he did not get it. As I have said, I might have

[12] This episode occurred about two months after I left Pierre Marie's service in the Hospice de Bicêtre, Paris, where I had naturally improved my knowledge of French. In Burghölzli too, there were many French-speaking patients. I was, therefore, quite fluent in French at that time.

known the name in ten or fifteen minutes. But I was a tyro and expected that it would be brought to me on a silver platter. Psychoanalysis is not easy. You must be alive to every association—much more so than in any other form of treatment. You have to pay particular attention to little things just as the surgeon who goes into the abdomen must know how to cut or avoid this and that.

Well, I could hardly wait that morning until nine o'clock when we had our staff meetings and reported everything that happened in each service. I recounted my experience with great excitement. My colleagues smiled and said: "Now you are a Freudian!" From that time on, I was convinced that by associations and interpretation you could really discover important things. Of course, this forgotten name was in the foreconscious. Had it been in the unconscious, I would never have gotten it.

To recapitulate, we have, according to Freud, the following states of mind: *conscious*, *fore-* or *pre-conscious*, and *unconscious*. They may be represented as in the following diagram:

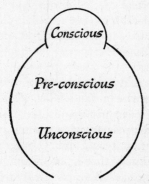

Consciousness is just a perceptive organ. The fore-conscious contains material which is under resistance because of its association with something that is disagreeable. It is not so forgotten as to be unconscious. One remembers the situation in general but cannot recall some important detail, e.g. the name, Lapin. The unconscious contains only what is very fully repressed. Now, I have said that we repress what is or was con-

ceived as disagreeable or painful. Whenever I make this statement, I am always sure to encounter opposition to it. My opponents admit that no one wants to suffer physical pain and
does everything to avoid it, but for some reason they cannot
assume the same for psychic or emotional pain. The fact is,
however, that the mind acts in the same manner whether it
concerns physical or mental suffering. Before the advent of
anæsthesia, whenever there was an amputation, the patient
fainted away or became unconscious when the pain became
severe. Serious accidents in which the organism suddenly finds
itself in a dangerous situation, whether they leave an injury or
not, are invariably followed by amnesia. All this shows that
the tendency of the mind is to keep the individual away from
pain. People frequently claim, however, that they do remember the worst things that have happened to them. Thus, one of
my dissenters claimed that the death of his fiancée was the
worst experience of his life. He said that he had never felt so
much grief, and yet, he remembered it. Nevertheless, when I
asked him to tell me when this event occurred, he could neither remember the date of the month, nor was he sure of the
year. It took considerable time and effort before he could recall them. To be sure, only schizophrenics can actually tear
themselves entirely away from such an experience and treat it
as *non arrivé*.

The unconscious, finally, consists of much that occurred
early in life, before the individual is word-conscious. These
early experiences leave only the affect or the cathexis of the
situation, and if disagreeable, it is naturally repressed. Later,
this material can be expressed only by acting it out through
similar and cognate situations, or it sometimes appears in
"masked" or "concealed" memories. Here the person vividly
remembers something as having definitely occurred which
could not possibly have happened. One of my patients claimed
to remember when he was baptized at the age of a few days.
Such memories conceal something which is unconscious and
repressed. Last but not least, the unconscious contains many
inherited engrams which are of a phyletic origin and which
ordinarily serve the two primary instincts.

QUESTIONS AND ANSWERS

Question : We have seen so many hysterics in older people, where it does not seem to be based on sex—but rather on money, as in cases of so-called traumatic neuroses. How do you explain this?

Answer : It is simply a question of interpretation. What is money? What is gold? Next to sex, money is the greatest substitute for libido. Its acquisition not only eliminates the problem of hunger but also sex. But money, or gold, as we shall show later, is intimately related to the anal-sadistic pre-genital phase of sexual development.

The whole thing is a question of the pleasure-principle in life. In the broad sense, a gratification of this principle is what the organism craves. The little child, you know, has no sexual life in the adult sense. Yet it wants lollipops and other sweets, and you can get the greatest favors from a child by catering to his mouth. Later in life, some people gradually give up genital outlets and regress altogether to oral outlets. In senile dementia it is often a total regression to infantile orality, such as thumb-sucking. Money undoubtedly plays a great part in our civilization, but to understand its force we must know more about its origin. At all events, traumatic neurosis is a more complex problem than may seem at first sight. Thus, it is well known that such cases recover as soon as they receive financial compensation for their so-called trauma or when they become convinced that there will be no compensation.

Question : Is it true that things with an emotional basis are remembered longer than things that are just casual?

Answer : Logically, that seems so. Memory is selective, however. Things that do not impress you obviously have no special bearing on your own life, and there is no reason for retaining them. I am sure that we never forget anything once experienced, but we cannot keep everything consciously before us.

On the other hand, we sometimes remember things that do not seem to be very important simply because they are appendages to something that has to remain repressed. The point is that you never forget anything that you wish to remember. If you make a date with a girl you love, you are right there on time. In the army too, you never forget to execute an order. If you do, your superiors are justified in thinking you were either careless or drunk. In brief, you never forget anything you feel you must do. If you do forget, it is because you do not wish to remember.

Question : Is there any difference in the repression between a neurotic and a psychotic?

Answer : The only difference, as I will show you later, is this: In both, the ego runs away from a disagreeable situation and thus tries to close any exit to it. In both the repression fails; but the neurotic keeps in touch with his environment. He may complain of all kinds of symptoms; yet he goes to work every day, and his friends may see nothing wrong in him. The psychotic, however, tears himself away entirely from reality and usually makes use of the mechanism of projection in the form of hallucinations and delusions. He turns his back on the outside world, and hence we consider him peculiar or unmanageable. The repression is the same in both, but the psychotic reacts more vehemently to it.

Question : Why is it that the hysterical symptom is not dissipated over a long period of time? Why does this neurosis last so long?

Answer : Well, I told you that the hysterical symptom is a substitutive gratification for the sexual act; and you know that sexual outlets may be dissipated for the time being, and yet after a very short time there is need for another sexual outlet. In other words, hysteria replaces an instinct which has to repeat itself. That is the nature of an instinct. After a good meal you often say: "I'll never want to eat again·" but in a few hours you are again hungry.

It is the same with the hysterical symptom, which, I don't want you to forget, is a substitutive expression for the sexual act.

Question : Is it possible by hypnosis to stop any physiological functions—say, stop the circulation of any part?

Answer : Some have claimed that. I was never able to do it.

One can influence by hypnosis only those things which are functions of everyday life. Ordinarily, when one does something of a dynamic, emotional nature, it will be accompanied by its affect. One becomes pale, for example, on seeing something terrifying, or grows red in the face on hearing something embarrassing. There is nothing miraculous about producing or influencing such phenomena. On the other hand, it can be done by everyday means. A hypnotist once claimed that he could produce a blanching of his whole arm by mere suggestion. It was found that he had a very hard rubber ball in his arm-pit; by pressing the ball against the blood supply of the arm, of course, he could readily shut off the circulation.

There is no hokus-pokus about hypnotism if you look at it scientifically. What you see on the stage is nearly all fake. Anyone can learn to hypnotize. I assure you that you can accomplish the same thing in the waking state if you are confronted by a person who looks up to you as an authority. Ignorant people as well as children can be easily influenced through hokus-pokus. But sensible people are usually influenced only by logic. Of all the wonders ascribed to hypnosis, you can discard about ninety per cent.

LECTURE IV

I HAVE endeavored so far to show you how we look at patients in terms of Bleuler and Freud, and I have pointed out that this process differs in every way from the methods used by their predecessors. We look upon patients as dynamic beings who, in their neurotic or psychotic states, strive to adjust themselves to reality much as we do in our so-called normal

state. In Freud's terms, all individuals—whether normal or neurotic—are a product of constitution and fate. We have also
seen why Bleuler and Freud believed that constitution, or personality, is inherited.

Now, the subject of personality has always been of interest
to psychiatrists, and many observers have found that people
differ right from the start in their behavior reactions to life.
Long ago Kretschmer claimed that there is a schizothymic and
a cyclothymic character in normal life. He presented these
views in his *Physique and Character*,[1] a book which you should
all read and know well. Bleuler modified Kretschmer's views
slightly by saying that whatever we find later in the psychoses
is nothing but an exaggeration of the original type of personality. In other words, persons from the very beginning are
either of the schizoid or the syntonic type,[2] and it is merely a
question to what extent a person is one or the other. A schizoid
person is one who weighs everything before making up his
mind. He strives to settle situations or the various elements in
any situation by saying: "I must think about it and see whether
that is so." He might be called the natural conservative. The
syntonic personality, on the other hand, immediately throws
all his feelings for or against the situation in question. He will
say: "That is wonderful!" or "That is terrible!" assuming an
attitude toward it at once. He may change his mind soon after,
but he has always a definite opinion one way or the other.[3]

If the schizoid type becomes insane, he will develop schizophrenia; the syntonic, on the other hand, will develop manic-
depressive psychosis. But these two types of personality are

[1] Cf. Ernst Kretschmer *Körperbau und Charakter*, Springer, (Berlin,
1921). English translation: *Physique and Character* (London: Routledge;
1936).
[2] Bleuler used these terms instead of Kretschmer's "schizothymic" and
"cyclothymic." Like many others, he considered "dementia praecox" a
misnomer since such patients are not always praecox nor do they necessarily show dementia. Bleuler instead coined the name, schizophrenia—
from Latin *scindo, scindere* ("to split")—basing it on the main characteristic of the disease, which is a splitting or a schizoidism. The other term,
syntonic, comes from *syn-tonus*—"Of the same or uniform tone."
[3] Cf. Brill: "Schizoid and Syntonic Factors in Neuroses & Psychoses,"
American Journal of Psychiatry, April 1925.

86]

also to be seen in everyday life, in all normal people. The syntonic is the old-time book agent, the ebullient, traveling-salesman type who can approach you easily and talk freely. The other, the schizoid type, is serious and reflective; he can control and accumulate emotions and bide his time before giving vent to them. For this reason, it is the schizoids who are largely responsible for culture and civilization. The syntonics, however, furnish the ergies, the dynamics to put things into operation. In partnerships you often see a combination of both types. If you want to establish a successful business concern, have a good schizoid executive in the office, and a good syntonic salesman on the outside. I have seen this combination so often that I have said to myself: "The good Lord must have purposely put those two fellows together." It works out excellently; but put two schizoids or two syntonics together and there is trouble. A certain amount of adjustment, of action and counter-action, is necessary in all these things.

At all events, these two types of reactions exist constitutionally both in the individual and the race. Sometimes one seems to merge into the other. Thus, children are in general syntonic in their behavior; but as they grow older they become more cautious, and their actions resemble more the schizoid type. All people, whatever their reactions, gradually become more schizoid as they grow older. Still, you can distinguish between a real syntonic child and a real schizoid child at a very early age, and in private practice you are often called upon to do so. I have now been in private practice for more than thirty-six years, and I have an ample number of cases which confirm my early diagnoses.

Like individuals, there are also schizoid and syntonic races. If you live among our American Indians or if you visit them, say, in their pueblos, you will be struck by their seeming stoicism, unresponsiveness, and reserve. This schizoid quality is characteristic at all times; it is not simply due to the fact that they do not know you and hence are suspicious. Thus, I have a good friend, a Pueblo Indian whom I have known for many years. He sometimes visits me, brings people to meet me, and shows in many other ways that he considers me a good friend.

Yet in my conversations with him I do about ninety per cent of the talking. (And I am not syntonic by nature; I am sort of mixed, according to Bleuler.) After I am all through, he will give me some such monosyllabic answer as: "Yes, that's so." The last time I saw him, I broached the matter of psychic suicide, a subject in which I am very much interested. I know that primitive people can die at will and frequently do so. I thought I had an excellent opportunity to discuss it with my Indian friend while on this visit to New Mexico. I began to explain to him some cases I had seen, and I told him what had been written about its existence among Indians. He listened very attentively; and when I was through, his answer was: "Yes, we know about it."

On the other hand, if you go to a neighborhood like Harlem, where the colored race predominates, you will be immediately impressed—even "infected"—by the vivid emotional emanation. The Negroes as a race are syntonic; they are very accessible, very ready to talk if you give them the slightest encouragement. You will find similar contrasts in other ethnic centers. But, of course, the schizoid and syntonic types are not always seen in pure form. As a result of cross heredity they are often very much mixed, both in individuals and in races. It is for this reason that we always had to use diagnoses like Meyer's "allied to dementia praecox" or "allied to manic-depressive psychosis," and why Bleuler coined the term "schizoid-manic" to designate the psychotic mixture of these two entities.

Now, our object in studying types of personalities in conjunction with psychotic and neurotic conditions is to ascertain how the average individual reacts to external situations. Freud tells us that personality depends on constitution and fate, and Bleuler tells us the same in different words. In brief, if an individual with a schizoid personality should get into emotional difficulties, he is likely to develop a psychoneurosis or a schizophrenic psychosis. My feeling is that one does not merge into the other as a great many people think; that is, I do not believe that a psychoneurotic—i.e., a person starting as an hysteric or neurasthenic—can later become a schizophrenic. I do not believe that any such thing exists. I did think so in the beginning

88]

of my career. But as I continued to study my cases I found that such patients were really schizophrenic from the beginning, that they were diagnosed as psychoneurotics long before the psychosis was fully developed. Neurasthenic, hysterical, or obsessive trends are frequently noticeable in incipient schizophrenics.

In other words, the schizophrenic personality represents an evolution. It is constitutional, and in many cases it seems as if directly inherited—because one finds schizophrenics or very schizoid personalities on one or both sides of the parents. Thus, in a recent case, the father of my schizophrenic patient was a very shut-in type of person. He sometimes did not talk for weeks; yet he was steady as a business man and was a good husband and father. He himself told me that he was "peculiar," and that there were also eccentricities on the mother's side of the family.

I said a few moments ago that psychoneurotic and psychotic manifestations follow special paths from the beginning—that one does not merge into the other. You must be careful in this regard when you are making a diagnosis. I once had a patient who came to me as a compulsive neurotic. He had many obsessions, phobias, and ceremonials. Yet I noticed that in comparison with other compulsive neurotics he was impervious to treatment. He began to develop hallucinations, and despite seeing him regularly four or five times a week, I could do nothing to stop it. He started by saying that the obsessions were so vivid that he could virtually hear them. Gradually he became inaccessible and finally showed a perfect picture of schizophrenia. It was the greatest surprise to me at the time because I had considered him a psychoneurotic. On further consideration, however, I found that his history, his heredity, and his whole mode of development were distinctly schizophrenic.

The prognosis may not be of so much importance in hospital cases. But in private practice you must be able to tell the relatives something definite about the patient's future, for your career depends on this. Here you must be guided mainly by the affect, or you will get into all sorts of difficulties. That is true not only in psychoanalysis, but in the practice of psychiatry as well. You will always be right in giving a fair prognosis if the patient has a good affect—no matter how actively his hallucinations may run.

It is often the little things that help you in diagnosis. Last week, you will recall, I told you about my experience in tracing the forgotten name of my patient, Lapin. But I did not tell you how I concluded that he was an epileptic, and not, as my senior had diagnosed him, a dementia praecox. I did not just guess at the diagnosis. I based my opinion not so much on the symptoms (for the patient was uncommunicative) as on a hint derived from a paper written by a Russian psychiatrist named Tchitch which I had read a year or two before. The paper, which appeared, I believe, in *The Alienist and Neurologist*, reported the history of a murderer who had butchered his whole family. The murderer had been found sleeping soundly near the mangled bodies, and he stoutly denied that he had ever killed anyone. Tchitch diagnosed him as an epileptic even though he had never had fits. His diagnosis was based on a sign which Tchitch claimed to have discovered in all epileptics, whether they had attacks or not—namely, a peculiar luster in the eyes, which the author described as a dull, metallic luster. Now, it is difficult to make up your mind just what a "dull, metallic luster" is when you look at anyone's eyes. I could not describe it definitely any more than Tchitch had been able to do. Perhaps I was able to recognize it because at that time I was very much under the spell of Fuhrman's *Diagnostik und Prognostik der Geisteskrankheiten*,[4] a little book which laid much stress on physiognomy. I used to go around the wards and study the physiognomy of the different patients; and, thinking of Tchitch's "dull, metallic luster," I imagined that I could see such a luster in the numerous epileptics in my service. Lapin seemed to be confused and to show a dull, metallic luster in his eyes. Subsequent examination revealed that he had never had any *grand* or *petit mal* attacks to his knowledge; but he undoubtedly had the psychic equivalents of the attacks.

I must control my temptations to reminisce about my early psychiatric experiences, for I am here to lecture on psycho-

[4] Barth, Leipzig, 1903.

analysis. As you can see, I got on this track in my endeavor to stress the fact that the psychoanalytically-minded psychiatrist must do more than just label cases. He must pay strict attention to every expression, to everything said and done by the patient from the moment he lays his eyes on him; and, most important, he must learn to translate the patient's symbolic language which can be understood only by the method of free associations. Thus, a patient may suddenly develop an inability to swallow. After a while you discover that the symptom goes back to a time when the patient, unable to accept something you said, had protested with the words, "I can't swallow that." Or, a patient dreams that she is trying to get away from someone and cannot run. Next morning she wakes up and actually cannot walk and then has an "astasia-abasia" which lasts for years. You can remove the symptom only if you trace it back to its origin. In other words, when you make your diagnosis it is not enough to note merely that you are dealing with, say, a compulsive neurotic or an anxiety hysteric. You will at once have to figure out what this patient is trying to tell or to do through his symptoms or how he is trying to dodge certain difficulties in order to get along in life. He is using his neurotic symptom to reduce some tension, and you must try to discover the nature and origin of this tension. The patient, for example, may complain that he cannot see well when all the oculists say that there is nothing wrong with his eyes. His new glasses are good for a day or so, and then they give him trouble. You ask yourself: "What is wrong there?" The patient evidently is exaggerating something which bothers him; he has certain anxieties which incapacitate him—which tend to interfere with his normal behavior. The eye trouble is merely his particular form of symbolic expression.

Another person may complain that he suffers from chronic constipation. After you see him for a while, he will tell you that he must go through certain ceremonials before he can have a bowel movement: he has to sit down and make a crude drawing of a woman and then throw his knife or some pointed object at this picture. Only when he makes a direct hit at the heart can he move his bowels; that hit acts as a cathartic. (I have actually reported such a case.) [5] Or, the patient may be a psychotic. He may complain that there is something very peculiar about the automobile he drives. He thinks either that there are people who are tampering with the engine or that the engine itself acts like a demon. "Doctor," he will ask in perplexity, "how does that happen?" You can see at once that you are dealing with a form of projection the mechanism of which can be compared to the mode of thinking in primitive people.

Such paranoid complaints and behavior may appear utterly meaningless, but there is always something definite behind them. Psychotic or strange behavior can often be seen among children and primitives. Thus, I recently read a book on Australia,[6] in which the author describes the ceremonial of burial and mourning. The description tells how the aborigines act and what sounds they emit, and goes on to say that their way of expressing real mourning is to move their bowels. In their ceremonial they become more and more excited until the function takes place, when the yelling group all shout the word "bowel movement." Now, if you know anything about the anal-sadistic phase of childhood, which I shall discuss later, such peculiar actions, instead of being merely strange or disgusting, assume very definite meanings. The little child in the nursery often moves his bowels to appease his mother. Feces is the first gift that children can offer to mother.

Behavior like that of my patient who had to aim and hit a symbolic woman's heart in order to move his bowels and like that of the savages just described, shows you that we still have not got away from our erstwhile primitive. We still do many things of which we are unconscious, and the neurotic and psychotic symptoms show them in disguised form. Not everything, however, has been solved. You have every opportunity to become famous. Freud and Bleuler are dead now, and if you will follow up any of the problems they brought up, you will have much to contribute.

I have been talking about the neuroses and the psychoses as

[5] Brill: *Freud's Contribution to Psychiatry*, p. 142.
[6] Cf. Bates: *The Passing of the Aborigines*, p. 174, Putnam, 1939.

they are formulated in terms of personality, and in this connection we must now consider Freud's scheme of the mental or psychic apparatus. Last week, you recall, I discussed the concept of the *conscious*, the *fore-* or *pre-conscious*, and the *unconscious*, and I sketched out what these stages of the mind are supposed to contain. But in 1923, after many years of observation and study, Freud described this psychic apparatus more schematically.[7] Freud states, to begin with, that the child at birth brings into this world a sort of primitive, unorganized mentality which he called the *Id*.[8] The id is vague, unclassified, and lawless. It brings along those ergies which help the child to maintain itself. The motive power which instigates the id into action is supplied to it by the two great instincts—hunger and love. The child wants food and it wants comfort, or love; it cries out for these from the moment of birth and obtains them from the mother. These instinctual needs are expressed freely and openly, for they are driving forces which are necessary for the child's self-preservation. Therefore, the id strives constantly to satisfy these demands. It knows nothing of time or space, and it always remains the same throughout life.

The id mentality is what controls the child's behavior, and that is why the child does not conform to what we call order and regularity. Yet, as time goes on and as the child comes in contact with the outside world, a part of the id gradually becomes modified; for the child soon finds that he cannot get things even though he craves them deeply. Through his senses, moreover, he learns that the outside world is not friendly but hostile and dangerous. He is attracted, for example, by the beauty of a burning flame, but his sense of touch teaches him that fire is painful and must be avoided. He learns through his sense of hearing that certain sounds mean danger and are to be feared. In other words, part of the id, coming into contact with the outside world, develops awareness of the hostile forces which threaten the organism. This portion of the id is then modified into what we call the *Ego*. Having gained these ex-

[7] Cf. *Das Ich und das Es*, English translation by Rivière, *The Ego and the Id*, Hogarth Press, London.
[8] *Id* is Latin for "it."

periences, the ego then tries to control the rest of the lawless id. Freud compares the ego to the bark of a tree which becomes hard and tough as a result of its exposure to the elements. The bark at the same time protects the tree, and the ego exercises a similar function in relationship to the id. The ego is its protective mechanism.

To be sure, when we speak of these mental components, we do not want you to conceive them as tangible things. They are terms invented to express certain forces. Yet the psychic apparatus, although an invention, is one based on experience — on observations of normal and abnormal people whose thoughts we have examined, on observations of children, and on a study of primitives in the manner described by Freud in his *Totem and Taboo*.[9] As Freud has aptly stated, the psychic apparatus is something like a microscope: it makes no difference whether its component parts are of copper or steel or pasteboard; what you see by looking through it is the important thing.

Now, the ego has been described in many ways by many thinkers. According to the Freudian concept, as I have just said, the ego is a modified portion of the first psyche or id which has developed a knowledge of the outer world and its hostile forces and henceforth restrains the individual from following the promptings of the id. Bleuler ascribes to the ego many other functions which in a way contradict Freud's formulation. Psychiatrists long before Freud have always maintained that everything in life is definitely determined. The rank and file of psychiatrists believe in absolute determinism. Ordinarily however, most persons feel that they can do what they want regardless of motives and according to their own free will. Bleuler explains this feeling of freedom of will by telling us that the complex of psychic functions which we call our ego has the peculiar capacity to observe itself. Now, it is in this complex of cerebral organization — in this ego — that the resultant of an individual's strivings is formed. That is, of the many strivings which struggle with one another, one gradually gets the upper hand; and this resultant, which is formed in the ego, we then conceive as our will. That is why we feel

---

[9] Cf. Freud's *Basic Writings*, p. 807.

that our actions spring from our own free choice. Thus, if I am hungry and go out for a meal, I think that I merely felt like getting a meal and hence do so. But any biologist will tell you that the desire to eat with all its attendant functions is the result of millions and millions of ancestral evolutions—that it started in the unicellular organism when life first began. We think we choose to do things because we so perceive it, but actually we perceive only a very small fragment of the act. The bulk of it we know nothing about. In brief, all our actions are definitely determined by definite causes. But since we know only one small part of our acts, and since this fragmentary perception occurs in the ego, we call it free will. Of course there is no such thing in psychiatry or in the natural sciences. Everything must be determined.[10]

Let us return, now, to the psychic apparatus as defined by Freud. I have said that the ego controls the primitive tendencies of the id, and thus protects the organism against the hostile forces of the outside world. If it were not for the ego protection and control, the individual would soon be annihilated. In the very young child, the ego which has not had sufficient time to develop is still weak, and thus there is the need for adult protection and guidance. The defective also has a weak ego—but here it is due to a lack of brains. Left to himself, an idiot or low-grade imbecile would not long survive. They never develop an ego strong enough to control their id tendencies; without protection, they would follow these tendencies blindly and soon meet with destruction. I was once consulted about a boy who had to be watched almost constantly, because otherwise he met with accidents on the streets of New York. He had been repeatedly run over, his leg had been fractured, and he had suffered many other injuries. A doctor had urged the parents to send the boy to the country out of harm's way. But there too he met with an accident at least once a week. When he was brought to me, I found that he was an idiot, attracted only by motion and sound. At the age of 15 he had none of the fears that one ordinarily sees in a child of one year

[10] Cf. Brill: "Determinism in Psychiatry and Psychoanalysis," *American Journal of Psychiatry*, Vol. XCV, No. 3 (November, 1938).

or less. He did not have a sufficient ego development to restrain him from following his id promptings.

While I am on the subject, I may add however that it is incorrect to compare such a defective to an animal as has so often been done. The idiot lacks in cerebral function both qualitatively and quantitatively, and, as in the animal, he has not the capacity to form associations like the normal. But the animal brain though a simpler machine, nevertheless, is perfectly adapted for the animal's needs. Observe birds for example, when they forage for food. They do not do it complacently. The other day I watched the starlings on my lawn and was impressed by their constant alertness for any hostile force that might be near: they thrust their mandibles into the grass in search of food but raised their heads every few seconds to make sure that there was no danger. The bird, or any animal which has a need for food, is free to go anywhere and get it; it has learned by previous experience, however, to be careful and keep out of harm's way. The ego controls its id demands. Even large beasts of prey do not forage in the daytime. The tiger prowls at night simply because in the daytime it would be too dangerous. Every animal has a good ego organization.

But in man (and by that I mean in all human beings) the ego undergoes a still greater modification. In order to be a civilized person—to possess sufficient morality to follow the Golden Rule—one has to attain a greater development in the ego. This higher modification we call the *Super-ego* or *Ideal-ego*. The ego alone prevents the id from putting its desires into operation by calling attention to the dangers from without. But the super-ego, which represents what we call "conscience," prevents the individual even from thinking of evil desires. It imposes a sort of categorical imperative—the "Thou shalt not!" of Kant (who was himself a terrific compulsive neurotic). Possessed of this super-ego, the individual refrains from doing wrong not because it is impractical or dangerous but simply because it is not the thing to do. The criminal, who usually has a good ego, will say: "I cannot go ahead and rob this place because it is daylight and I will be caught." But the average person will never think of doing such a thing under any circumstances. To him it is honesty for honesty's sake, morality for morality's sake. If that super-ego develops, the person is civilized. If not, he may be a criminal or otherwise difficult to deal with in civilized society.

Thus I once examined a criminal who, in trying to rob a bank, had murdered two of the employees. "Why did you shoot them?" I asked him. "Well, doc," he replied earnestly; "I gave them a fair chance. If they'd stuck up their hands, like I asked, I wouldn't have shot them." A man like that, of course, has a sort of moral blind spot; he lacks a super-ego. Or take the case of Fierenza, who, while sexually assaulting Mrs. T., suffocated her. I asked him whether he had ever gone to prostitutes, and he replied that he had consorted with them regularly for many years. "Why did you have to assault Mrs. T.?" I asked. "Why did you not go to a prostitute?" His answer was that ever since he had become engaged to marry a nice girl, he had given up consorting with prostitutes. This too shows a weak ego and hardly any vestige of a super-ego. Giving these two super-ego weaklings psychiatric names did not prevent the State from electrocuting them.

To be normal in our state of society, a person must have a super-ego or conscience. But even primitive people, so-called savages, have a super-ego or conscience. Naturally, it is different from ours for it is based on different values, but it is equally strong. What our conscience tells us is right in our society differs greatly from what is judged right by the conscience of the jungle pigmy. In the ultimate analysis however, it works much in the same fashion.

You will notice in the diagram (copied from Freud) the three mental states I described last week: the *unconscious*, the *fore-* or *pre-conscious*, and the *conscious*. As you see, the repressed and the unconscious are in the id below the level of the ego.

These forces of the psyche are constantly at work, both in normal and abnormal mental states, with the ego in the center of the struggle. The id tendencies remain the same throughout life: the primitive instincts of hunger and sex are continuously

Psychoanalytic Psychiatry

and imperiously demanding new gratifications. A glimpse into the innermost recesses of the average citizen in fact would probably reveal incredible situations—phantasies which are extremely shocking to himself. There might be death wishes

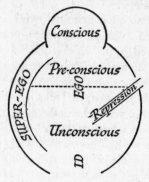

against his competitors, desires for someone else's wife or property, cravings of the type that he would dread if they became conscious to him. However, an average person with a good ego and super-ego unconsciously disposes of them through suppression, repression, and sublimation. The neurotic, whose ergies run deeper and faster, is likely to become disturbed when something untoward affects his primary instincts.

Thus I was once consulted by a man who had developed a sudden attack of anxiety. He was afraid that he was going crazy, that his lungs were diseased, and that many other dire things were going to happen to him. After I talked with him for a while, he said: "You know, doctor—the strongest man in the world would get sick if he had to go through all the troubles I've had in the past year. My wife is dying of cancer; there is no hope for her. I must be with her all the time. She is in constant, terrible pain, and the doctors can do little to help her." Of course, such a situation is a very sad one. The man was a devoted husband; he was in his early forties, and his wife was even younger. Still, he was organically in sound health, so that there must have been some additional reason for his neurotic symptoms. I discovered soon enough that his sister-in-law had become a devoted helper in the home because of her sister's illness. She took care of his children and even went out with him to help divert his mind from his troubles. He confessed that—for "solace"—he would occasionally kiss her; and he added naïvely that she was a very fine woman. Well, you know that we "evil-minded psychoanalysts" do not believe that a man can kiss an attractive sister-in-law and have the incident pass unheeded by the organism. And, in fact, my patient confided before long that the thought had come to him that if his wife should die, he might marry her sister. It seemed dreadful to him that he should think of such a thing when his wife was not yet dead, and he added that his sister-in-law was really the last one he would want to marry.

Now, here was a man whose love life—particularly in so far as the instinctive part of it was concerned—had been suddenly cut off as a result of his wife's illness. His sister-in-law, who resembled the wife whom he so deeply loved, undoubtedly stimulated him, but he repressed it. Yet we know that repressed libido in neurotically predisposed people frequently changes to anxiety; or, in the light of what we know about the psychic apparatus, we would say that the anxiety was the result of tension between the ego and the super-ego. But when anxiety is generated, it has to be "bound" to something. If a person suddenly becomes frightened but does not know why, the fear or anxiety is intolerable to him. He is overwhelmed by it and immediately tries to attach it to some specific cause.[11] It is much easier to control fear if one is able to say: "I am afraid because of a disease or a snake or a thunderstorm." Thus my patient tried to bind his anxiety to some specific reason. There were, as you see, good reasons why this devoted husband developed the anxiety. His effort to bind it to his brain (insanity) and his lungs was also well determined. In other words, his id tendencies were actively reminding him that his sexual needs should be gratified. But as far as he knew consciously, he was just nervous. If he had not come into such close contact with his sister-in-law, whom he met only on rare occasions prior to his wife's illness, the anxiety attack might

[10] Brill: *Freud's Contribution to Psychiatry*, p. 220, W. W. Norton, (New York, 1944).

not have occurred. From my study of the case, I can definitely state that she acted as an *agent provocateur* for his neurosis. Of course, the forces that were contending within him were entirely unconscious to him.

The story is told about a man whose wife died and who was suddenly missing the next day just as the funeral procession was about to start. Everyone began looking for him, and finally his brother-in-law found him in the kitchen with the maid on his lap. "Jack!" he exclaimed. "What's the matter with you?—At such a time!" "Well," came the reply, "does anybody know what he's doing at such a time?"

Well, this joke belongs to what we call tendency wit or the type of wit which serves to express sexual feelings which modern civilization strives to suppress. Tendency wit gets around such taboos by presenting the sexual situation in a distorted manner and thus affords us pleasure from sources otherwise forbidden to us. The joke just mentioned, one might say, expresses rank sexual cynicism—as if to say the greatest loss this husband sustained through the death of his wife was his sexual outlet which any other woman could supply. Indeed, it recalls the cynical saying, *Sublata lucerna nihil discrimen est inter feminas.* But the comic effect of this wit comes from the element of surprise. The last thing we would have expected the husband to do at this time would be to indulge in love-making; and his excuse was equally surprising. If a person is under a strong spell of acute depression, he might do something very drastic but harmonizing with that affect. In this case he might have wept aloud, or might even have attempted suicide—but not something so entirely alien to the situation. His act would show that he never loved his wife and that he did not possess the decency to hide it on this sad occasion. We would not hesitate to say that he lacked a super-ego or conscience. But why do we laugh at this joke? Simply because of our resistance to the institution of marriage.

Technically, the mechanism of this witticism depends on displacing the accent from the inexcusable immoral behavior to something which would in no way mitigate it. The man is reproached for brutally violating the moral code of matrimony on a most solemn occasion—his wife's funeral. His excuse implies that the transgression was due to the overwhelming depression occasioned by the loss of his wife; but he ignores the fact that the depression should have caused him to act in an entirely different manner.[12] In everyday life, such pleas are often made in murder cases. The jury sometimes justifies the crime if the act was unpremeditated and committed under an acutely developed affect—as in cases involving the so-called "unwritten law."

However, the fact that we have such jokes only shows that the primitive, the id tendencies are forever lurking about and seeking expression. Modern marriage implies more than just mating. The average married couple is kept together by social and spiritual forces which transcend in time the sexual factor which put the marriage into operation. Nevertheless, it is a fact which we cannot ignore that whenever men are threatened with the loss of their love objects, as in the case just mentioned, their libido seems to flare up and they consciously or unconsciously begin to look for a new love object.

I could report many cases of this kind, although not all of them become neurotic as in the example just given. I have in mind two very good and steady husbands who confided in me that they were annoyed by erotic phantasies and dreams whenever their wives were ill. Neither of these men wanted to get rid of his wife, and one of them occasionally had extra-marital relations. It seems that the id has no moral sense. Beaver[13] tells about a native of New Guinea who left his wife in care of his father while he went on a trip. When he returned, it was only to find that his wife had died during his absence. He bitterly upbraided his father for not having cared for her properly; and in his anger, says Beaver, he "violently raped the first woman he met in the bush." Judge Beaver, who could not understand the native's peculiar reaction to his wife's death, adds that anger and grief were the only reasons the native could

[12] Fierenza's excuse for assaulting Mrs. T. was based on displacing the accent (brutal sexual assault) to a trifle—to the fact that sexually promiscuous men sometimes stop running around with prostitutes when they become engaged to respectable girls.

[13] Cf. *Unexplored New Guinea*, Lippincott & Co., 1920.

give for the crime. We would say that the native openly expressed what the neurotic patient did through his anxiety and what modern man does through such jokes as the one mentioned above. To be sure, we have advanced morally and spiritually, but unconsciously marriage is nothing but civilization's way of curbing modern man's sexual aggression.

To return to our anxiety patient—I wish to add that he told me in all sincerity that his sister-in-law's kisses were maternal in nature despite the fact that she was a woman of only 25 or 26. There was no doubt that the patient's anxiety was also determined by fear of losing his mother for whom his wife was a good substitute.

That men of intelligence and culture frequently act like morons in matters sexual only shows how strong the repressive forces of sex must be in this type of person. Such cases are often surprising even to me. Thus many years ago I was consulted by a clergyman—let us call him a bishop. He was brought to me because of an anxiety hysteria. He was a man past sixty, and his main fear was that he would go insane. He had been repeatedly assured by physicians that there was no sign of insanity in him. "Nevertheless, doctor," he told me, "I begin to have a tingling in my ears when I hear of certain things or when I read of someone committing suicide because of a nervous breakdown. At such times I am almost beside myself."

Now, in those days it was still a common belief that masturbation produces insanity. Everybody was plagued by this idea because the museums "for men only" and the quack clinics exploited this fear for their own advantage. As far as I recall, every normal young man suffered from a "masturbation complex;" I myself was freed from this idea in my senior year at the College of Physicians and Surgeons, after attending a clinic on masturbation by Professor Taylor, our instructor in genito-urinary diseases. I am sure the whole class was in sympathy with the dejected patients, all of them "confessed masturbators," who had applied for treatment because they feared insanity. After presenting a number of such cases, Professor Taylor turned to us and said: "Gentlemen, I think that all these ideas about masturbation are exaggerated. I do not believe masturbation produces insanity; I do not think it does any harm at all." At this, the whole class burst into spontaneous applause, so strong was the feeling of relief with which we heard these remarks. Taylor was an old, experienced professor, of the type one now rarely sees; he was an empiricist and he knew what he was talking about. I recall that when we were dispersing after the clinic, one of the audience, an elderly physician, came up and said: "Now, Professor Taylor, you made the remark that everybody masturbates. I would like to take exception to that; I never did." "Well," Taylor replied, "you missed a good thing!"

When the bishop told me about his fears, then I immediately thought of this wide-spread belief. The bishop had been a widower for over twenty years, and it occurred to me that at least he might be worried by nocturnal emissions—another *bête noire* of those times. I delicately got around to this subject, but the patient assured me that he had no such worries. In brief, his story turned out to be this: He had a ward, the young daughter of a deceased relative, who had been virtually brought up in his home with his own daughters. She was now away in college, and she would only visit him when she came to the city. At such times she would occasionally sit on his lap as of old, and he would pet her like any of his own daughters. But suddenly he began to notice that his feelings had changed toward this ward. He no longer felt indifferent when he kissed her, and on one occasion, about a year or so before seeing me, he had actually had an erection. It was, of course, a great shock to him, but it soon passed from his mind and the episode was forgotten. It was not long after this incident that the symptoms of his neurosis began to appear.

Here again, the need for sex gratification, which was evidently dormant in this man for so many years, was suddenly awakened by his innocent behavior with his ward. His ego ordinarily controlled this impulse, but having unwittingly allowed himself to be led into temptations, his id, as it were, ran away from his ego. It was only natural that his strong superego should participate in the struggle and thus produce feel-

ings of anxiety. In other words, his conscience reacted power-
fully against these primitive feelings, and the tension thus
generated produced in turn a strong need for punishment—
which manifested itself in the phobia of insanity and in other
fears.

When you study mental behavior, then, the main thing to
remember is that we are controlled by the two systems I have
previously mentioned—the intellectual system based on experience and the emotional system based on the ergies. In the
normal, this noöpsyche and thymopsyche are proportional; in
the neurotic and the psychotic, there is a disproportion between the two. How to find your way in these apparent in-
congruities I endeavored to show you in the simple analysis of
the forgotten name, Lapin. I wanted to demonstrate to you,
by a simple example of the type you will find in *The Psychopathology of Everyday Life,* how difficult it is to unravel anything by the use of free associations and interpretations. But
the analysis of simple examples of forgetting, mis-writing, or
mis-reading, which are frequent occurrences in the life of every normal person, demonstrate that there is hardly any gap
between the so-called normal and abnormal. Both kinds of individuals express themselves practically in the same manner in
all their activities, be they normal or pathological. It would be
an excellent thing to apply this investigation to yourself. (I can
assure you that you are as good a subject for study as any you
can find in the textbooks.) If you will only observe yourself
and see how you constantly try to dodge difficult situations in
daily life by means of slips, you will learn to understand the
utterances and acts of your patients.

In other words, there is very little difference—as far as adjustment is concerned—among the neurotic, the psychotic, and
the so-called normal. They are all trying to keep their emotions
under control; they are all trying to reduce the tension which
is constantly accruing within them. The tendency of the human organism is to keep tension at as low a level as possible,
because an increase of tension is felt as painful, and a decrease
as pleasurable. (That is known as Fechner's principle of the
tendency to stability.) Thus, if you are hungry, you are apt to

be more irritable than usual. Every married woman will tell you that her husband acts this way if the dinner is not ready on time. It seems that as soon as a man's heart is reached through his stomach, he becomes a different person. I have no doubt that the same is true of the other sex. That is why we have so many fine restaurants and night clubs in New York. The young man who does not take his girl to dine at one of these places hasn't much chance of reaching her heart.

To remove or reduce the constantly rising tension is the task of every living organism—of all human beings. All normal behavior, as well as most abnormal symptoms, are calculated to help people move around in their environment with as little tension as possible. Our whole cultural development, as well as all comforts of civilization, are based on that one mechanism. I do not know whether you are aware of the fact that the schizophrenic process is itself an adjustment of this nature which the patient constructs for himself in order to disburden himself of intolerable tension. It was for this reason that Freud was originally loath to treat such patients by analysis.

When the above-cited young woman strove to repress the seduction episode and developed hysterical attacks, she merely defended herself against an excess of painful tension. Imagine her predicament following this experience. On the one hand, she would have liked—was even anxious—to have lived through that experience; but on the other hand, the moral forces within her were adamantly against it. Following the episode, the struggle continued unabated: she was constantly assailed by the contending forces of desire and rejection. The resultant hysterical attacks were annoying, to be sure. Still, they were a means of dismissing the original and more painful experiences from consciousness, and at the same time they afforded her a substitutive gratification for what she had missed.

Select any praecox in your service and devote time to him, and you will find that the patient has made a little world of his own because he could not stand the outer world. Praecoxes have torn themselves away from the world they could not tolerate and retired to their own little world to live more peacefully. In the world that they construct, they need not care whether a Roosevelt or a Willkie is President or whether Hitler invades a continent. Judging by their apathetic behavior in regard to external impressions, you infer that they do not feel anything; yet, as I have already shown, they do. Sometimes after many years, when they suddenly seem to wake up and become accessible — (or if you can bring them back in the manner I described) — you will then find out about their inner world, and if you will contrast it with their former life, you will see that they were merely trying to reduce painful tensions. The schizophrenic as well as the psychoneurotic processes are adjustments in themselves.

Briefly, every individual is dominated by the two primary instincts of hunger and love: he has to have food, and he has to exercise his sex functions. What was the matter with that girl who seemingly suffered from the epileptiform attacks? She was really trying to live through her maternal instinct — sex, and she was thwarted by her civilized standards. It is easy enough to think ill of those who suffer shipwreck on the rock of sex, and to designate them weaklings, degenerates, or perverts. But if you study them you will find that they are merely unfortunate beings, who, for some special reasons for which they are not at all responsible, became sexually abnormal. Constitution and fate, as I have said, determine whether the individual comes out well or badly. If you will look upon his struggle in terms of the forces of the psychic apparatus, you will not only see why he acts in this particular manner, but you will also see the whys and wherefores of his whole behavior. Here I also want you to remember Bleuler's theory of identism, which states that the psyche is nothing but a cerebral function. If you will understand the way the psyche functions, you will have no trouble in diagnosing and in treating your cases intelligently.

Before closing this lecture, I would like to make a few remarks about a class of patients who consciously suffer from sex tension and who come to you for advice. I can best illustrate what I wish to say by the following case: I saw a young widow not long ago — one of those enlightened, artistic types who feel that they are enlightened particularly about sex yet find it impossible to manage their own sex problems. She spent some time bewailing her lot, and then exclaimed: "I think I am just a damn fool." I assured her that psychiatrically I considered her normal. Yet she insisted that there must be something wrong with her, adding that many men had made sexual advances to her, but because of her high moral standards she had rejected them all and then suffered for it. She had come to me now because she was having an unsatisfactory affair with a young man. He was a nice enough fellow who took her out and traveled around with her a good deal, but he made no advances whatever toward her. She sought help because she was full of intolerable tension and just did not know how to rid herself of it.

When you see such patients, you wonder what you can do for them. They do not show any pronounced symptoms by which you can classify them as psychoneurotic or psychotic. Nor can you label them as "psychopathic" or "constitutionally inferior" because they show no such characteristics. They invariably struggle with a manifest sex problem which the average person not seldom encounters; but they, being very sensitive or neurotic (that is the only appellation I can give them), cannot settle it. In years gone by, they consulted no physicians about such problems. They got around them in some way or other or finally developed a neurosis. Nowadays they know that they can talk to us freely about sex, so they consult us. Invariably they pose the question: "Shall I or shall I not?" and expect you to tell them to go ahead. There is only one answer that you can give—and that is: "Follow your moral code."

This woman, as I said, was neurotic; that is, she was a sensitive person who could not just do something and forget it. If I had said to her: "Why don't you go ahead and sleep with this fellow?" I doubt whether she could have done it. By virtue of her upbringing, she really did not know how to size up the situation confronting her. Evidently the young man liked her as one would a sister; as a sexual object, she apparently had no appeal for him. There may have been something wrong with him; he may have been a homosexual. I do not know. But if I advised her to go ahead and have a sexual affair with him—

as some psychiatrists and general practitioners do—the young man might have rejected her, and that would have enhanced her feeling of inferiority. If she had had a sexual affair with a man who creates such doubt about himself, there would surely have been trouble. You will always make a mistake if you advise any person about his course in sexual behavior. The only thing you can do is to enlighten and help clarify the problem. Thus if your patient thinks he is getting softening of the brain because he masturbates, or because of some unusual sexual practice, you naturally explain that that is not so.

Why should you not give them any sex advice? Sex is an instinct which dominates every animal at a certain period of its life. The average person despite our modern way of suppressing and controlling sex somehow manages his life fairly well in this respect. We now have very good works on the subject of sex, and the average person has had a chance to read them and derive enough knowledge to serve his needs. If he is nevertheless ignorantly inhibited, there must be something wrong with him. One cannot just tell him to go and get a girl. I have seen people who followed such advice and then came back in great disgust. Some of them contracted venereal disease; they did so in spite of the fact that the man who gave them the advice warned them and instructed them how to guard against it. All of this means that there is something neurotically wrong with such a person and that it necessitates treatment rather than mere advice. Hence, never give any advice on sex behavior. The average person does not need it, and the moron or defective will always go wrong regardless of advice. If the patient is of normal mentality, give him enlightenment.

My statements apply to sex in general. Nor do I necessarily mean illicit sex. As a psychiatrist, especially if you are also listed as a psychoanalyst, you will be asked all sorts of questions about sex. Thus, I have in mind a doctor of about forty who consulted me not long ago. When I asked him what his problem was, he replied: "I would like to get married." "Well," I said, "this is a funny place to come to. This is no marriage agency." He then explained that actually he did *not* want to get married. It seems he had no urge for sex at all; sex simply never appealed to him. He was one of those people whom I have termed "sexual idiots." [14] There are such people —people who have no sex sense whatever. This doctor convinced me that he never experienced any feelings that I could connect with sex. His parents however, could not understand why he remained single, and they naturally urged him to get married. I have seen a number of such sex defectives. They are like people who are born color-blind. To understand such problems, it behooves you to make yourself proficient in sex knowledge. This man had no neurosis; it was seemingly constitutional. He was very pleased when, after a few hours' examination, I gave him this opinion.

In the case of neurotics, if you once remove the inhibitions, they will then do as well as you and I. They will find legitimate or illegitimate outlets without need of physicians' help. The young widow whom I mentioned before had a mild neurosis, and I sent her to someone for analysis. When she recovers, she will be able to manage herself like anyone else. She will then, like all average women, sense very quickly whether the man with whom she comes in contact is normal or abnormal. It is only the neurotics who get mixed up and need help. In brief—don't advise! Explain!

QUESTIONS AND ANSWERS

Question : You spoke about constitution and fate—can you give us a definition of fate?

Answer : Fate is whatever strikes you from the environment: in other words, accidental factors. For instance, you might get the measles if you happen to be around someone who has the measles. On the other hand, you might inherit a certain diathesis. That is constitution.

Question : Last week someone asked you about traumatic neuroses.[15] I was wondering whether the same thing applies to the war neuroses.

[14] Brill: "Sex and the Physician," the *Urologic and Cutaneous Review*, Vol. XXXIII, No. 11 (1929).
[15] Cf. Lecture III, p. 82.

Answer: I visited Bleuler soon after World War I, and I discussed with him the war neuroses. I have also been connected with the Veteran's Hospital Number 81, which was originally a neuropsychiatric hospital. Bleuler said that the so-called war neuroses had nothing to do with the war. I asked him whether the war might not at least be considered as a provoking agent. "You can call it that, if you want to," he replied. "All the so-called war neuroses are of the same old type as those we have always seen—the same schizophrenics manic-depressives, or traumatic neuroses which we have always known. The war has not increased any of them, despite the enormous hardships undergone for four years by millions of men."[16]

Every once in a while I see cases that are supposed to be traumatic neuroses, but they never are. Some people take refuge in disease; they are prepared for it, and any accident may precipitate an attack. Not long ago I happened to witness an accident in New Jersey. It involved some young men and women who were going to a party when their automobile was struck. One of the young women was badly shaken up, and I urged her to go to the nearest hospital to have herself examined. "Oh, no," she replied; "We have this party to go to." Well, if she had gone right home she might have gotten a bad traumatic neurosis, and the illness would then have been attributed to the smash-up. But that young woman had no time for a traumatic neurosis.

Question: You spoke about the hysterical young woman who reacted neurotically to the man's attempts at seduction. How could she have conducted herself at that time without getting neurotic over it?

Answer: She could have said something like this to him: "My dear fellow, if you think you are going to get me by force, you are crazy. You will have to do better than that." A normal woman would have acted that way and nothing would have happened to her. You must remember that the average person does not get into such a commotion as she did.

[16] For a fuller discussion of this subject, cf. Brill: "The Etiological Relationship of Trauma to Schizophrenia, *Medical Record*, March 5, 1941.

She was naïve about sex as many neurotics are. That is why sexual enlightenment has been advocated for the past fifty years or more. In my opinion however, this has not modified the situation as much as some think. The neurotic retains a blind spot for sex despite all available knowledge and information.

I myself have worked very hard for sexual enlightenment since 1908 because I felt that it was particularly valuable for those who are sensitive. It saves a lot of trouble later if parents know the forces of sex and start early in controlling them. Yet, with all the sex enlightenment of the past fifty years, the neurotics and psychotics are still here. The other night at a lecture, I was asked what will happen to us if the psychotics continue to increase at the present rapid rate. My questioner cited very high figures. "Well, I do not worry about it," I said. "If most of us are going to be crazy in so many years, the psychotics will take as good care of us as we are taking care of them now. It is not going to be so bad."

Question: That point you mentioned about schizoid personalities being hereditary. I was at a gathering last night where there were school teachers and general practitioners. They could not understand how a schizoid personality could be inherited in that strict sense of the word. They felt that a thing like that was like "nature versus nurture." One man cited the case of his own brother-in-law, a professional man, whom the family had known for years. There was no trace of any mental illness in the family. They were highly educated people. Yet this individual became mentally ill with dementia praecox, and they could not understand it. His environment seemed to be good.

Answer: Well, doctor, you should have been able to answer this question. Dementia praecox has nothing to do with education. I am very sorry for people who know so little about this problem. I can forgive ignorance in teachers but not in physicians. As a psychiatrist, you must have often heard people say "My brother (or son) never showed the slightest sign of dementia praecox until the disease suddenly appeared." You undoubtedly know that every mother of an idiot child will tell you, "He fell and hit his head when he was a baby." If I had been in your place, doctor, I would have said to them: "Gentlemen, you don't know a damn thing about schizophrenia."

Question : Does *everything* come down to the two instincts, hunger and love?

Answer : Yes—hunger and love, and ramifications of them. Some people have separated those instincts into partial impulses, but self-preservation and procreation of the species are what it all comes down to. Freud modified these concepts, as I will show you later, but still it comes down, fundamentally to the same instincts.

What human activity is there that does not come under these two instincts? Of course, some activities may be very much deflected from the main instinct so that the average person will find it hard to classify it. For instance, I had a patient who was interested just in stones. He called himself a "petrologist"—not a geologist. He had no scientific interest in stones, but simply liked to collect them wherever he traveled. Thus, he had a stone from Rome, a piece chipped off the Pyramids, and so on down the line. Can you imagine anything drier than collecting stones in this way? You will understand however, when I tell you that he was a bachelor of 48, with a marked anal-erotic component. He was very tidy, very pedantic, very systematic. He rarely bought a new suit and once boastfully showed me an overcoat which he had worn for nineteen years, mending it and cleaning it himself every spring. He had no interest in anyone. He was a teacher of mathematics, lived on a small income, and simply collected stones. The connection will be more obvious when I tell you that he also suffered from extreme constipation.

Of course, I need hardly add that the further the libido is displaced from the original source, the more difficult it becomes to recognize it.

Question :Where does the super-ego come from?

Answer : It comes originally from your parents, your school, from the police, from the surrounding society. In the beginning however, it comes from the father and mother. The father is the great authority in the home where everyone fears him. The child's first fear therefore emanates from him. The mother also plays a large part in the development of the super-ego. The mother is the great aggressive force in childhood: she gets hold of the child, washes and cleans him, and does many other things which the child resents. It is, as I shall show you later, a very complex development, but it starts with the parents, who lay the foundation for it.

You will see this remarkably in your psychotic cases and particularly in people who have committed crimes. As I have said, the normal person has a super-ego which prevents him from committing crimes. Of course, I do not mean that the normal person will not cheat a little on his income tax or that he will not drive his car beyond the speed limit. Such offenses are distinguished even in law as *malum prohibitum*—that is, merely prohibited crimes, in contradistinction to what the law calls *malum in se* or things that are crimes in themselves, such as murder and robbery. The average person refrains from committing such crimes not because the law will punish him, but because his super-ego, his conscience, prevents him even from contemplating them.

LECTURE V

TOPICS:

IN discussing determinism last week, I described the ego as it is presented in Freud's psychic apparatus and also as it is conceived by Bleuler. The psychoanalytic conception of the ego is broader; I might say that it is meta-psychological in the

114]

Freudian sense, whereas Bleuler's concept of the ego is more or less restricted to psychiatry. In any case, I went into this subject because I am particularly anxious that you try to formulate for yourselves what we mean by "free will" and what the process of "willing" actually is. I believe that no one explained it as simply as Bleuler. I can assure you that, for all intents and purposes, his description is true and covers everything perfectly.

The moot question of "free will" has occupied the attention of psychiatrists from the very beginning of this science. Philosophy and religion have quarreled from earliest times over that concept. According to science, as I said in my last lecture, there is no free will. But when we are asked as experts to testify on the question of criminal responsibility, we are forced to testify in accordance with the legal concept, which states that if the person knew the nature and quality of his act and realized that he was committing a wrong, he was sane and responsible. Yet, as believers in determinism, we know that those who think we have perfect control of our actions see only a very small part of the whole—not more than perhaps a drop of the ocean. I devoted much time to this problem, when I was first confronted with the question of responsibility. If you are interested, you will find this subject discussed in my paper, "Determinism in Psychiatry and Psychoanalysis," [1] which I wrote several years ago.

But to demonstrate to you the process of determinism at work, I would like to cite something that happened right here last week. At the end of my lecture, one of you asked me for a definition of "fate." I answered that fate refers to environmental or accidental factors, and by way of illustration I said that you might contract the measles if you were accidentally exposed to them. Now, that is what I answered—and to all appearances my choice of illustration was simply something that happened to pop into my mind.

But, as you will presently see, there was much more to it. I

[1] *American Journal of Psychiatry*, Vol. XCV, No. 3 (November 1938), also "Is Punishment a Deterrent?" *Federal Probation*, Vol. VII, No. 1, January-March, 1943.

had been talking to you for two weeks, you recall, about determinism and free will. Well, I was reading the *Times* two Sundays ago when I saw an advertisement of $1.98 books. Ordinarily, I do not look at ads, and besides, I have more books than room for them. This time however, I was struck by one of the titles advertised; it was Mark Twain's works. I thought to myself: "You have not read Mark Twain since you were in college, forty-five years ago." Now, I am one of Mark Twain's greatest admirers, and on occasion I have referred to him and his writings. When I saw this advertisement, it occurred to me that I had only one of his books, *Tom Sawyer*, in my home. I decided to get his works and read them again. I had what you might call a sort of nostalgia for Mark Twain. I therefore ordered the book—and at the same time I ordered two others from the list. One was *Lincoln's Own Stories* and the other a book on jokes. I found out later that I already owned the Lincoln book. I ordered the joke book because I am interested in wit as you have probably observed.

Now, ordinarily one would think that I ordered those books simply because I felt like it—but listen! The first thing I did when I received the volume of Mark Twain was to page through it until I came to "The Turning Point of My Life." For some reason I stopped there and began to read. As I said, I had not read those works for at least forty-five years. I can assure you that I did not remember the title of this essay. In fact, I did not remember anything about it at all. On reading it however, I found to my great surprise that Mark Twain here gives the whole theory of determinism. Indeed, everything I have tried to tell you in ten times more complex form you will find presented in "The Turning Point of My Life" in a concise and delightful way. The essay is really a treatise on determinism, but instead of employing the terms "constitution" and "fate," the author uses *temperament* and *circumstance*. How delightfully he defines them! He starts by saying that the *Bazar* had asked people to write on the turning point of their lives, and this had impelled him to write his essay. He goes on to say that a turning point means a special event in one's life. But, he adds, there is no reason to call it a turning point, for it is

116]

only a conspicuous event which really is no different from tens of thousands of other events that led up to it. He then states that the conspicuous event in his own life was the occasion when he became a literary man.

He goes on to tell how this happened. His father had died when he was eleven years old. Evidently he was an unruly boy, and his mother had a hard time taking care of him. Matters reached a climax when an epidemic of measles broke out in the small Missouri town where he lived. Every day children died of the disease. All the other children were kept at home for fear of infection, and the young Sam Clemens had no one with whom to play. There was no fun; as he says, "All you heard were hymns." In desperation, he decided to visit one of his little friends who had the measles and catch the disease from him. He ran over and got into bed with his friend. The patient's mother discovered him and brought him home. But young Sam had already caught the disease and was soon confined to bed with a severe attack.

After his recovery, his mother decided that she could no longer manage him. She therefore apprenticed him to a printer. There he read a lot, became interested in literature, and so developed into a writer. This, concluded Mark Twain, was the conspicuous episode of his life. The measles were responsible for his becoming a literary man.

You can now see how my memory worked! When I answered, "Fate is getting the measles," my illustration was determined by what I had read more than forty-five years ago and then completely forgotten. That is also the reason why, after talking to you on determinism, I was "accidentally" attracted to Mark Twain. Unconsciously I must have remembered "The Turning Point of My Life." But, consciously, I assure you, I did not. In short, there is a definite determination for every memory, and there is no way of getting away from it. That is why you must look for psychogenesis in your patients if you want to understand them and their symptoms.

I spoke to you last week about the psychic apparatus as Freud has given it to us. I tried to show you that when we look at the neuroses and the psychoses we now have in mind their relation to the ego, the id, and the super-ego. The id, as I said, contains the primitive impulses and ergies which are brought along at birth. The individual, if left to himself, would try to live through these primitive instincts and impulses just like any other animal. The result, however, would be chaos, and so, from the very beginning, civilization strove to curb these blind ergies. It is just that struggle which produces what we now call anomalies of adjustment in the form of neuroses and psychoses. When we say that *a neurosis is a conflict between the ego and the id,* we mean that the primitive instincts—or the tendencies that emanate from the id—conflict with the ego which represents the outer world. The id tendencies always remain the same, and if you are not in a position to gratify them, you develop tension which is painful. The individual, whether he is a child, a savage, or a philosopher, always strives to reduce that tension. Ordinarily this can be done only by satisfying the need which generates it. An animal which tries to do this either succeeds or is destroyed in the attempt. But we civilized beings cannot do this directly. On the basis of morals, religion, or whatever you may call it, we have developed within us a super-ego, or conscience, which works against the primitive tendencies. Conflicts then develop which, in neurotics, cannot be settled definitely one way or the other. The id tendencies are repressed, but then the repression invariably fails, and the result of the struggle manifests itself in distortions which we call symptoms.

Let me illustrate our theory by another hysterical case I once analyzed. The patient was a young woman of about 29, who for years had been treated for a pain in the arm. It was supposed to be rheumatism or neuritis. But her doctor, after hearing me speak at a meeting of the Academy of Medicine, decided that she belonged to the type of case I had described. He sent her to me, and in a short time I had the following story —a story which you might hear from any young woman. About eight or nine years before, when she was a high school senior, she had met a young man who was studying at an Eastern college—say, Princeton. A friendship developed which continued right through his graduation, when he went to another university to study engineering. But he continued to correspond with her and to visit her at vacation time. Things went very nicely, and the young woman (as well as her family) expected that he would marry her. The proposal, however, never came. The young man confided in her all his hopes and plans for the future, but, unlike more aggressive fellows, he never spoke of marriage.

The young woman naturally thought that he was merely waiting until he had a job and a sufficient income to support her. Time went by, until finally she received a letter announcing that he was coming to see her because he had just obtained an excellent post as representative of his company in South America. Her hopes rose. The young man came and spent a week at her home. They had a fine time together. He walked and talked with her, held her hand, pressed her arm—but that was all. Eventually the hour for parting came. The young woman anticipated that now at last he would declare himself. But again the young man departed without saying a word about the subject uppermost in her mind.

Of course, the poor girl was left terribly dejected. Her family, too, was greatly disappointed. All the members rose in open wrath, and her older brother even threatened to kick the young man out if he ever appeared again. Now, the young woman might have dismissed the whole thing if she had been able to talk about it freely, as did her family. But she was a schizoid type of personality. (Remember, all real neurotics are schizoids.) She brooded over the affair for a time and then tried to forget it. A few months later she began to complain of pain in her left arm. It was at first diagnosed as a type of rheumatism and later as neuritis. When I saw her, two and one-half years after the onset of the pain, she showed all the symptoms of hysteria.

Now, let us consider the situation: under primitive or even ordinary conditions, these two healthy young people could never have met so often without mating. Something would have happened one way or the other soon after the first few meetings. But because they were both cultured and religious people, they concealed their feelings—or, I might say, deferred the end aim for many years. The postponement must have produced tension in her. What she unconsciously or perhaps consciously craved was feminine fulfillment. Her primitive impulses were there, but they were countered by her sense of morality. She could not say to herself: "What is the matter with this fellow—why doesn't he get busy and do something?" She probably could not even think this way; whatever she felt she had to keep even from herself. The one thing she did expect, however, was that proposal of marriage, which covers everything a good, Christian girl craves. When the young man left for South America, after repeating what he had done for seven or eight years, she began to feel tense and to doubt whether he had ever really thought of her seriously. She then began to feel the pain, which in its full development was a monument of the whole situation. It was a *conversion pain*, the meaning of which was unconscious to her. When she thought: "He really does not care for me," she also thought of the walks with him and of how he had pressed her arm—so that she added: "He must have some love for me." The pressure of the arm, which she recalled, was then repressed along with the whole episode. But when the repression failed, the affect then forced its way up to consciousness as a pain in the arm.

I once described for my students a patient who at first had terrible headaches but then lost them and had painful feelings in the vagina. They laughed when I added that I thought we were making progress because the feelings, though still negative, were now in the right spot instead of being displaced from below to above. Well, our young woman too had displaced the libido from below to above. This is a well-known mechanism in dreams, symptoms, myths, and in fairy tales. Things that should take place below the waistline are always displaced to some organ above. In everyday life you see this mechanism all the time. For example, one of my patients sent me a telegram saying that she would not keep her appointment next morning because she suffered from an attack of laryngitis. Later in the day her husband, in talking to me on the phone, said: "It's too bad that Edna cannot come in to-morrow; she had a terrible attack of diarrhea this morning." My patient could not tell me she had diarrhea because it would have been indelicate to speak of it, and so she had displaced it from below to above. The same mechanism is strikingly illustrated in another patient I once had in Central Islip State Hospital. He was a praecox who was constantly trying to masturbate. They put a long-sleeved camisole on him and so prevented him from masturbating during the day. But then I noticed that the patient had developed the habit of rubbing the top of his head. He continued this habit for years and in time had rubbed a large bald spot there. He had displaced his masturbatic activity from below to above.

Our young woman—to get back to our hysterical patient—brooded over her sad situation for some time and tried hard to forget everything. But instead of being forgotten, the whole situation was repressed into the unconscious, and by the usual processes she then developed the hysterical conversion-symptom. In other words, there was a struggle between the ego and the id. The erotic phantasies in which she had lived for many years were all shattered, and she could no longer indulge herself in them. The ego, so to say, tried to run away from the whole situation, but since the repressed material could not be kept down, it took a devious path and resulted in a hysterical symptom.

You can see all the implications of the forces of the psyche from such a simple case. Of course it was not so simple for the girl. She was very wretched for years and made life miserable for everyone at home. She would awake at night with terrible pain, and everyone would try to help her. But none of the plasters and medicines did any good. Why? Because the pain, though she perceived it as physical, was really mental. As the ancients used to say, *Nullus amor medicabilis est herbis*—"No love can be cured by herbs." After we analyzed and discussed the underlying factors, she gained new understanding of the situation and the pain then disappeared. You must understand, of course, that it took a long time before this happened, and that in the process she underwent a definite change in her view of life. One might say that she was educated by analysis to think of love and sex frankly and openly and so was able to solve her problem. That is really what we do. We get the patient to think in actual, realistic terms so that she can call a spade a spade; and after a long elaboration, running for months or longer if necessary, the patient understands her way in life and solves her problems accordingly.

You may be interested to hear the outcome of this romance. Well, when that patient was all through with the analysis and understood her problem, she asked: "What will I do with that fellow? I still get letters from him." By that time, you see, he had been in South America for more than two years. After a long discussion I finally suggested that she write him and say: "We have known each other for more than ten years, and you have seemingly been courting me for all that time. How long are you going to keep that up? I still do not know what you intend to do about it." Well, she was at first a bit aghast at the prospect of such a step. But she finally did send him a letter to that effect. He sent her a cable in reply, and soon married her. He was one of those fellows who have to be pushed!

This case, as I said, seemed quite simple. But do not forget that the girl had been treated for years by many physicians, none of whom ever imagined that her pain was anything but physical. Her family physician finally decided that it might be hysterical and so referred her to me. It was not difficult to obtain this romance from her. If you bear in mind that you have to investigate every patient's erotic life and that you can ask any kind of question without giving offense, you will find it easy to get at the facts. Some patients who are enlightened speak freely, particularly if you yourself are objective about sex. Others will hedge. But sooner or later, directly or indirectly, the patient reproduces everything. In analytic cases, the patient soon realizes that he is to tell everything that occurs to his mind, and he usually tells whatever he consciously knows. If you are not analyzing, you ask yourself: "Where is the main stream of libido?" Everyone has a certain sum of libido at his disposal which can be easily observed in its positive or negative form—that is, as a direct sexual manifestation or as a symptom. The latter, as I said, is a substitutive gratification for the sexual act. If you call it hysteria, you may think of what the French writers used to designate as "hysterogenous zones" —regions which, when touched, produce sensations either of pleasurable pain, anaesthesia, or hyper-aesthesia. If you think in psychoanalytic terms, you will say that the symptom represents a displaced erogenous zone—that is, a part of the body which, when stimulated, gives pleasure. In the patient just discussed, the painful arm was a hysterogenous zone or a displaced erogenous zone. To put it still another way, it was a displaced and disguised outlet.

Outlets, as you will learn, are not always pleasurable. I define an outlet as a path of discharge for accumulated tension. An outlet, therefore, need not be pleasurable; it may even be very painful. Even in normal life, our outlets vary qualitatively and quantitatively. For example, children are undoubtedly the greatest outlet for their parents, but a good part of the time they are not pleasant outlets. Just the other day I talked with the parents of a boy who used to be a brilliant student but who is now a schizophrenic. As an only boy, he has largely absorbed his parents' interest. He was their great outlet, and up to a few months back it was a very pleasant one, but now it is changed. Similarly, many people find their work not particularly pleasurable. Yet it provides an absorbing interest and hence a useful outlet. It seems that the organism was meant to be in motion from the beginning to the end; if a person is occupied—pleasantly of course—his problem is solved. As psychiatrists, you will sometimes come in contact with people who accumulated a lot of money, retired, and then got nervous break-downs. In many instances, experience taught me that the only way to cure such people was to send them back to work. As soon as they started to worry about whether their stocks were going up or down, they began to improve and to live again. I need not tell you that occupational therapy is based on this principle. To be sure, unpleasant occupation long continued will sometimes produce neuroses in sensitive people.

The symptom, which is a masked representation of a libidinal frustration, is still an outlet for the patient. Our hysterical young woman could talk about her arm as much as she desired. She could show it to everybody and obtain sympathy from her family, friends, and physicians; whereas she could not possibly talk about her great misfortune in having been courted ten years by a man who had never proposed marriage to her—or even less about the sexual phantasies which followed her disappointment.

Now, this is a simple example of how we look at the psychic symptoms. But the most complicated symptoms show the same technique, and hence I cannot impress upon you too strongly the desirability of understanding the distortion mechanisms in the simple errors and mistakes of everyday life, and in wit.[2] Every slip, no matter how insignificant, and every joke not only has a meaning, but the distortions which produce them also teach you how to analyze dreams and symptoms. Thus, you never lose anything unless you want to lose it.

Whenever I say this, people always take exception to it. "I lost something very valuable," they always argue, "and I certainly did not *want* to lose it." I explain that the person only gives the conscious version of the situation, and I insist that there must have been some unconscious reason for it. For example, a patient of mine once told me about her experience in losing a ring—or rather, a large and valuable ruby set in a ring which had been given to her by her husband. She and her husband were going out to the theater one evening, and as she put the ring on she remarked to him, "The setting is wearing out, and the stone is loose." He suggested that she leave the ring at home and have it fixed before wearing it again. "Oh no," she replied; "I have been wearing it that way for some time." Well, they were in the theater only a short while when she noticed that the stone was gone. Her husband was naturally furious, but he simply said: "Don't look for it now. When everybody goes, we'll get the usher to look for it." After the show was over, the usher brought a flashlight—and immediately they found the stone near by.

Such a thing might be dismissed as a trivial accident if one

[2] Cf. "Wit and Its Relation to the Unconscious," Freud's *Basic Writings*, p. 633.

did not know that this woman had also lost a valuable bracelet and a brooch two or three months, respectively, before this accident. For some time she had told her husband th̲ she was seriously thinking of leaving him. And if not for ̲er attachment to her child, whose full custody she feared ̲e might lose through divorce, she would have actually st̲ted legal proceedings. It is therefore safe to assume that l̲ing these jewels symbolized a desire to get rid of her husba̲. The husband, an intelligent layman, knew the meaning of these losses without any interpretation. He said to her: "Y̲u dislike me, so you lost the jewels which were worn b̲ my mother and grandmother."

What did my patient mean by l̲sing and then refinding the stone? We know that the evol̲on of the marriage ring goes back to the time when the c̲emonials of coitus at marriage were no longer tolerated ir̲ ̲blic. Instead, a symbolic coitus was performed by puttin̲ a ring on the finger. That is the origin of the marriage r̲ng. People have always looked upon the wedding ring as a̲ ̲efinite symbol of marital fidelity, and a married woman f̲ls very badly if she loses her ring. In analysis, one often ̲ ̲nds all kinds of symbolic actions expressed by the marriage ̲ng. The ring is a symbol of union between husband and w̲fe, and when a woman loses her wedding ring it may be assumed that there is something wrong with her marriage.

As I said, my patient struggled with the idea of divorce for months before she brought the problem to me. I then found that she was very neurotic, and that she would have had difficulties with any other man. As a matter of fact, her attitude to her husband was very ambivalent. He possessed many qualities which she liked and admired, but due to her own maladjustment she could not tolerate certain weaknesses in him from which she herself suffered. She was very indecisive about everything—it was really pathological doubt—and it happened that her husband showed the same fault. Instead of telling her what to do, where to dine, or what play to see (a behavior which was only too familiar to her from her home), he always asked her what she would like to do. He wanted her to make the decisions. I believe Shakespeare says something to the effect that we dislike most our own faults in others. Originally, this particular trait in her husband appealed to her, because it was just the reverse of her father, a rather domineering person against whom she was in full rebellion when she first met her husband. But as soon as they began to live together, she missed her father, looked for him in her husband and, since he was not there, she became critical of what she called her husband's weakness. There were other factors which caused friction between them into which we need not enter here. At all events, after she had been under analysis a few months, she obtained a different perspective of the whole situation and then began to doubt the wisdom of a divorce. In view of the fact that her husband really suffered from a compulsion neurosis and was quite willing to be treated for it, she decided to give up the idea of a divorce "for the time being," as she put it. It is also interesting to note that she lost the ruby about a month after his physician informed her that he had every reason to expect that her husband would make a good recovery.

Had that been the first time I had heard of such an accident about a ring, I might have been willing to accept her own view that it was just an accident. But I have seen too many women who used the wedding ring as an expression of their marital status. To be sure, this woman did not really want to lose the stone itself which was costly and which she greatly admired. But the whole episode was a symbolic act of what had happened to her marriage. She had almost gotten a divorce, she had almost lost her husband, but she had recovered the stone —that is, she had gotten her husband back. That was why she warned her husband that she might lose it, and that is why she dropped it in a place where no one else could find it before she herself looked for it.

This episode happened about three years ago. The wife has gone through a successful analysis, and the husband, who was treated by another physician, has evidently also made a good recovery. At all events, they seem to live together amicably with their children of whom there are now two. The refinding of the stone obviously presaged that the marriage would continue—although at that time my patient thought that she would drop the proceedings only "for the time being."

Such symbolic actions are frequently observed in normal people and in neurotics and invariably show what goes on in the unconscious. The schizophrenic expression is somewhat different. Instead of contemplating a divorce, feeling guilty toward her husband, and depriving herself of something valuable to atone for it, the schizophrenic can split herself away from all reality and project everything to the outside. Instead of phantasying marriage, she actually feels that she is already married to the man of her phantasy. She even hears him hallucinatorily and actually sees him by mistaking someone for him. In brief, unlike the psychoneurotic whose symptoms manifest themselves in hysterical conversion or obsessive measures, the schizophrenic projects her repressed feelings to the outside because she has the capacity to tear herself away from reality. She can then feel and say that she is married to someone else and at the same time live with her husband. Bleuler explains this kind of behavior on the basis of *dereistic* [8] thinking or unreal thinking—which is also characteristic of dreams and myths. Nevertheless, when the praecox woman complains that everyone is calling her "a bad woman," her auditory hallucinations are nothing but outward projections of self-reproach for her desire to have another man.

Dereism thus explains the strange behavior of those unhappily married women who, instead of contemplating and obtaining divorces, become schizophrenic and say that they are already divorced and married to the other men. Normal women in similar situations take some action about it without merging into a neurosis or psychosis. They do not come to us nor are they brought to us, because they are constitutionally different from the schizophrenic. The latter keep everything to themselves; they try to repress everything, but in time the repression fails and the submerged material comes out in hallucinations and delusions. We usually see such patients after they have been overtly psychotic for a year or longer when they are inaccessible to psychotherapy.

[8] From *de-reor*—"away from reality," "illogical."

I recall one such patient whose mother expressed the wish to talk to me after I had seen her daughter a few times. The mother then informed me that years before, when she urged her daughter to have a child, the daughter had confided in her that her husband was sexually impotent, and that after all those years of marriage she was still a virgin. The mother had urged her repeatedly to get a divorce, but the daughter would not do it. That attitude, of course, was the conscious expression of this sensitive patient. In her unconscious, the struggle raged on until she tore herself away from her disagreeable reality and became schizophrenic. Without knowing about her past struggle with her impotent husband, we could not understand her hallucinations and delusion.

You may ask what we can do for this kind of patient by knowing the meaning of the symptoms. The answer is that theoretically we can do very little to restore the patient to normality. This particular patient is still in a hospital where I feel that she will remain. But, having learned a lot about the mechanisms of the symptoms (or better, the dereism of the schizophrenic processes) and the etiological factors that enter into the production of the disease, it will help in the treatment of other patients whom we might have the good fortune of seeing in childhood, or early in the disease, or perhaps before the patient resorts to dereistic mechanisms. For if you trace back the history of such patients, you will find that they have always been sensitive and shut-in personalities. Such children should be diagnosed early, and their education should be guided by a psychiatrist or by a psychiatrically-grounded pedagogue. For if such children are later subjected to a poor environment, if life does not run smoothly, they begin to brood and gradually to withdraw from active life.

I could best illustrate such a history by telling you something about the onset of the psychosis in the schizophrenic woman I just described. As I said, she had always been of the reserved and shut-in type. She was an only child, whose father died when she was just three and a half years old. Both her mother and her husband noticed that for about six to eight months she daily spent many hours lying in bed or on a lounge.

She did not complain of anything in particular; when questioned by her mother, she would complain of a cold or of indigestion. But one morning she remained in bed with her eyes closed, and when the servant finally went into her room, she paid no attention to her. Her mother was then summoned, but she too could elicit no response from the patient. The family doctor got her to speak monosyllabically—such words as "nothing," or "yes," or something entirely meaningless. The patient became increasingly somnolent and careless in her natural habits, and she continued in this state for a few weeks. No coherent answer could be elicited and no physical signs were found on examination. It was then decided to do a lumbar puncture, and following this, the patient suddenly, as it were, woke up. It was then noticed that she spoke "out of the way," and a mental disturbance was suspected.

To sum up: On the basis of a predisposed constitution, there was a prolonged prodromal stage during which the patient was seemingly depressed and hypochondriacal. This ended in a period of somnolence in which the patient was almost unconscious as far as responding to outward impressions. From the description of her state during these weeks, she resembled what the old psychiatrists used to call *amentia*—but which we would say was an acute schizophrenic shift. During this period the patient shut herself off from all outer perceptions, and responded to very strong stimuli in a rather senseless and disproportionate manner. When she emerged from this state she showed the secondary phenomena of schizophrenia—hallucinations and delusions—as well as a complete indifference to everything else about her. The apathy she maintained with increasing force throughout all these years. At present she no longer speaks of her hallucinations and delusions, but she is very childish in her whole demeanor. She does nothing spontaneously nor does she ordinarily resist much. She smiles to everybody near her, mistaking their identity, speaks in an embellished manner, and to all intents and purposes behaves like a little child. In terms of the psychic apparatus we would say that here we deal with *a struggle between the ego and the outer world* in which the ego first strove hard to shut out the

[129

outer world.   Something broke through which gave us an inkling of the basic struggle. The secondary phenomena showed plainly that she craved another man (the one to whom she fancied herself married was a movie hero), and the voices that called her a "bad woman" showed her feelings of guilt. Her husband had been impotent, and this in my opinion was the precipitating factor of the disease. From my observation of many similar cases, I am inclined to believe that if she had been married to a normal man and had lived the life of an average woman, she would not have become schizophrenic. If I do not speak in absolutely positive terms, it is because I am perhaps too conservative.

No matter what else you find in schizophrenia, either physical or mental, you will always find one thing: the schizophrenic is unable to make what we call a normal, object-libidinal adjustment. That is the one situation which you will invariably find; and that is why, too, we must pay close attention to the psychosexual development of children—especially to those who have a schizoid background. Looking at this patient as she was being fed by a spoon—otherwise she would have swallowed everything in a few gulps, or would not have eaten at all—I said to myself: "We are dealing here with a typical regression to the earliest organization of the autoerotic stage of development."

It is to be noted that the ego is in the center of the struggle. In the neuroses, the ego struggles with the id; in the schizophrenic psychoses, with the outer world. There is another psychosis termed by us as melancholic or depressive states which Freud classifies as *narcistic neurosis*. Here *the struggle is between the ego and the super-ego.* If we think of a typical case of depression—as, for example, in an involution melancholia—we usually find the following symptoms: The patient is depressed and often also agitated; she shows delusions of a somato-psychic nature, of self-condemnation, of poverty, and other similar delusions. The patient feels either that she (or he) is going to be arrested or electrocuted, or else feels unworthy and wants to die. Such patients often attempt and do commit suicide. When you investigate patients of this type, you find that, unlike the struggles in the other neuroses, the ego here admits its guilt and expects condign punishment. As I told you, the super-ego represents the highest mental evolution of modern man; and as his conscience, the super- or ideal-ego strives to keep the individual on the straight and narrow path. In a psychotic depression, this conscience often drives him to commit suicide.

Let us consider the case history of a patient I saw recently. The executor of her estate told me that she was worth about two million dollars. Yet she imagined that she was poverty-stricken: she wanted to save every scrap of paper, mistaking it for money or stocks. When her nephew asked her for a piece of writing paper, she refused to give it to him and insisted that he use a piece of wrapping paper instead. (You have probably seen dozens of such cases.) This patient feels that she has no right to live, that she has ruined everybody—and so on. Her symptoms mean simply that she has nothing to live for because she is libidinally poor; she simply feels that she cannot give or get libido. Of course, even the average, normal woman when she goes into menopause often becomes nervous over this prospect. I saw a woman recently who voluntarily stopped having children after she was thirty-one. She is now forty-three and is frightened and upset because she thinks that she "is changing." I explained to her that menopause simply means no more child-bearing. "No, it is not that," she replied; "I don't want any more children. But I fear that no one will love me, that my husband will not care for me any longer—that men will no longer think me attractive." Unconsciously her fear was that she was becoming libidinally impoverished.

The more I study psychotics, the more I am convinced that not only do they show regressions which can usually be traced to some fixation in their early life, but that the regressions are also phyletic—that they hark back to early racial evolution. To explain, let me recall that in the lower forms of life, as in some insects, the parents die very soon after copulation—that is, right after they have performed their mission in the preservation of the species. And when you observe women in states of melancholia, women who are barren, and average women in menopause, it is hard to dismiss the thought that all such women seem to be obsessed by the death instinct: they seem to regress to that period of racial evolution when the female actually died after she laid the fertilized eggs. More of that later.

In less glaring form, some men too show this peculiar phenomenon. Their reaction to coitus is, *mutatis mutandis*, of the same nature as that of the male day-fly which becomes so fatigued after coitus that it soon dies. Modern man also feels exhausted and readily falls asleep after coitus—*Post coitum omne animal triste* is an old saying. Impotent or sterile men are often compared to dead men, and some sensitive men actually go through a climacteric period in many ways comparable to the feminine menopause. To be sure, in the course of time higher species came into being, and their mating processes became correspondingly more complex. The anthropoid apes, our nearest relatives, live in communities ruled by the strongest patriarchal male, but the latter is invariably killed by his oldest son in a sex fight when he can no longer maintain his primitive dominance. We also know that some primitive people do away with the old parents. Ceremonials such as the "ripening of the fruit" point to the ancient origin of this practice. This is probably a repetition-compulsion of the old way of dying spontaneously when the parent's sex mission came to an end. To be sure, our mode of living has been so thoroughly changed in the course of the ages that we forget how man, like any other animal, is only a weak link in the chain of procreation. But we can still observe that the day-fly, the ant, or the drone all die spontaneously. The male spider and the praying mantis are devoured soon after copulation, and some of the male species of fish meet with the same fate.

The life of *homo sapiens*, however, is so well arranged that ordinarily they go on living long after their mating activities cease. Nature has helped to solve this problem much better in the case of the woman than in the man. In the latter, the sexual act is the only function that he has to perform, and as long as he is healthy, he is apparently forced to continue it. In the woman however, the sexual act is only the beginning of a long process—pregnancy, child-bearing, and rearing—all of which involves many activities not strictly sexual. Man can impregnate literally hundreds of females, while a woman, no matter how fertile, can successfully rear only a limited number of children. Unlike the male, her biontic function ceases at the menopause, and with it, as a rule, there is a gradual diminution of desire for copulation.

Impoverishment, which is a frequent delusion in feminine involutional melancholia, is, as I said, a symbolic expression for the lost power of child-bearing. We are living in an anal-erotic age where, besides actual libido, money procures everything. But the average woman as a rule finds many satisfactory substitutes for this loss. The maternal instinct comprises so many activities besides mating in the narrow sense that when the latter ceases women can usually live a satisfactory life through numerous related activities. The situation is different in the case of the elderly man. He is expected to adhere to the rules of matrimony as long as his wife is living. But it is a natural law that only females of mating age really attract. The "lead us not into temptation" attitude can be strictly followed only by few men, relatively speaking. The majority of elderly married men are rank adulterers if judged by the dictum: "Whosoever looketh on a woman to lust after her hath committed adultery with her already in his heart." [4]

As an intelligent and well-behaved representative of this group expressed it, "How can you remain sexually calm in the face of present-day feminine cultivation! Judging by the eagerness of young and elderly females to embellish their bodies by natural and artificial means, they seem hell-bent to lead us into temptation." Add to this group the widowers and a host of others who, though elderly, are nevertheless in need of sexual outlet, and you will understand why we hear of "sugar daddies" and similar species. There is no doubt that elderly men, both married and single, have to cope with this problem—a problem which modern society entirely ignores. I could give you a number of lectures based on tragic and comic material obtained from such cases. They are not analytic cases; in their

[4] *Matthew*, V: 29.

despair, they come to you because you are supposed to solve sex problems. The by-paths which ordinarily serve to release pent-up sexual tension are not of much help to this group. The average married man may see a stimulating show and then go home to roost, but the single, elderly man can only resort to illicit sex, and that frequently brings him disaster.

The many jokes which one hears about elderly gentlemen fully confirm our views. Thus, I once heard the following joke at a very nice after-dinner party. It was about an elderly gentleman who was courting a show girl with all sorts of expensive gifts. The girl however was quite a nice person—not the ordinary gold-digging type who is always on the lookout for just such a daddy. Knowing what the man was after, she decided to make matters clear once and for all. One evening, therefore, upon receiving a handsome bracelet, she said to the man: "It is very sweet of you to have given me this beautiful bracelet, and I can't tell you how much I appreciate it. But I want you to know, Mr. Smith, that my heart is already given away." "Don't worry about it, my dear," the old gentleman replied. "I never aspired as high as that."

This joke, like the one I gave in the last lecture, shows a sexual tendency. The wit here lies in the answer, "I never aspired as high as that," and the distortion mechanism which produces the laughter lies in the *manifold application of the same material.* Ordinarily, "high aspirations" refers to the ideals of civilization, but here the same words recall a different image—one that is more anatomical than spiritual. She tells the old gentleman that her heart is already given away, meaning "I love someone else." His answer is that he doesn't want her heart or "I never aspired as high as that."

The outburst of laughter that followed this old man's answer left no doubt that the audience understood the joke without the need of such explanations as I have just given. It shows frankly the problem of sex gratification in old gentlemen who can procure it only through money. As I said, among animals and primitives such old males are soon eliminated. Among the former it is done outrightly; in the latter it is done ceremoniously and forms the occasion for a sort of holiday. In the "ripening of the fruit" ceremony, which I mentioned before, the old man plays the part of the fruit and climbs up a tree. As the "ripe fruit" falls down he is clubbed to death by the assembled youngsters. In our civilization the old men are subjected to no such games. Yet the laws of nature cannot be changed. As long as a man is healthy, his sexual impulses continue to function, and since he has to suppress them, he finds pleasure in jokes of this nature. I heard this joke from an old gentleman of the type I just described.

It is remarkable that something suggestive always comes to mind whenever I wish to illustrate the nature of wit. Why? I can assure you that I am not any worse in this respect than you are. But we are all subject to the same social oppressions, and those feelings which we must bury and repress are precisely the ones that are likely to crop out whenever a favorable occasion arises. In extenuation, I wish to say that only those who control their primitive impulses find pleasure in cracking jokes about them.

Many years ago, in 1923, I recall, the *New York Herald* ran a Sunday feature which contained the favorite jokes of prominent persons. To my surprise, the editor wrote and asked me to give him my best joke. I thought of the best one I had ever heard, but then said to myself: "He will never print that." To make a long story short, I finally sent him a letter which read as follows: "My dear Mr. Editor: I have collected a great many witticisms, but hardly one would be fit to print. Your request, therefore makes me think that you may get a great many very good stories and anecdotes, but they will not be the most favorite of the persons questioned. After discarding a half dozen stories that came to my mind, I am sending you the next most favorite." He published the whole thing—letter and all. Then, for weeks, I was bothered by people who wrote or telephoned to ask: "Well, what *is* the best joke?"

To repeat, wit is a product of civilization. It is a by-path for emotional outlet. Jokes that are particularly desirable are those dealing mainly with sex control or with other oppressions put on us by civilization. If you can crack a joke of this type and thus give vent to some of your repressed feelings, you and your audience obtain a good, vicarious outlet. It is for this very reason that we can look upon jokes as disguised expressions of something that is very deep and fundamental but which must be held in check by civilization.

But wit serves as a path not only for sexual but also for aggressive outlets. We have baseball and football games, prize fights, tennis matches, and other games of competition. Basically, these are conventionalized aggressive outlets which help the average citizen to control his primitive aggression. When you read Malinowski and Rivers (who have lived among primitive people and who can speak authoritatively about them) you will discover that since head-hunting was abolished, the primitives have lost their zest for living and are actually dying out.

In other words, the aggression for which the organism was constructed, and which all animals must exercise, was suddenly taken away from them, and as a result they are pining away. Several medical missionaries who worked in all parts of Africa told us the same thing recently at a meeting held at the Board of Foreign Missions. It seems that human beings were not born to be the gentle, kind creatures that Christianity and all the other religions want us to be. Without aggression, we could not maintain ourselves in the struggle for existence or in mating. "Faint heart n'er won fair lady" is merely one of the sayings which express this situation in regard to sex. All religions —particularly Christianity—have always striven to do away with aggression, but they have only partially succeeded. The lion and the lamb may some day lie down together as the prophet foretells—but, judging by the present and past, it will probably be a very senile lion who is about ready to die.

Lest I appear too pessimistic, I wish to say that we have learned to control our emotions and to express them vicariously through regulated competition in sports, in elections, and last but not least in holidays. In the latter, the ordinary restrictions are somewhat eased, and so the individual can relax. "Alcoholidays"—as one wag called them—expresses the situation. That undoubtedly explains why Christianity was never able to abolish the holidays which the converted pagans celebrated before they became Christians. I am referring to Easter, which was a Spring holiday devoted to Ostera-Venus, and to Christmas, against the celebration of which there is still a law in the Commonwealth of Massachusetts. The human being can never renounce a pleasure once experienced.

During elections you can see quite plainly how regulated aggression works, for here we deal with a very fundamental factor. When we choose a president or any other officer to lead us and, as it were, regulate our lives, we are unconsciously thinking of our childhood, when we needed someone to protect us and to provide for us. The person whom we wish to elect, however, must unconsciously be a replica or a composite image of our first leaders. In the ultimate analysis, he is the father, and the type of man that the individual elector wants depends on his struggles with his own father. Thus, in a great many homes, the father is actually referred to as "the governor" or "the president." The Pope, head of the Roman Catholic Church, derives his name from *papa* meaning father. We all try to identify ourselves, in other words, with that chieftain who was our childhood father toward whom we now have an ambivalent feeling of love and hatred. That is why an election always expresses itself in powerful terms. The average citizen lives through his ambivalent feelings by refusing to see the faults of his own candidate, and by finding nothing but wrong in the opponent. All you have to do is to read the remarks made by the followers of the various candidates during the heat of a campaign. They do not call each other openly a "son-of-a-b — —," but the implications are there.

Tendency wit is also used as an indirect or masked expression of aggression. Thus, the story is told about Wendell Phillips the abolitionist who one day found himself on the same train with a group of Southern clergymen on their way to a conference. When the Southerners learned of Phillips's presence, they decided to have some fun at his expense. One of them approached and said:

"Are you Wendell Phillips?"

"Yes, sir," came the reply.

"Are you the great abolitionist?"

[137

"I am not great, but I am an abolitionist."

"Are you not the one who makes speeches in Boston and New York against slavery?"

"Yes, I am."

"Why don't you go to Kentucky and make speeches there?"

Phillips looked at his questioner for a moment and then said: "Are you a clergyman?"

"Yes, I am," replied the other.

"Are you trying to save souls from hell?"

"Yes."

"Well—why don't you go there?"

Technically, the wit in this joke consists of the *manifold application of the same material*, in the form of repartee. Of course, if Wendell Phillips had not been a nice, cultured gentleman, he would not have bothered to respond with this elaborate repartee. He would simply have said to the clergyman: "Say —you can go to hell!" But gentlemen cannot be frank when they wish to vilify. They use euphemisms, indirect expressions, and in this particular joke the manifold application of the same material ("Why don't you go there?")—as well as other concealing techniques to batter down their opponents.

Wit uses the same forms of distortions, in other words, that you find in the neurotic and psychotic mechanisms. For example, one of my schizophrenic paranoid patients used to ask me whenever I visited her: "Where is your red carnation, Dr. Hill?" At first I thought little of it, but when this kept up for more than a year I began to wonder what she meant. I said to myself that it must be assonance or sound association—"Dr. Hill, Dr. Brill." But one day I discovered the real meaning. There is a well-known surgeon in New York, Dr. A. A. Berg, whose initials are the same as mine. He had once operated on this same woman some time before she became my patient. Moreover, the patient knew German quite well, and in that langauage *Berg* means "hill." The patient thus identified me with Dr. Berg: he was the surgeon who had cut deeply into her body as I was the doctor who had tried to do likewise with her mind. Moreover, as everyone knows, Dr. Berg usually wears a red carnation or red necktie. Thus, my patient's apparently "crazy" remark was not just sound association; it was a condensation of real ideas such as you find in dreams and in wit.

Let us turn now to Freud's classifications of the neuroses. As you know, Freud began as a neurological researcher. For many years he worked in Brücke's laboratory and then with Meynert on cerebral anatomy. Those of you who are interested should read his works on aphasia and diplegia.[5] Here we are interested only in his psychoanalytic work which he developed in relation to the neuroses. He started with Breuer on hysteria but soon found it necessary to devote more attention to the other neuroses. Hysteria and neurasthenia were at that time the two all-embracing neuroses. The average psychiatrist put everything into these two entities. Neurasthenia was called by Forel the garbage-can of medical practice: whatever did not fit into any other disease was thrown into neurasthenia. Freud soon narrowed the concept of neurasthenia by separating from it all the anxieties, and gradually he formulated the neuroses into the classifications you note on the blackboard:

1 — Actual Neuroses   *(Neurasthenic syndromes,*
(Hypochondriasis,
(Anxiety neuroses

2 — Transference Neuroses   *(Hysteria*
(and
(Compulsion neuroses

3 — Narcistic Neuroses
or
Psychoses

I believe these classifications are more logical than those of other authors which are still more or less bungled. Before Freud gave us these entities, I never knew which was which. His classifications enable you not only to diagnose your patients but also to give the proper prognosis and the corresponding treatment.

In investigating the anxieties which he separated from neurasthenia, Freud came to the conclusion that here too sex played a major part, and he finally stated that inadequate sexual

[5] Cf. S. E. Jelliffe: "Freud as a Neurologist." *Journal of Nervous & Mental Diseases*, Vol. LXXXV, No. 6 (June 1937).

outlets—masturbation, frustrated sex, interrupted coitus—were always found in anxiety neuroses and in neurasthenics.

One of his pupils, Stekel, later on showed that anxiety neurosis was rarely seen in pure form: that even when it starts as pure anxiety it soon attaches itself to some ideas and becomes what he called anxiety hysteria.[6] In other words, pure anxiety cannot exist for very long without being "bound" to some specific thing when it can be more or less controlled. When so "bound" to an idea, the anxiety may result in being afraid of open or closed places, of crossing bridges, or in any other of the endless phobias.

Freud thus placed the anxieties into a separate entity and called attention to the fact that the neurasthenic symptom-complex often forms part of incipient tuberculosis, paresis, and other organic diseases, as well as of incipient manic-depression and schizophrenia. Looking at it in this way, the syndrome of neurasthenia became markedly restricted. For many years now I have rarely seen a pure case of neurasthenia. In short, if we restrict it in this manner, we find only a few cases of neurasthenia and a large number of anxiety hysterias. The latter naturally merge into the psychoneuroses (hysteria and compulsive neuroses) which are also called transference neuroses for reasons that you will presently hear. Then, in addition to the actual neuroses and psychoneuroses, we have the narcistic neuroses or psychoses—the psychoanalytic therapy of which still leaves much to be desired. More of this later.

Now I have spoken about the schizoid and syntonic types of personality. I wish to state that the psychoneurotics, whether they be hysterias or compulsive neurotics, are all preponderantly schizoids. It is for this reason that many schizophrenics begin with hysterical or compulsive neurotic mechanisms, and it is for this reason that quite a number of such cases at first look like psychoneurotics and are diagnosed as such.

Let us now return to the psychoneuroses which we designate as the transference neuroses. By "transference" we mean the ability of the patient to displace to the analyst or the analytic situation hostile and pleasant feelings which in reality belong

---

[6] *Nervöse Angstzustände* (Wien, 1908).

elsewhere. Hysterics and compulsive neurotics have a strong capacity and desire for love and hate—in contrast to psychotics who either cannot transfer libido to an object or can do so only in a difficult and peculiar manner.

You hear a lot of nonsense about the term *transference*. Transference does not mean, as some people seem to think, that the patient falls in love with the analyst. I saw a doctor recently who had superficially read *Freud's Basic Writings*. He is not a psychiatrist; yet, after perusing this work, he began to use what he imagined was psychoanalysis in treating patients whom he thought suffered from hysteria. He had come to see me because five of his patients were in love with him and he—poor fellow!—did not know what to do. "How do you manage it?" he asked me. From what he had heard—and not, he admitted, from what he had read—he imagined that in order to achieve success one must get the patient to fall in love with him. I replied that I have been in private practice for more than thirty-five years and have never had such a problem. The psychoanalyst who understands the nature of transference does not become entangled in love affairs with patients. I told this physician that he had no business treating patients by a method for which he was untrained. He of course now found himself in a quandary; he was in fear of being driven out of the community. He admitted finally that he was in love with one of his patients. In other words, he was trying to excuse his misdeeds by make-believe analytic treatment.

Actually, by "transference" we mean that during the treatment the patient, whether male or female, *displaces* both hostile and affectionate feelings to the analyst. These feelings belong to earlier situations—to relations between parent and child—which crop out during the analysis. When you analyze, you unwittingly bring back such situations—actual occurrences of love and hatred; and they are now displaced to the analyst as the father or the mother substitute. Consequently, the difficulties which arise are not due to the analyst but to the patient. In a way it is a repetition-compulsion which anyone can see in his own life. One always reacts to situations in the same way that he did in childhood, when everything centered on the parents. When such erstwhile occurrences are acted out, the analyst is endowed with the love and hatred that were formerly heaped on the parent. This mechanism comes into being throughout life in all human relations; the analyst is well aware of it and knows, or should know, how to cope with it. Such emotional repetitions are often referred to as the so-called "pursuing fate" about which one reads and hears.

Let us take an example: a patient called me up on the telephone and asked me a question. I dislike talking on the phone when I analyze, but I have to answer some calls—particularly if my secretary thinks so, but this patient simply wished to know whether her appointment was for three o'clock. Now she should have known this without telephoning; I therefore confirmed the appointment and brusquely hung up. When she came to my office at three o'clock, she immediately burst into tears. Of course, one might think from such conduct that something terrible had happened to her, but if you are experienced you just sit and perhaps read something until the patient cries herself out. Then you ask: "Well, what is the trouble?" In this case, the patient said that I had been rude to her over the phone. I pointed out that she would not like me to carry on telephone conversations during her own analytic hour, and, besides, that she had no business asking me something that she already knew well enough. In reply, she gave me some apparently plausible reason for her act.

I could have dismissed this episode by saying that she was just foolish. But if you knew that she was an only child who habitually called her father on the phone at least four or five times every day when she was accustomed to hearing nice things from him, you would then understand why she telephoned me. I was in loco patris, and she expected the same attention from me. Since I had not reacted in the expected manner, she hated me. On other occasions when I was nice, she loved me—although she naturally kept this to herself. I always tell my students not to feel flattered when a patient shows them affection: they must remember that the patient came to them not for love but because she was sick.

That is what we mean by the transference mechanisms.

They operate in everyday relationships as well. Thus, we always transfer feelings to friends. The transference is of an affectionate nature when we have common identifications of past experiences—as with classmates and people who were brought up with us. On the other hand, strangers often innocently suffer from such unconscious excursions which are fixed in us early in life; we treat them, in other words, on the basis of some image which has been formed in us during childhood. If that image happens to be pleasant, we treat them pleasantly. If not, we treat them unpleasantly—even though they themselves are perfectly innocent.

Transference, then, simply means the emotional reactions that an individual displays toward any human being with whom he happens to come into contact. If the contact is between male and male, the transference is of a homosexual nature; if between male and female, it is of a heterosexual nature. The homosexuality that I have in mind is the normal component present in all human beings. In the neuroses, of course, things are different. Yet, whether in normal or neurotic, these forces are always at play. I once said that when a man meets a man, the thought which runs through his mind is: "What does he want?" In other words, he is immediately on guard. But if the man comes to him with a card of introduction from a friend, the feeling is different. Ordinarily, one is always in fear that the other fellow wants to put something over on him. That feeling of rivalry always exists between the males. But when a man meets a woman, the thought which courses through his mind is: "Is there anything doing?"—to put it into classical terms! He may not express it in words, but that is the feeling which he experiences. To be sure, the average man has learned to control his emotions. He does not at once attack this newcomer even if he does not like his face.

Similarly, when we meet people of the opposite sex, the end aim usually is controlled or inhibited. The end aim is inhibited because as civilized humans we cannot always put our desires into operation; that is particularly true of sex. The women we meet are as a rule protected by society, and they cannot be exploited sexually with impunity. The aim can only be attained in a manner regulated by society. Yet nature does not know these restrictions of civilization: the transference mechanisms come into play despite all prohibition, and it does not matter whether the woman is so-and-so's sister or wife. The end aim is also inhibited if the woman happens to be beyond the mating age. She may then be identified with a mother or a grandmother, and you will like or dislike her accordingly. Our patients unconsciously do the same thing when they first meet us. Depending on the cathexis which you evoke in them, they either like or dislike you.

In the beginning of my psychoanalytic career, I tried to find a way of getting around this difficulty. I knew that if the first interviews did not establish a favorable impression—a good rapport—I would lose the patient. For no fault of yours, some patients sometimes drop you after the first or second visit, and return to the doctor who recommended them to you and say that they just did not like you. There is no argument to such a reaction. I finally said to myself: "If I can discover the type of masculine or feminine identification which the patient seeks, I might know how to control the situation." I then began to ask every patient, during the first visit: "What personage from history or legend appeals to you most—or is your ideal?" I gathered hundreds of answers, and in this way I was able to learn much about the patient's strivings. Thus, the person who answered "Napoleon" or "Lincoln" or "Frederick the Great" certainly belonged to a different type than the man who answered "Florence Nightingale." Everyone unconsciously harbors such an ideal and strives to emulate it. I called this the *empathic index;* [7] and at the time I wrote a paper on it.[8] If you can determine this empathic index of your patient, you will be able better to control the transference mechanism—especially in the beginning of the treatment.

Transference neuroses—to return to our classifications—are the most promising for psychoanalytic therapy; they are the

[7] From *en patein*—"to feel" or "to read oneself into" another person, thing, or situation.

[8] "The Empathic Index and Personality," *Medical Record*, January 24, 1920.

only ones that, given time, are curable. The actual neuroses (neurasthenia and the anxiety states) can also be cured, but are not always easy to manage. The narcistic neuroses were at first not considered amenable to psychoanalytic therapy because the psychotic is incapable of proper transference. Years of experience however have taught us that the psychotic does transfer his libido, albeit in his own peculiar way, and in my own experience of many years I am convinced that, with much patience and skill, they can become accessible and can be benefited by us. Moreover, there are all kinds and degrees of psychotics. Some can undoubtedly be influenced by psychoanalytic therapy.

Some time ago I was visited by a patient who seemed a nice enough sort of fellow. When I asked him what was the matter with him, he replied: "Well, doctor, I have been treated for years by Dr. N——, and I have made up my mind to kill him. I hope you will agree with me." This patient was not an overt paranoiac, but he had ideas of reference and vague ideas of persecution. Nevertheless, his apathetically expressed idea of killing was based on marked hostility to his father and older brother which he transferred to Dr. N——. I changed his mind by getting in touch with Dr. N—— and asking him to write me a letter speaking well of the patient. I then read the letter to the patient; he was pleased to hear that Dr. N—— had a good opinion of him and thereupon gave up the murderous idea. This patient is really a compulsive neurotic with paranoid tendencies.

When we study the narcistic neuroses or psychoses (the schizophrenics, paranoids, and depressions) we find that such patients express their wishes in different ways. Thus, the wish to be pregnant is shown by the hysteric in morning vomiting and in other characteristic symptoms of spurious pregnancy. The compulsive neurotic may express the same wish through a touching-phobia or through the fear of becoming infected by germs. The same wish is expressed by the schizophrenic in the delusion of being poisoned.

In other words, they all have their own expressions, and to

understand them you will have to be versed in the characteristic expressions of the various neuroses as well as in the laws
of association.

QUESTIONS AND ANSWERS

Question : Would it be possible some time to see an actual
psychoanalytical examination?

Answer : You could see it, but you would not learn much
from it. In the first place, no patient would be willing to talk
in the presence of a third person, let alone for a class. Secondly,
in psychoanalysis, there is no examination in the psychiatric
sense. You might say that every interview is a sort of examination; yet the doctor may say very little. It sometimes takes
hours before anything is revealed. You cannot do this in public.

Question : Concerning dereistic thinking—do you find that
in manic cases?

Answer : Yes—they, too, sometimes utilize it but in a different way. Thus, manics often show "flight of ideas"; they
run from one thing to another and do not finish the idea often
in order to disguise it. That is why you cannot grasp what
they say. Manics who are not so productive or who are in the
depressive state often use dereistic mechanisms although they
are always in touch with reality and can be brought back to it
—whereas you cannot bring the schizophrenic back to the actual problem.

Thus, I recently saw a manic young man who claimed that
he was a genius. I soon discovered that this idea was a new
symptom. At first he was very depressed because he failed to
pass his exams, but then he began to react with a manic state
and imagined, or just said, that he was a genius. If not for this
sudden turn, he might have committed suicide. But in talking
I could always bring him back to reality, and he then admitted
that he was not a genius just now but hoped to be one in the
future.

Question : How about a person who has no predilection for
any kind of joke—who has no sense of humor?

Answer : There are few people of this type. They are either people who for some reason do not repress much or who are laboring under an acute repression where everything is still kept down. Primitive people—I mean very primitive people—never resorted to joking because they still lived in the midst of inexorable reality. You can measure the amount of civilization by the number of jokes you hear. Genghis Khan never cracked a joke (all his biographers say he had no sense of humor) and I doubt whether Hitler ever used wit.

The sense of humor appears in children as soon as they begin to repress. I have collected considerable material on this subject. The child begins to show a sense of humor when it begins to dream, for as you know, the dream is nothing but an effort on the part of the mind to give you something which you cannot get in reality. A little child of course will laugh when you play with it. But I am talking about *wit,* with its distortions, displacements, *double entendres,* and indirect expressions. The child knows nothing about that. Those are mechanisms which come later when the child begins to feel the stress of civilization and finds it hard to adjust himself to it. It is then that he tries to get an outlet from such by-paths as dreams and wit.

LECTURE VI

TOPICS :

I ENDED my last talk by speaking about *transference* and the empathic index. I told you how I tried to gauge and control the transference mechanisms of new patients by asking

148]

them what personage from history or legend appealed to them the most. "Empathy," you recall, means "to read yourself into" a person or a situation, and through the empathic index you can judge, particularly in the beginning, what any given patient is striving for.

I gave you some illustrative examples from among my patients, but as a matter of fact we all do the same thing unconsciously. I recall when I was in college long before I ever thought of being a psychiatrist I used to size up my fellow students whenever I came into the classroom at the beginning of the term. When the roll was called, I used to jot down in a notebook my estimate of all those students with whom I was coming into contact for the first time. Thus, I would note that Smith was a "N— — F— —" or a "S— — B— —," or Jones a "D— — F— —." I just happened to do that—although perhaps it was the nature of the psychiatrist already functioning in me! Well, I then wanted to find out whether these first estimates of mine were right or wrong. I was always right.

After I became a Freudian, I discovered why I was always right. It was impossible for me to be wrong, for the simple reason that my evaluation had nothing to do with the fellow's make-up. The image which my classmate aroused in me had already been present in my unconscious. In other words, my damning or exalting the different students depended wholly on what they reminded me of in my own past. There were only two instances I recall when I later changed my estimate. One classmate asked me to tutor him in chemistry; he paid me for it, and naturally he became a fine fellow! The other exception was a student who happened to have a part with me in the same cadaver. You know how at such times you discuss general things as you work together, and in this case we got to talking about William Jennings Bryan who was then running for president. I was a great admirer of Bryan, and this was the first election in which I was really interested. Well, I made the remark that since St. Paul there had not been a greater orator than Bryan. "What the hell do you know about St. Paul?" retorted my partner. As it happens, I studied theology before I entered medical school, and I knew the Bible as well as anybody. My classmate was surprised when I told him this—and so we became further acquainted. I found out that he was just a nice, quiet, good boy. I had at first pitied him for that reason, but I changed my mind about him.

We always form such prejudices. In other words, you are never neutral; you never meet a person to whom you do not immediately make some transference. Charles Lamb in one of his essays tells about two men who met for the first time: the moment they looked at each other they began to fight. Unconsciously people are always doing things like that. We judge people on the basis of what we already know. Those who do not belong to our circle, who do not resemble us, or who do not possess our culture, have already been considered by us as wrong, bad, or suspicious. From the beginning of history we have had *ecthronyms* [1]—"hostile names" which were applied to foreigners or to people outside one's immediate circle. Thus, the word "barbarian," with its present connotations, comes from the Greek, *barbaros*, which means a stranger. These ecthronyms you find everywhere, in the smallest as well as the largest groups. We apply them not only to people who differ from us in color or race but also to those who belong to a lower stratum of our own group. For example, in this country the Italians are called "wops," or the Germans "Dutchmen," or the Jews "kikes." The latter ecthronym was originally applied by the Americanized Jews to their newly emigrated countrymen from eastern Europe. Within the group, we use ecthronyms for people who are financially or socially below us. Freud calls such discriminations "narcism of small differences." Political parties have always had such names; in our own history, for example, you will recall the "mugwumps" and the "carpetbaggers." In short, anyone who does not fit in with our image impresses us as being strange and untrustworthy and hence deserving of some discrimination.

The same mechanism operates in *zenophobia*—which means a fear of strangers. We have definite feelings of hostility toward strangers just because we do not trust them. Biologically, this is perfectly justified. An animal cannot trust any stranger;

[1] From Greek *ecthro—anumo*.

a primitive person cannot trust anyone but the people of his own clan. (I have previously mentioned that in New Guinea a native is instantly killed if he ventures into the waters of a strange clan.) Today, we still have the same feelings. Attend any engagement reception, and on the surface the two families are apparently well disposed toward one another. They seem to be delighted over the union of their children, but if you could accompany both families home and listen to their remarks, you would find a different state of affairs. Most likely, the dominant note would be struck in the question: "What kind of a gang are we getting into?"

In other words, we are all governed by the "better than thou" attitude, but the more people deviate from you in behavior or in color, the more you feel justified in venting your hostility upon them. Professor Weekly, the Cambridge philologist, pointed out in one of his books that language referring to strangers is always hostile. As illustration, he related an incident which occurred when he was in a little town in the Black Country of England. While standing on the street he overheard the following conversation:

" 'oo is that?"

"Dunno."

"Then 'eave 'alf a brick at 'im."

I have always maintained that anti-Semitism is not primarily a Jewish problem. Because the Jews have been disseminated all over the world for thousands of years constituting unprotected minorities everywhere, the suspicion and hatred which is always directed to strangers clung to them more tenaciously.

As I have pointed out, such reactions to people are based on the images we have formed in childhood. The child who has learned to dislike a rigid father, for example, will later react to all men in the same way. Thus his relationship to rigid teachers will be similar, and even if the teachers are not actually so, he will view them as father substitutes and displace the same kind of feelings to them. This mechanism operates over and over again in the case of the "boss," the department head, and other people in positions of authority. History shows that regicides evinced extreme expressions of the same mechanism. In fact, you come to the conclusion that in order to be normal, one must have the right kind of father and mother to start with, for those early impressions are authoritative and hence to a large extent determine the rest of our behavior.

When you meet patients for the first time, therefore, you must be careful about these preconceived prejudices. Whether it be an old lady or a young person who has not reached puberty, you have to know very soon where you stand. Otherwise you will waste a lot of the patient's money and your valuable time. Let me give you an example: A young girl of eleven is brought to me by her parents. She has symptoms of a gastrointestinal nature: she belches, can balloon up to an incredible size whether or not she eats, and can vomit at will. She has puzzled many physicians until they finally decide that she is hysterical.

That girl was very talented, wrote good poetry and was generally precocious. After I had spent about an hour with her, she became tremendously enthusiastic about me. She wrote a poem comparing me to Napoleon, Lincoln, Washington, and other great figures of history. I can assure you that I have done nothing to deserve such encomiums. I knew at once that the girl was merely transferring her affection from her father to me, to whom she was quite ambivalent. The parents themselves expressed doubt whether she would be willing to come again after the first visit and were surprised at her sudden attachment to me. I said to myself: "Whenever you have such a marked, positive transference, you must also expect the opposite reaction." Well, she came about three times and suddenly refused to come again. The whole thing of course had never been meant for me. It was a displacement of her relationship to her own father. On the one hand, she was very much attached to him; on the other, she hated him and often would not speak to him for days. She was a psychopathic, hysterical girl.

That is, in brief, the transference mechanism with which you have to cope in psychoanalytic treatment. As I told you last week, transference has nothing to do with the ordinary idea of falling in love. Any psychoanalyst who allows his patient to fall in love with him does not know his work. As a matter of fact, when the erroneous idea first became current, I began to keep statistics on the subject. Since I was the founder of psychoanalysis in this country, I was usually the one consulted whenever there was any trouble or problem between patients and analysts regardless of whether they were doctors or quacks, and it is still so in a great measure. A woman who had trouble with the doctor invariably came to me to complain. She would either wish to show me that he was a poor therapist or that he should be barred from membership in the psychoanalytic society.

In addition to these statistics, I also gathered records of neurotic women who had become erotically involved with men in other walks of life. Well, I found that there were more women who got into trouble with butcher-boys and ice-men than with psychoanalysts. Mind—I am talking about "nice" women! In fact, there were only two cases of psychoanalysts who, to my knowledge, became involved with women patients. The first case concerned a bright fellow who was however quite psychotic. I warned the woman in question not to marry him, but she did not heed my advice and later had to divorce him. The other was an older man, a widower, who fell in love with one of his young, married patients. She was a very rich woman, and her husband was just a nice neurotic. The husband complained, and I was to serve as a member of the committee of investigation. When we talked to the doctor, he said: "Is there any reason why a physician cannot marry any woman he likes even if she happens to be a patient?" My answer was that ordinarily this would be perfectly all right. But I reminded him that he was more than twice the age of his patient and that she belonged to an entirely different social group, so that in the natural course of events she would not have looked at him as a potential husband; and I added that she had come to him for treatment and not for love-making. To make a long story short, she got a divorce from her husband and married another man—not the doctor. As soon as she got under objective analysis and realized that her love for the aged doctor was a father displacement, her feelings changed. The whole situation was based on an unconscious incestuous desire for her father.

At all events, those are the only two cases I know in which bona fide analysts were involved. Neither of them was so very bad. Of course, you must not forget that if a woman has to come for treatment, she has a floating libido which might attach itself to any man who happens to come into her life and who will give her sympathy. To be sure, we must sympathize with our patients. We must feel that they are persons of good character who deserve help; otherwise, they are not cases for analysis. We must listen to them sympathetically, allowing completely frank expression; but we must never forget that they are sick. If we direct their floating libido to the right channels, the patient will not fall in love with the analyst. True, there is always some danger whenever two people of the opposite sex meet so often and engage in intimate talk. But, psychoanalysts have been taught precisely how to recognize and direct this force. One of my former pupils recently came to me and said: "Look here: I discharged this woman three years ago. Is there any reason why I cannot have an affair with her now?" I said: "No, you can't." When he asked why, I replied: "Because you feel forced to ask my permission. If you had a different conscience, you could have made your own decision. Asking me means that you cannot do it—and you had better not." In further discussion I said that any man or woman who wishes to have an affair does not find it necessary to consult a doctor. If a person has so strong a conscience as to get into a conflict over it, we must advise against it.

Of course we psychoanalysts are no more moral than the average person, but we do know more about those forces. Consequently the moment we come in contact with a patient of the opposite sex, we know what might happen and we regulate our conduct accordingly. In this way the patient gets help —instead of a temporary little tickling which in the long run may do much harm.

I have dwelt long on this topic in order to illustrate the transference neuroses—which, as I mentioned, are based on unconscious factors. The hysterics or compulsive neurotics are unable to adjust their libido properly; yet they constantly strive to do so, and the symptom is the result of the struggle.

In the narcistic neuroses or psychoses, the libido is mainly centered on the ego; the individual finds it very hard to transfer it to an object and usually cannot do so. Nevertheless, as I pointed out last week, the psychotics are not altogether lacking in the ability to transfer hostile and affectionate feelings. This phenomenon exists with them too, but it is a more difficult process and it is differently expressed. In the beginning of my psychoanalytic career, I was firmly convinced that the schizophrenics were absolutely inaccessible to any analytic influence. Their libido, I thought, was turned in—or "introverted," as Jung later called it, but my experiences since then have led me to modify this opinion. I told you in the first lecture about Bleuler's experience in rousing his own sister from her catatonic state and of my own experience with the patient in Burghölzli. Many similar instances have convinced me that you can influence any psychotic if you will devote sufficient time and effort to it. In fact, I am almost convinced that if you had one understanding doctor devoting all his time to one or two schizophrenics, they could be adjusted or perhaps cured. I am sure that the patient's problems can only be solved through the process of giving and taking libido.

Close observation teaches that every schizophrenic shows some kind of transference. Some like the doctor; others hate him. There was a schizophrenic whom I had known ever since she entered the state hospital almost thirty years ago. During all these years she has been falling in love—now with this ward doctor, now with the other. A few years ago I happened to visit her ward. She remembered me immediately, and the first thing she said was: "Will you take this letter and give it to Dr. Knapp?" It was a love letter. She is a chronic paranoid praecox, but she is able to transfer the original, congealed situation to the doctor. Through her dereism, she can readily substitute the doctor for her lost lover. I have seen numerous patients of this kind, and as a result I am convinced that there is more to praecox transference than we know about.

I spoke about this subject once at the New York Psychiatric Society. I recalled a patient who was known to several of the doctors present at the meeting. This patient was paranoid, absolutely inaccessible, and very assaultive. We all diagnosed him as a chronic paranoid praecox, and the only thing that I expected was perhaps a slight change in his behavior. As it happened, the patient had a devoted sister who used to come to me often. Her husband was a college man—an engineer, I believe—and they decided to take the patient home. They wanted to see what they could do with him. They then devoted all their time to him, and as a result the patient changed and became so tractable that they could travel with him here and abroad. They themselves became so interested in the situation that they went to Vienna and had themselves analyzed. Since then, I was told, the patient has behaved well. Of course, he is paranoid. But he behaves well, and had they given him all their attention earlier, and had they possessed the knowledge they now have, I am sure that they could have produced enough restitution to allow him to live in society. I have done it myself with several patients of this type who have maintained themselves at large for twenty and thirty years. Naturally, if you knew them intimately, you would note the mental scar. But to all intents and purposes they are well adjusted to life.[2]

That a schizophrenic has the capacity to transfer—albeit with difficulty—was impressed upon me years ago when a doctor brought a schizophrenic woman of about thirty-five to see me. He was an elderly man of almost seventy, and, as the family physician, had known this woman ever since her birth. After expressing the desire to have everything confidential between us, he quietly informed me that he had been having sexual relations with the patient. "When I saw that she had become sick," he said, "I thought of those Freudian theories, and between you and me, I gave her sex." I just listened and thought to myself: "That is true philanthropy—he did all that for the poor patient!"

Now, this patient was a paranoid as anybody could be, and I naturally thought that she would speak freely about this relationship. Praecoxes supposedly have a poor affectivity, an

[2] Brill: "Schizophrenia and Psychotherapy," *American Journal of Psychiatry*, November 1929.

emotional deterioration. Yet, though I tried in every way to get her to tell me about her affair with the altruistic doctor, she remained just as mum about it as any normal woman would have been under similar circumstances. She was loyal to her man. The fact was that the doctor had grown tired of this amour. When I asked him why he had brought her to see me, he frankly said that he wanted to get rid of her. There was no use in arguing with him about the merits of his therapy. I did, however, tell him not to attribute his technique to the Freudians, and at my suggestion he sent her to a mental hospital.

Through this case I became very much impressed by the fact that schizophrenic women react to sexual situations like any other women. Judging by the usual behavior of schizophrenics, you would expect that this patient would have spoken freely of her affair with the doctor. For although she was no longer actively disturbed by the secondary phenomena of her malady, she still was hallucinatory and delusional. She imagined that men were blowing sensuous smoke from the street into her apartment and had many other somato-psychic delusions of this type. Nevertheless, she kept her secret so well that no one in her family suspected her relation to the doctor as being anything but strictly ethical. I therefore concluded from this and similar cases that psychotics can and do transfer—that they can give and take emotions in their own way. As time went on, I came to the conclusion that this is particularly true in matters of sex, which, we must not forget, are determined not only ontogenetically, but also phylogenetically.

The behavior of this patient recalled to me the same kind of reticence displayed by immature young girls in matters sexual. I recall cases where I was asked to give judgment about men who had affairs with little girls from six to eleven years of age. In no instance was the relationship discovered through the little girls. In some of the cases, outsiders would accidentally notice something which would arouse their suspicions and then report it. I never knew it to work out differently. In the last case that I saw, a very prominent man, a pædophiliac, had been carrying on a sexual affair for about four or five years with a little girl. When he was caught, the girl was only ten and a

[157

half years old. This old bachelor was a friend of the family and
he took that little girl every week end to his home in the city.
Ostensibly, he brought her in to attend concerts and other such
events. In any case, that went on for years. It would never have
been discovered if the little girl had not brought along a friend
on one of those week ends. This girl was about a year older
and evidently knew a thing or two. The bachelor made advances to her, and when she got home she told her parents
about it. They in turn told the principal of the children's
school, and so the whole thing was discovered.

The parents of the first little girl were terrifically shocked.
They could not understand why the child had never told them
about it, for they had her confidence in all other matters. But
the little girl never gave them the slightest hint of what was
going on. I had a good opportunity to obtain the details of this
case because the culprit, anxious that I should save him from
the law, made a clean breast of his whole sexual life, and the
little girl, once I gained her confidence, gave a full account of
everything. In my conversations with her, she spoke and acted
in such a manner that I had to remind myself several times that
she was only an immature girl of ten. Throughout this whole
affair, which lasted for about five years, she behaved like a
mature woman.

In my analyses of women patients, many of them have told
me about similar sexual traumas which had been forgotten for
many years; in every case the behavior was the same. Such
reactions, I feel, show that the individual remembers unconsciously the sexual reactions of the past generations. To use
mnemistic terms, one would say that the inherited sexual
engrams become ecphorized as soon as they are stimulated into
action by some association. In this connection, you will recall
my starling, who began to bathe as soon as he had drunk water
for the first time.

The fact that girls are not supposed to have sexual experiences before they grow up, is of course an artificial state of
affairs. Among animals and primitive people there is no such
hiatus between infancy and puberty; there is no latency period
as we see it in the civilized human being. The instinct is always

there, and even the very young girls seem to react to it, as it were, naturally. When I was a student taking my obstetrical course in the Sloan Maternity Hospital, I recall they brought in a Negro girl of eleven for a Cæsarean section. The thing which surprised me most at that time was the way in which this little girl comported herself. She behaved like any of the other grown-up women there. I said to myself at the time that she was prematurely developed, and undoubtedly she was, judging by our everyday standards. But what developed her was the biontic situation. That is what I feel happens to all of the other youngsters. They know what it is all about; they understand it just like animals—like the chick which knows as soon as it emerges from the shell how to catch grain thrown to it. The instincts, though seemingly immature and dormant, are so deeply rooted that a slight association can always bring them to the surface.

Some years ago I received a German booklet from an English therapist who wrote under the pen-name of Teulon.[3] The booklet was issued in Germany because the author feared that the prudery of English-speaking countries would have refused to countenance its publication and might even have led to his being criminally prosecuted for it. This therapist was not a physician. He claimed to be a naturalist, educator, and sexologist, and in this booklet he gives the case history of a very unruly, crazy girl of about ten. From the description, I would say that she was a schizophrenic although the therapist diagnosed her as hysterical. He describes his method of treatment, which, as far as I could see, consisted in divining her actions and in explaining and gratifying everything up to actual coitus. He states that he never had anything "to do with her sexually," but allowed her to see, touch—and so on. After this treatment had gone on for a certain period, she developed "from a little animal into a perfectly normal girl."

The author published his booklet years after these events had occurred and sent it to people who he thought would be especially interested. When I read it, I thought that indeed this was heroic treatment—but something which, in my opin-

[3] *Psycho-sexuelle Heilbehandlung*, Die Neue Zeit, Verlag, (1930).

ion, could not be given by a physician. The case was interesting however inasmuch as it showed that thwarting a fundamental instinct produces in some people a violent disturbance which can be alleviated—or "cured"—by gratifying it. Our technique is different, for believing as we do that psychic reality is equivalent to actual reality, there is no need for any physical contact with patients. They can be cured by mental and emotional abreaction or by the psychic elaboration which is entailed in any *lege artis* analysis. In time psychotics too have the capacity to give and take libido. With them however, it is not direct and does not manifest itself in the same way as in the transference neurotic.

Here let us return for a moment to Freud's classifications of the neuroses. As you will recall, we have actual neuroses (neurasthenias, anxiety, and hypochondriacal conditions) where there are definite physical disturbances. Then there are the transference neuroses (hysterias and compulsion neuroses) and the narcistic neuroses. All of these neuroses result from a libidinal disturbance in the love life of the individual. When we treat our patients must show them that their biological development was hampered in many ways, and that they did not direct their libidinal stream in the right direction. Now, we define *libido as a quantity of energy directed to an object*. The goal of normal life—the goal we want all our children to reach —is to attain genitality. To be normal, in other words, an individual first must reach the stage where the genitals can function in the act of procreation, and second, he must crave an object of the opposite sex for this function. In our civilization, mating must be controlled, but the goal remains the same— namely, the development of normal genitality and the finding of an object. People who go through life that way are normal; the others are not. Our investigations show that some do not find the right object. Instead of a heterosexual object or a person of the opposite sex, they want a homosexual object or a person of the same sex. Others crave immature objects—children or animals (zoophilia)—or are satisfied with a lock of hair or with some other inanimate object obtained from the love object (fetishism). Still others are contented with a partial impulse of the whole instinct. They make a meal of the *hors d'œuvres*: all they crave is to touch, to look, or to taste. To the average person, such partial satisfactions are only a fore-pleasure. A certain amount of touching and looking is normal, but in the average person it is merely an incentive which leads to genital activity.

I shall devote the rest of these lectures to showing you how this genitality develops. Through Freud's scheme of psychosexual development, I will show you the course it takes in the neuroses, psychoses, and in the normal. That scheme I have outlined for you on the board.

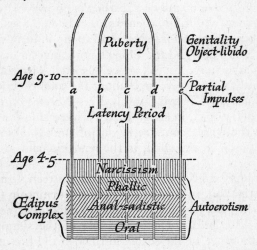

According to Freud, sex shows itself right from the beginning of the child's life, and contrary to those who believe that there are no sexual manifestations until puberty, Freud maintains that sex is born with us and functions from the beginning of childhood. To be sure the infantile sexuality expresses itself differently than that of an adult but these functions are no different than the other non-sexual activities. The child has legs but cannot walk; he has pulps but it takes some time before they develop into teeth. In brief, the child is born with all the germs of sex which gradually develop into what one later calls sex. Sex does not fly into human beings at puberty as is generally believed; it simply functions differently in childhood.

[161

That is the reason why we have known so little about the psychosexuality of man. Before Freud, there was a large literature of sexology, but every one of the early investigators (and I have read them all) described only certain isolated phenomena; they made no effort to give a uniform classification of sex or its functions.

When I entered the state hospital, every one of us was eager to read Krafft-Ebing's *Psychopathia Sexualis* which the hospital library had just acquired. I did not know until after leaving the hospital that Krafft-Ebing was also a first-class psychiatrist who wrote one of the best textbooks on psychiatry of his time. All I knew about him then was that he had been the first to write about sexual abnormalities and to say in print that they existed. As you know, Krafft-Ebing's book gives a description mainly of perversions. Yet he, as well as Moll, Hirschfeld, and the other early writers give little about the total psychology of sex. It was not until Freud published his *Three Contributions to the Theory of Sex*, in 1905,[4] that we were able for the first time to see the whole cohesive layout of the sexual instinct as it manifests itself in the child, in the neurotic, and in the pervert.

Freud published his work on sex after thirteen years of analytic investigation. In tracing the neurotic symptom from the present to the past, he naturally came to childhood, and at the same time he learned not only the fate of the symptom but also the importance of the sexual instinct in the life of the individual. In his usual way of proceeding from the abnormal to the normal, he divides the abnormal sexual manifestations into two classes: those which deviate from the sexual object and those which deviate from the sexual aim.[5] To be normal, one must attain what we call genitality. In contrast to the infantile sexual activity which is disseminated in different parts of the body (as will be shown later) the adult sexuality is mostly centralized in the genital zone. Whatever the stimulation, the adult reaction always manifests itself in the genitals through which alone the species can be propagated.

[4] Cf. Freud's *Basic Writings*, p. 553 etc.
[5] The sexual *object* is the person from whom sexual attraction emanates; the sexual *aim* signifies the goal toward which the instinct strives.

This brings us to the second condition for normality—namely, the finding of a suitable sexual object. Children show no such distinctions: they can obtain outlets from different parts of the body. The same is true of the so-called perverts whose sexual aim does not strive toward the procreation of the species but toward self-gratification in the manner of the child. Freud shows that the neurotic whose symptoms are substitute formations for sexual gratification stands midway between the so-called normal and the pervert. He concludes that *the neurosis is the negative of the perversion.* For one who is not well versed in psychoanalysis, this may sound peculiar; but I will try to show you later what it signifies.

Let us now return to deviations from the object. The best example of this deviation is furnished by those individuals who crave sensuous gratification from persons of their own sex. Homosexuality, as you are aware, has been known since the beginning of civilization, and there is no question that it has also existed even among primitives. The Spanish found it well established when they first came to this hemisphere. There are other deviations from the normal object. Thus some persons crave sexual gratification from immature objects—children (pædophilia); others use animals for sexual purposes (zoophilia). We shall have more to say later about homosexuality and its relation to the neuroses.

In discussing the deviations from the sexual aim (which normally consists of genital union in the act of copulation), Freud states that some of the partial impulses or components of the sexual instinct—like aggression, looking, touching, tasting, smelling, and hearing—which normally participate in the sexual act, may for some reason become accentuated and become an end in themselves. Normal aggression may thus develop into sadism, sexual curiosity into mixoscopia, etc. A perversion thus represents an anatomical transgression from the region normally destined for the sexual aim (the genitals) or a lingering at some stage which normally is rapidly passed on the way to the sexual aim. A certain amount of looking, touching, tasting, and smelling is quite normal. All the senses, as I have said, participate in the sexual act as fore-pleasures to it. The pervert, however, does not want genital union; he can get full satisfaction through any one of his senses. Of course with the time at my disposal, I cannot go very deeply into these problems. But as they are intimately related to the neurotic symptom, I shall discuss them in connection with psychosexual development— with the pregenital organizations as they appear in the child.

Freud divides the psychosexual development into three principal phases: autoerotic, latency, and puberty. The first is the most important phase, for it forms the foundation for all the others. It normally runs to the age of four to five, and if you look at the diagram you will note that during this period there are the following organizations: the oral, anal, and phallic— the so-called pregenital sexuality. You will also note that this phase is labeled *autoerotism*, which means self-gratification— for, as Freud says, the child's life is autoerotic. Following the autoerotic phase is the one labeled *narcism*, which is a very short but no less important phase. Then comes the latency period and finally puberty.

The latency period is characteristic only of civilized man. There is supposed to be no active sexual manifestation during that period. But this is not altogether true. If you observe a little boy or girl you will always see certain definite indications of it, and anthropologists, notably Malinowski, claim that latency does not exist among primitives. (This is also true among some semi-enlightened people.) In the Australian bush, according to G. Roheim,[6] and in other places, boys and girls play sexually as they develop. As soon as they are able to move around and play, they begin to manifest sexual interest in the manner of animals. They are not restrained, and they indulge in things we would consider immoral or disgusting.

The latency period in civilized life corresponds mostly with the school age. It is the age when the child no longer shows those infantile manifestations which are inhibited through shame, sympathy, disgust, and morality. Freud speculates that the latency period in civilized mankind represents a remnant of the glacial period when the struggle for survival was so ex-

[6] Cf. "Psychoanalysis of Primitive Cultural Types," *International Journal of Psychoanalysis*, Vol. XIII, p. 96.

treme that man could not mate. True or not, when we look at the terrific struggle imposed on our children—through training, education, and the elimination of everything sexual during the most fertile years of life—it would seem logical to assume that these mental labors exert the same effect as the ice age did on early mankind.

It is during the latency period that the organizations formed during the autoerotic and narcistic phases become more or less consolidated for the next important phase of the individual—that is, puberty. If all these organizations go through their normal evolutions, the individual develops normally. If, as not seldom happens, some trauma takes place, a weakness is left which we designate as a *fixation*. Such a *locus minoris resistentiae* in a sensitive person may later absorb so much libido that it will form a symptom.

I repeat that the first four years of development are mainly characterized by autoerotism, which normally decreases with age. The new-born child needs no gratification from the outside world except from the mother. As I told you in describing the psychic apparatus, the child's psyche or the id is stimulated into action by the two primary instincts of hunger and love which are satisfied by the mother. But the child considers the mother as a part of himself; he is in what we call an *anaclitic* relation to the mother.[7] This relationship, although it later disappears, nevertheless remains in the unconscious and now and then comes to the surface.

The id, as I said before, soon becomes modified into an ego, the first organization of which shows itself through the mouth at the level which I have marked *oral*. By the oral organization we mean that the child's needs for nourishment as well as for pleasure are effected through the mouth. The child naturally gets his nourishment from the mother's breast which satisfies both hunger and love. This oral organization becomes enhanced with age. At first it is quite simple, but as the child grows older we observe that his oral gratifications become more complex. To be sure, this outlet is in every way enhanced by the mother who wants the child to grow and be healthy.

[7] From Greek *ana-klino*—"to lean on."

The better the child's appetite, the more pleased is the parent.

In grown-ups, the oral outlet not only serves for satisfaction of hunger but also to gratify the other senses. We want the food and dishes to look colorful and savory. There is no limit to oral satiation in normal times. We eat a hundred times more than we should. We stimulate our appetites by all kinds of methods. We do not feel that we have had a really nice dinner unless we have had some alcoholic drinks with it. In nice society we have cocktails as appetizers, white wine with the fish course and red wine with the beef, and at the end a variety of liqueurs.

Eating has become an important institution. We have special societies for the cultivation of fine eating: in New York there is at least one Gourmet Society. This group meets once a month and dines in some good restaurant. Everything is served in the highest style of culinary art. The menu is carefully selected, and the dinner card tells exactly how each dish is prepared. The various courses are brought in with great ceremony: the roast duck, for instance, is a thing of beauty, a gratification to the eye as well as to the taste. Then the chef is ceremoniously ushered in by the host, and everyone applauds him. Ordinarily one does not give a thought to the cook as long as the food is good, but the members of the Gourmet Society pay homage to the artistry and skill which furnishes so much pleasure to all the senses. The chefs, I have noticed, are always very pleased by this recognition.

There have always been such societies in the great cities of the world. France which has given civilization most of its pleasure principles has long led the world in its cuisine. If you have ever lived in Paris—that is, the old Paris—you know that even in the most inexpensive restaurant the host meets you and often tells you what great pride he takes in his sauces and special dishes. In civilized man, there is always an additional gratification besides the mere satiation of hunger. Primitive people, on the other hand, eat very simply and always the same kind of food. But with the advance of civilization, even the humblest housewife racks her brains for something new to give her husband every day. He is not satisfied with a roast beef no matter how good it is if it is given to him twice or thrice in succession. The various senses need different meats, different flavors. I do not know how it is now in the state hospitals. . . . From your outburst of laughter however I can judge that it is the same as it was in my own time. We were very critical because we knew every day exactly what was coming. The food was good enough. But we craved variety—and the first thing we did when we were on leave was to go to some neighborhood restaurant, perhaps a beanery, simply for the change. (Hostesses always vie with one another to give their guests a new stimulus for their taste buds. In fact, they invariably force the food upon you, and if you cannot do justice to it the hostess feels badly.)

In brief, our eating habits like everything else in civilization are very artificial. But when you observe the child, you will see that his first erotic object is his mother's breast which he does not at first differentiate from his own body. He wants only mother's milk. If you try to give him anything new, he absolutely refuses, and it takes time and effort to get him accustomed to it. The mother may think that spinach is wonderful, but because it does not have the taste of the original food —mother's milk—the child refuses it. Some psychoanalysts, unlike the pediatricians, do not believe that bottle-feeding is as good as breast-feeding even when the formula is correct, but Freud himself agrees with the pediatricians. As eating belongs to the first ego-organization of the child, it will be best to listen to Freud's own words.

In his last expression on the subject,[8] he states: "In the beginning the mother's breast is surely not differentiated from his own body. When it has to be separated from his own body and displaced to the *outside* because the child had so often missed it, it takes with it as an 'object' a part of the original narcissistic libido-cathexis. This first object later becomes merged with the personality of the mother, who not only nourishes the child, but also takes care of him and evokes in him so many other pleasant and unpleasant physical sensations. Through the phys-

---

[8] *Schriften aus dem Nachlass,* p. 115, Imago Publishing Co., (London 1941).

ical care of the child she becomes his first seductress. These two relations contain the roots of the strange and unique importance of the mother as the first and strongest love object, which is firmly established as a model for all later erotic relations—in both sexes. The phylogenetic determinants are here so greatly superior to the personal or accidental experiences, that it makes no difference whether the child has actually suckled the breast or was bottle-fed and never enjoyed the tender care of his mother. His development follows the same path in both cases, although in the latter there may be more longing later. And no matter how long the child lived on the mother's breast, he will always carry the conviction, after the weaning, that it was too short and too little."

You will undoubtedly better appreciate these statements later when we go into the deeper developments of the ego organizations. At all events, not only our later eating habits, but our whole adjustment is based on these experiences of early childhood. But some child analysts, as I have already said, claim that a child who gets his food from the breast is better equipped than the child who gets it from the bottle, and they recommend that even if the mother cannot nurse, she should hold the child at her breast at certain periods of the day. This difference of opinion recalls the man who, when told that he had a very beautiful wet-nurse until he was about a year and a half old, exclaimed: "Look what I missed!" From this remark it would seem that Freud is right; in either case they are not satisfied.

The first ego organization, as I said, starts with the mouth, and the child uses that organ not only to satiate hunger and obtain pleasure, but also to express his displeasure. If angry, the child refuses the breast or may even bite it. I have been consulted about breast-biters. When forced to eat certain foods, even a very young child may eject them through vomiting. Neurotics invariably express themselves through their oral habits. I am sure all of you have seen persistent vomiting cases in hysterical men and women. We now know too that ulcers of the stomach are produced mainly by mental factors.

You will often be consulted because the child will not want

to eat. That is a problem that you find only in civilization. I am sure that in primitive society and in animals that problem never exists, but in civilization it invariably comes up often. I have been consulted any number of times by mothers who told me that their children did not eat anything—sometimes for days! Yet the children looked perfectly all right to me. In such cases I sometimes quote Virchow's reply when his attention was called to the case of Louise Lateau—who was supposed not to eat, and showed all the stigmata of Christ on the Cross. Virchow is reported to have asked whether she had bowel movements, and when the answer was in the affirmative, he said that although God had created the world out of nothing, he was sure that there could not be any bowel movements without food!

I saw a boy who was a little over two years old. The parents brought him to me at the suggestion of a pediatrician because the child would not eat anything. "If you will look into his mouth," the parents said to me, "you will see that he still has food in there which we gave him yesterday." I could not at first get the child to open his mouth. I finally had to use the ruse of lighting up the interior of my own mouth with a flashlight—which the little boy imitated. Sure enough—there was food in his mouth. He would not swallow. He evidently had terrific resistances to his mother and expressed them in that way.

You may be interested to know that I cured that child by taking the mother away from him for a few weeks, and by not giving him anything to eat until he practically asked for it. I learned that method from Mark Twain! Mark Twain once wrote a story about a sanatorium somewhere in Austria for the treatment of indigestion. The story went on to tell that all patients were cured one hundred per cent by a very simple method. When a patient was admitted, he was put in a small cell and left there all alone. They gave him nothing whatever to eat. After a few hours, the patient would ask for some food. No one paid any attention to him. Mark Twain strings the story out so that in a few days the patient was so hungry that he finally ate shoe leather avidly and was thus cured.

[169

The above-mentioned little boy looked perfectly well, and I knew there was no danger in giving him a modified Mark Twain treatment. Besides, since the object of resistance (his mother) was away, he soon learned to eat normally. Food is the one factor by which children are judged at home. The parents boast of it if the child eats well; they complain if he does not. And as the child is in an anaclitic relationship to the mother, the oral organization soon participates in his behavior toward her. Grown-ups, whether normal or abnormal, similarly utilize the oral activity, both as a compliance and as a resistance.

The oral manifestations of our patients are of particular interest. I now see a hypo-manic case that I have known for ten years. During an attack, she still talks almost incessantly whenever she is with me or with friends, but she refuses to speak to her husband, maintaining that she cannot talk to him. In my office she occasionally feels like screaming. I pay no attention unless she gets too loud for my comfort. Ordinarily, I let her indulge in her oral activities to her heart's content, and she has a wonderful time. On other occasions, she shows an oral rejection by vomiting and belching. Some schizophrenic cases, especially catatonics, do not eat voluntarily or talk for years. Suddenly however they become very loquacious, shout, or make senseless speeches. They show the same behavior about taking food. Similar manifestations are observable in children as regards both eating and talking.

Not all of the early oral manifestations in children are directly connected with the intake of food. Thumbsucking, for example, according to Freud, is a libidinal manifestation which has nothing to do with hunger or eating. Freud was not the first physician to reach that conclusion. Thumbsucking was recognized as an infantile sexual outlet as early as 1879 when a Hungarian pediatrician named Lindner wrote an essay about this phenomenon. Many other physicians have held the same opinion. My own professor of pediatrics, Dr. Abraham Jacoby —who, I am sure, never heard of Freud—told us when I was a student that thumbsucking is to the child a sort of pleasurable gratification akin to what we would ordinarily call sex. The

Germans always called it *Wonnesaugen*, which means pleasure-sucking. When the child is hungry, he does not usually suck his thumb; he simply cries. He sucks his thumb after he has been satiated and is about to fall asleep. In other words, the child acts like the man who takes his cigar after a good meal.

Mothers never liked their children to suck their thumbs and have done everything to stop it. They did not know why they objected to it until the modern dentist made thumbsucking responsible for deformation of the palate, for adenoids, and what not. There is no truth to these assumptions. A deformed palate is usually found in a badly constructed skull, which has nothing to do with thumbsucking. Nor has thumbsucking any relation to adenoids. It is my opinion that mothers are jealous of thumbsucking; they unconsciously feel that the child is taking a substitute for their own breasts. It is the first effort of the child to make himself independent of his mother. The latter is annoyed and resents it—just as later she resists when the boy wishes to take a substitute for her. Fathers never seem to care about it. I need not tell you that doctors have employed all sorts of devices to stop thumbsucking. The usual thing is to put all sorts of nasty stuff on the thumb. They also tie the hands—and I know of one case in which a plaster cast was put on the child's hands whenever he went to bed. They soon found however that children know how to get around these obstacles; they then suck the lower lip or click the upper palate or suck the covers.

Left to themselves, normal children give up thumbsucking when they become more interested in the outer world—long before the latency period. Some, who are mismanaged, retain this habit in later life as shown by the following case: At sixteen this young lady was an ardent palate-sucker. Her mother did everything to stop her infantile thumbsucking. After considerable labor on the part of her mother, the child finally gave it up but then started to suck her palate instead. When she came to me, she was very anxious to break this habit, but she evidently started it as she was falling asleep and continued making a clicking noise while she slept. There were many other features of an autoerotic nature in this case which definitely showed that her thumbsucking was only a variant of breast-sucking.

By virtue of the deep impressions it leaves, the breast for-ever remains an important erogenous zone. The breast plays an enormous part in the sexual economy of man—and for that matter, in woman also. The dressmaking art has always taken note of this fact; it has always utilized the breasts as a sort of sally-port for concealed attraction in modern women. This ob-ject is achieved by rendering the breasts prominent, or by leaving them slightly exposed. To illustrate the relation of thumbsucking to adult sexuality, I will cite the case of a woman who sucked her thumb regularly until she got married, when her husband objected to this "filthy habit." She then stopped it and never thought of it again until her husband died some years later, when she returned to it. In other words, as long as she lived a life of sexual abstinence, she continued her infantile sexual outlet, but during her married life she had no need for it.

In senile dementia, some persons regress to this infantile habit. I was once called in to see an old man of about ninety. I found him sitting in his chair, sucking his thumb. His son said to me: "You see, doctor, he sits there just like a child, sucking his thumb." Upon investigation, I found that this habit was revived when the family physician ordered the old man's pipe to be taken away. He thought that smoking was detri-mental to his physical health. We know of course that smok-ing in any form is a substitute for the erstwhile nipple. One might almost say it is a direct continuation of it.[9] To be sure, smoking is a substitute also for other things. The Indians orig-inally developed the habit of smoking by using certain weeds to generate smoke in order to frighten their enemies. The mod-ern boy smokes because he wishes to be "big." People will tell you that when they began smoking they got headaches and sometimes nausea and vomiting; yet they all continued. Why? Because they want to feel big. (Invariably it is the little fellows who walk around with the big cigars in their mouths.) In any case, this senile man who had been deprived by the doc-

[9] Cf. Brill: "Tobacco and the Individual," *International Journal of Psychoanalysis*, 1922.

tor of the only pleasure left in his life regressed to the earliest autoerotic outlet and sucked his thumb. You know, of course, that old age has often been called a second childhood.

Sublimation of accentuated orality in later life sometimes manifests itself in the form of biting, sarcastic expression. For every child actually uses biting for defense and sometimes for attack. Normally we break the child of this savage outlet, but it often remains as a characteristic trait. Teddy Roosevelt tells us in his autobiography that he recalls being spanked twice as a child—both times for biting his little sister. On the second occasion he was almost five years old, which was rather late for such an oral outlet. Of course, you know that cartoonists always pictured Teddy Roosevelt with a biting expression on his face and with the teeth showing very prominently. He was a fine speaker, a great oralist. In fact, all of the dictators in history (the Hitlers, the Mussolinis, the Calvins, the Luthers) [10] exerted their power through the mouth—through oratory. Hitler never advanced beyond the oral and anal-sadistic levels.

Years ago, I came to the conclusion that poetry too is nothing but an oral outlet. Of course, poetry is a highly sublimated oral expression, far removed from the original aim. Nevertheless, investigation shows that it has always been connected with food. The old Arabs indulged greatly in poetry; they held poetic contests long before the advent of Mohammed. But the desert Arabs are always hungry; they are satiated only a few times a year on the occasion of some special celebration. In more recent times, the true poet was always supposed to be a hungry man. Now and then, you will find poetic manifestations in your patients. I saw patients in hypo-manic or manic states who suddenly began to write poetry. They never penned a line of it before. For instance, one of my hospital patients, a butcher, suddenly began to write poetry during his manic periods. Of course, as you will note from everyday observation, children have a marked tendency to play with words and make rhymes. This whole subject is a very fascinating one, and

[10] Judging by his *Tischreden* and his disputes with the Pope, Luther was also strongly anal-erotic. He seemed to enjoy using frequently and forcefully such words as *farzen*, *scheisen*, and *Dreck*.

if you are interested, I can refer you to a paper I wrote about it many years ago.[11]

We have other oral outlets which are distinctly erotic. This is especially true of kissing, which is not known among primitive people—or even among civilized oriental nations. The Japanese abhor it. Some years ago in Tokyo there was a loan exhibition of painting and sculpture which had been brought from Paris. One of the exhibits was Rodin's famous "The Kiss," which marvelously depicts in marble this great western outlet. It caused a riot when it was displayed. The Japanese public would not stand for it, for to them kissing is disgusting. I am interested in the motion pictures, and I know that the one thing censored in our movies before exhibition in Japan is what we call "soul" or sloppy kissing. Such scenes must be cut out before the movie is projected on the screen. The nearest thing to kissing in the Far East is a purring by the mother into the child's ear—or, as among the Eskimos, a rubbing of noses. The latter of course means smelling, a form of salutation among many primitive tribes.

Why have we westerners developed the art of kissing about which so much has been written? In my opinion it is a form of displacement resulting from the restraints imposed by civilization upon the sexual instincts. Because of these restraints, substitute expressions were later developed. Kissing is a displacement ·from below to above—a well-known concealing mechanism. To be sure, kissing also takes place between people in whom the end-aim is inhibited—as between parents and children. Nevertheless, it is nothing but a gratification of the sense of touch and often also of taste. In other words, it is an oral erotic outlet.

QUESTIONS AND ANSWERS

Question : I did not understand you at first—does the child consider himself a part of his mother all his life?

Answer : Unconsciously—yes. For example, an American

[11] Cf. "Poetry as an Oral Outlet," the *Psychoanalytic Review*, Vol. XVIII, No. 4, (October 1931).

doctor who had served in the English army in the first World War described to me how those Scotchmen—big, sturdy fellows—would always call out: "Mother—Mother—Mother mine," whenever they were severely wounded and in distress. He said he could not understand it, and it always brought tears to his eyes to see those big giants weeping and crying out. I also heard the same thing from an Italian officer, who said the soldiers had a habit of crying out: "*Madonna mia,* or "*Madre mia*" on similar occasions. Of course, the madonna cult of the Catholic Church is well known as a mother cult. If you study some of the art masterpieces, you will find that the madonna and child is an idealization of the artist and his mother. A good example is Leonardo da Vinci and his feminine artistic creations. I would suggest that you read my translation of Freud's *Leonardo da Vinci.*[12]

In analysis, we find that every woman who comes into one's life is gauged by one's mother. You accept or reject women depending on whether or not they fit in with the mother cathexis. That mother image is always there, and the behavior of the individual toward women is always guided by it. If I had the time, I could show you this mechanism in many cases. Of course, the child's anaclitic relation makes him absolutely at one with the mother. This is naturally repressed with age, as I shall show later. But quite often the mother does not allow that anaclitic relation to stop. This is noticeably true if there is only one child; in that case the mother will hold on to him tenaciously and frequently rob her son of his virility. More about this later when we shall speak of homosexuality.

Question : What is your attitude about thumbsucking? From what you said, my impression was not to pay too much attention to it.

Answer : Yes—we consider thumbsucking an autoerotic outlet which some children (perhaps most of them) indulge in during the first year of life. It is a self-gratifying outlet because it relieves tension. The child soon learns that the breast or bottle satiates and gives pleasure, and he wants to repeat this later. During stress, we adults smoke too much. We chew or

[12] Dodd, Mead & Co. (New York, 1932).

we bite our nails or we make bread pills and knead them. In China, where civilization is much more advanced, they actually manufacture jade beads for this purpose. Smoking, chewing, drinking, singing, and talking are oral outlets which are used to reduce tension; they mitigate the stress of civilization. I have known people who were not allowed to smoke and then began to gorge themselves with food or drink—which was much worse for them than smoking.

Naturalists and explorers everywhere have noticed that primitive people too do the same thing to relieve their tension. For instance, the South American Indians chew coca leaves; in the Far East, everyone chews betel nuts. There is surely a strong need for such release. If you read the history of smoking in the 15th century, you will find that in the beginning strong efforts were made to stop it. In Turkey, people were decapitated for smoking; yet it could not be stopped. Children, if left alone, will gradually stop thumbsucking and masturbation, of their own accord when they emerge from the auto-erotic phase of development, when they get a little older and start playing with toys and with other children. They do no harm. But if you try to stop them, you will often lay the foundation for some neurotic disturbance later.

Question : Does the term "actual neuroses" mean there is an actual injury?

Answer : Yes. Thus, Freud found that the anxiety neuroses were due to *coitus interruptus, reservatus,* and other abuses which produced real somatic injuries of a chemical and toxic nature, the manifestations of which are in the emotional spheres. Many people who do not know how to use contraceptives or who do not have the money to buy them, resort to these and similar practices. In time the man develops anxiety attacks, usually before the woman. For the man always has an orgasm, while in the woman it does not always take place. All sexual indulgences wherein the act is not allowed to live itself out adequately in the manner prescribed by nature sooner or later leads to anxiety. The sexual act has been compared by many observers to a sort of epileptoid attack, and whenever it is accompanied by consciousness—that is, by the idea: "I must

176]

be careful not to ejaculate"—it is inadequate. In *coitus inter-ruptus,* the man and the woman must necessarily think about it.

Again, take masturbation. It does not do any organic harm. But those who indulge in it not only get a very inadequate outlet from it, but also develop conflicts about it. The result is that sooner or later they try to stop it and usually develop an anxiety neurosis. Freud called them "actual neuroses" in contradistinction to the psychoneuroses—that is, to the hysterias and compulsion neuroses, which result as a consequence of psychic traumas.

LECTURE VII

TOPICS :

1. *Anal-sadistic phase*
   Bowel Control
   Chinese Method
   Professor Holt's method
   Hiding of excrement by primitives
   Sense of sight substituted for sense of smell
   Cartoon in Le Rire
   Continuation of sense of smell in a grown-up
   Repression of smell and perfumes
   Sense of smell in different races
   Aggression in childhood
   Sexual manifestations more prominent in boys than in girls
2. *Phallic phase*
   Stimulation of genitals through cleansing
   Infantile masturbation
   Thumbsucking as a sexual activity
   Erogenous and hysterogenous zones
   Motion outlets in children and adults
   Motion pleasure in amusements
   Swaying in religious rites
   Opposition to dancing by leaders of religion
   All senses cooperate in coitus
   Moll's tumescence and contrectation
3. *Havelock Ellis's tumescence and detumescence*
   Lewin's "body as phallus"
   Chronic tumescence as result of modern wooing

Necking as cause of anxiety
4. *Œdipus complex*
   Early family romance
   Sleeping with mother as seen in civilized, in primitives, and semi-enlightened people
   The father as an intruder
5. *The castration complex—usually based on a threat*
   Becomes effective when the boy sees girls who lack the penis
   The disappearance of the Œdipus complex and adjustment to father
   Selection of vocations and empathy toward father
6. *Œdipus in girls*
   Penis envy
   Inferiority in girls and the wish to be a boy
7. *Narcistic phase—noticeable about the age of 4 to 5. In girls it does not appear until pubescence*
8. *Questions and Answers:*
   Does the manipulation of the penis in the phallic stage serve to localize the libido in that organ? And what should be our attitude toward the boy who craves that?
   Do you consider modern women feminine?
   What is your attitude toward perversions?

178]

LAST week I outlined for you the phases of psychosexual development as described by Freud in his *Three Contributions to the Theory of Sex*. I told you that the goal of normal life is, first, to attain genitality, and second, to crave an object of the opposite sex for this function. The sexual instinct is present in the child at birth, but it must go through various levels of development before it reaches the normal adult stage of genitality. Up to about the age of four, we say that the child's life is autoerotic. It is during this period of so-called pregenital sexuality that the child lays the foundation for his later adjustment.

The first ego organization in this period is the oral phase which I discussed at length last week. Hand in hand with this, in civilization, is the second or anal-sadistic phase. We must train the child right from the beginning to control his bladder and his bowels, and you know what a great problem this is in the nursery. Every time the diaper is opened the mother (assuming that she is caring for the child) will say something like: "You dirty little boy." She herself has had to go through so many years of training and repression of her anal and urethral activities that a feeling of repugnance inevitably crops up when she sees and smells the diaper.

The child, of course, does not know what she means by "dirty little boy," but he does get the feeling that invariably accompanies it. The mother's emotions are carried right over to the child, leaving in him a disagreeable affect. Naturally, we as civilized westerners have to act in this way; we must control these excrementitious acts and repress what we once liked. But it is only we Occidentals who make such a fuss over it. In China they take the little child and put him in a bag of sand, leaving him there the whole day. At night they simply empty out the bag and fill it with fresh sand. That is why the Chinese, so far as I know, do not suffer nearly as much from compulsion neuroses—for that malady, as I will show later, is based on an anal-erotic fixation. Be that as it may, our mothers begin to train their children to control their bowels and bladders from the beginning of their existence. Bear in mind, please, that these

[179

activities are perfectly natural, but that our mode of living—
our æsthetic and social feelings—demand that they should be
controlled. And since we have done so for many thousands of
years, it has now become sort of second nature to us. Every
civilized being must learn to do it, and every mother has her
own way of getting the necessary results.

When I was a student, one of my teachers in the subject of
children's diseases was Professor Holt. He was a first-rate
teacher, and I liked him so much that I thought seriously of
becoming a child specialist. Holt used to tell us that it was very
easy to train even very young infants in the control of their
bowels. For this purpose he had invented a glass rod with
rounded ends. Every so often, he said, the child's anus should
be stimulated with the rod; the child would then learn to move
his bowels at a particular place and time. We all thought that
this was a brilliantly ingenious way of mastering a difficult
problem. I would have forgotten all about it—since I gave up
the idea of becoming a child specialist—had not two people
come to me as patients years later, who had been trained in
childhood by this method. They were both marked anal-erotic
characters, and I had no doubt that this early glass-rod condi-
tioning had something to do with their neuroses.

You must not forget that so-called character, too, is nothing
but the sum total of early impressions. In our efforts to control the primitive impulses, we often use means which leave
peculiar impressions on the whole personality. This is especially true concerning the reaction formations to anal control.
More of that later.

Nowadays, a well-to-do woman does not have to bother
with diapers. There are companies which deliver clean ones
and take away the soiled ones for a few dollars a week. But that
does not in any way help the child; he still must learn to control his anal functions. One might say that to do away with the
excrementitious is simply a question of hygiene, but primitive
people have different reasons for it. They consider that excrement, being a part of one's own body, can be utilized by an
enemy with malicious intent—that is, to kill or hurt its erstwhile owner. Some primitives, therefore, are particularly care-

ful about hiding their excrements. My belief is that phyletically this concern about excrement was originally due to the odor which feces and urine emanate. Animals trace each other by the sense of smell; and in some primitive (and even semi-enlightened) countries, detectives, like our blood-hounds, still trace criminals by smell. This fact may have been the origin of present-day efforts to conceal the excrementitious. Remember —we all lived by the sense of smell before we stood up on our feet. When we assumed the erect posture, we gradually repressed the sense of smell and instead used the sense of sight. We say, "How beautiful she is!" In the olden times it was, "How nice she smells!"—as one can still observe in dogs when they meet. Among humans, if a lady smells, even of the finest perfume, it is not always to her credit.

A pagan god—or anything that was once pleasant—turns when repressed into a demon or into something unpleasant. What was nice and agreeable in early life, when it is repressed becomes hideous and disgusting. That is the only way in which it can be held down. In the neurosis, which results because of a failure in the repression, the original material can only come back in disguised form. Nevertheless, some neurotics like to pick out an old shoe from a rubbish heap, smell it, take it to bed, and sleep with it.[1] Reference to the sense of smell can be found in folklore, fairy tales, myths, and in modern wit. Not long ago a patient brought in a copy of *Le Rire*, one of the leading French humor sheets. In it was a cartoon showing a male and a female dog, both very beautiful and well-groomed. The male dog was smelling the female dog in the usual place, and the French—who have a sense of humor and frankly express it—had used the caption: *"Qu'elle est charmante!"* That cartoon was very interesting to me because modern men look at women from a distance and say just those words. The reaction is produced by the sense of sight, instead, as it used to be, by the sense of smell.

There are still some people who have a very strong sense of smell and who utilize it in the primitive sense. Freud has called attention to the fact that this is true in all compulsive neu-

[1] Cf. Brill: "The Sense of Smell in the Neuroses and Psychoses," l.c.

[181

rotics.[2] When I was a student in the College of Physicians and Surgeons, a classmate used to say that he could tell a menstruating woman by the sense of smell. He had discovered this ability or gift at home, where he claimed that he was always able to tell when his sister was menstruating. A few of his classmates tested him one day by going with him through the waiting room of the nose and throat department of the Vanderbilt Clinic. As he passed by the women patients who were sitting on benches and waiting for treatment, he indicated which ones he felt were menstruating, and in every case he proved to be right. He seemed to be an average fellow in other respects—although he did not turn out to be such a good doctor.

Repression of the sense of smell is responsible for many changes in the behavior of civilized man. But the interest in odors has not been given up. Millions are spent annually on perfumes and odoriferous powders and pomades which are supposedly used to disguise our dislike for human odors. Yet all these artificial perfumes come from the same source as the human odor. The most expensive perfume is made from the sexual glands of the civet cat, musk ox, and of certain deer, obtained when these animals are in rut. A drop of such secretion can make gallons of perfume. The other ingredients of perfume are from blossoms or the sexual glands of plants. These odors are in such great demand simply because they unconsciously serve the same purpose as the original ones—namely, to attract the sexes.

On the other hand, we usually sense and object to the odor of those human beings who are not of our own race or color. I have talked to Japanese and to peoples of other races who assured me that they are just as sensitive to the odor of whites as we are to theirs. There undoubtedly is an *odeur humaine*—even in those who keep themselves very clean—to which we are still quite sensitive. It plays quite a part in everyday life, as you can see by all the advertisements for odor concealers and mouth washes. In the child, this sense—like all the others—is very active. I once went to visit some friends, and I took along

[2] Cf. Brill: "The Sense of Smell in the Neuroses and Psychoses," l.c.

a box of candy for the hostess. We all went for a walk leaving the little boy of about three at home. When we returned, we found that he had taken every piece of candy from the box and spread them all on the floor. He had eaten none of them, for his mother was very rigid with him and allowed him only two pieces of candy at a certain time of day; he just sat there smelling them. He had unwrapped the candies one by one, and was having a wonderful time merely smelling each piece.[3]

In the average person however, the sense of smell is repressed, and as the excrementitious odors are particularly obnoxious, everything is done to control and repress them in early childhood. We call this second phase of ego organization *analsadistic* because at this age, when the child has difficulties learning to control his bowel movements, he is also very aggressive and destructive—and, as will be shown later, often utilizes his anal functions to express his aggression. Left to himself, he would shout and break everything that came in his way. Even when he is already more or less controlled, he still likes to take everything apart, and his behavior towards other children is thoughtless and often cruel. The little boy of two or three displays no feeling of consideration or sympathy. It is an "age without pity," as La Fontaine said of childhood.

Now, when I refer my remarks mostly to the "boy," it is not necessarily out of deference to the ladies. That may be a factor—but the main reason is that we can study the sexual life of the human being more easily in the male than in the female. This is so because by nature the female is passive; she usually conceals her feelings, whereas the male is active and so aggressive that he finds it hard to control his feelings. This differentiation should not be taken in a sense derogatory to the female. I have never believed that there is a "superior sex," but there are two sexes who differ both physically and psychically in many respects. Thus, the egg lies passively in the uterus and waits for the spermatazoa to come to it, and this characteristic manifests itself throughout life. It constitutes the vital differences in the division of labor between the sexes. An obstetrician of

[3] It is of interest to note that this little boy, now about thirty, is being treated for a compulsion neurosis.

wide experience told me that when he delivers a little boy, he frequently hears the bystanders remark, "He cries just like a little boy;" and he confirmed this by stating that the boy's demeanor is different at birth from that of the little girl. This aggressive attitude increases with age as soon as the boy is able to walk. He has to be watched lest he break things, and the more commotion he makes, the more he will like it.

When I was giving courses in the department of pedagogics at New York University, some kindergarten teachers asked me why it was that little boys have a habit of taking pencils, putting them into keyholes, and breaking them off. They said they never noticed this in the little girls. It occurred to me that to penetrate—to go into something—is a very important part of the masculine function, phyletically speaking; and that the little boy unconsciously remembers this and strives to exercise this activity as soon as he can. We know for example that the Hebrew word for "male" means a *borer*, a *piercer*, while the word for "female" means a *hollow*. The name of the Greek god who brought fire to mankind—Prometheus—means to rub and bore into something.

The little girl on the other hand is graceful and demure; she loves colors and strives to be attractive. To understand the manifestations of sex, then, we must study them where they are most prominent. The male cannot hide his active aggression, whereas the female passivity allows her to remain quiet—at least on the surface.

I should spend more time on the anal-sadistic phase; but, as we must cover ground, we shall now consider the next pregenital phase in the child's development. It is the *phallic* or *clitoric* phase, which treats of the predestined erogenous zones which are often quite active in childhood. The little boy very soon becomes aware of his penis; when he is cleansed or accidentally touched in the genital region, he perceives it as a pleasurable sensation and he naturally wants to have it repeated. As a man said to me once when I was talking to him about masturbation, "It is not so simple, doctor. If you touch your nose accidentally, you do not think of it. But if you accidentally touch your penis, you want to keep it up." That is undoubtedly true. The nerve distribution in this region is perhaps more prolific than in any other region of the body, or it is nature's way of preparing this organ for the important function allotted to it. At all events, once the boy becomes cognizant of his genitals, his interest in them continues. I was only lately consulted by a mother who said that her little boy showed distinctly that he wanted her to use the washcloth on his penis several times, that she was sure that he wanted the pleasurable sensation repeated. I heard from another mother that her boy would say on similar occasions: "Do it again."

Another little boy, when washed, would suddenly begin to laugh. When his mother asked him why he laughed, he explained that it tickled him. Mothers soon become aware of these things and try to prevent them, but it is not always possible to do so. Pleasure once experienced is not easily renounced, and that is as true of the child as of the man. Very often such an experience is the beginning of infantile masturbation. Whether the mother is compliant or not, the boy will usually try to repeat this touching, but naturally he prefers to obtain it from the mother. Little girls show a similar behavior in the clitoric region; they often go through all sorts of motions with or without friction of the clitoris.

The phallic, clitoric, and other activities are of a masturbatic nature, and depending on the constitution and the environment, they are more or less in evidence during the first years of childhood. We designate these activities as infantile masturbation in contrast to the later masturbation which starts around or during adolescence. What should we do about it? It is best to ignore it and to remember that, like thumbsucking, it is only an autoerotic activity which ordinarily disappears sooner or later when the child begins to take more interest in the outer world. I have seen however many neurotic disturbances which started at that age because the parents—sometimes even doctors —mismanaged this early budding sexuality.

Before Freud called attention to the existence of an infantile sexuality, such behavior was considered monstrous and sometimes found its way into medical literature as sexual curiosities. Thanks to Freud, we now know that we deal with a natural development—with the so-called pregenital or infantile sexuality, which, in contrast to adult genitality, is not centralized and subservient to the primacy of the genitals. The child obtains his or her outlets from erogenous zones: that is, from a portion of the skin or mucous membrane, which, when sufficiently stimulated, produces feelings of a sexual nature. Some of these zones are predestined for further genital activities, and the others—the mouth, anus, and other parts of the body—usually fall into disuse during the early years of life. Because of its disseminated nature, Freud called the child's sexuality "polymorphous-perverse"—that is, in the adult sense it is perverse in all directions.

But to illustrate the essential features of the infantile sexual activity, Freud selected thumbsucking, which involves a part of the body that ordinarily has no relation to sex, and thereby demonstrated that the production of pleasurable sensations depends more on the quality of the stimulus than on the nature of the bodily region. The thumb, by virtue of its location and mobility, readily lends itself for pleasure-sucking, and thus accidentally becomes an erogenous zone. The predestined zones (the penis or clitoris) are naturally preferred, but the erogenous feelings can readily be displaced to the thumb or to any other part of the body. And this tendency to erotic displacement is also found in hysterical symptoms. From what we have learned from psychoanalysis, we know that in the neurosis the repression mostly affects the genital zones proper, and their excitability is in turn transmitted or displaced to other non-sexual zones. The conversion symptoms, of which I mentioned a few, behave exactly like genitals, and the hysterical symptom is a substitutive gratification for the sexual act. Freud thus shows the direct relation between the infantile sexuality and the neurotic symptom, and concludes that *erogenous and hysterogenous zones show the same characters.*[4]

Before leaving the infantile sexuality, let us consider the desire for motion which every child loves. Motion of course stimulates the skin and the muscles as well as all the other sensory organs. This craving is noticed in early life: while

[4] *Basic Writings of Sigmund Freud,* l.c., p. 588.

suckling the breast or the bottle, the child will at the same time rhythmically pull his ear lobe or some part of the mother. Motion, in the form of running, jumping, riding, swimming, and now flying, forms one of the greatest outlets for the child and grown-up: the faster the motion, the better one likes it. Thousands of people are annually killed in auto accidents, but the quest for speed continues. If you go to Coney Island or to some other such place of amusement, you will not only see much dancing, but all sorts of motion outlets of the most primitive form. At these entertainment places you will see elderly people indulge in the most infantile forms of motion pleasure. Some of those attractions loudly proclaim things like "Shoot the chutes," or "Do the rollicking reel and be young again." Some of them offer a mixture of infantile motion with adult sexuality.

I remember, on my last visit about twenty years ago, seeing a place called "The Cave of the Winds," where you were made to walk on a crazily moving platform until at the end you found yourself on a stage in front of a good-sized audience. Every woman who happened there was directed by a clown to leave the stage by a special pathway, in which there was a contrivance to blow up her dress. Ordinarily, when a lady's dress is blown up by the wind as she goes into or comes out of the subway, one looks the other way out of delicacy. Here however there was a whole arena of people waiting for such a sight. What did one see? A girl's dress would suddenly be blown up, and the girl would utter a short scream, but actually nothing was seen. Yet everybody there was boiling with avid anticipation. The man who ran the show told me later that it was one of the most successful and profitable exhibitions there.

Motion is also observed in emotional states of a religious nature. The Jews, Arabs, and other races sway their bodies while praying, and our Negroes, though long away from their original land, still show much of it during their religious ecstasies. That conventionalized motion in the form of dancing has been recognized as a sexual outlet in the broad sense is shown by the fact that some religions have always disapproved of it. The Quakers for example never allowed dancing, and a great many Presbyterians were always opposed to it. Moreover, whenever the style of dancing changes, there always are some people who are dead against it. No less a liberal than Byron was horror-stricken when the waltz first made its appearance in Europe; and when the turkey trot and the other new steps were introduced in New York, all standard religions rose against them.[5] To be sure, every child, as soon as it can stand on its feet, will sway and move to the rhythm of music no matter how simple it may be. The desire for motion may be the secret of all our outlets, for what are music and art but gratifications of rhythmical motion? However, lest we give the appearance of indulging in mysticism, let us return to our main discussion.

In brief, the pregenital or infantile sexuality serves the auto-erotic needs of the child, and later it still serves as a fore-pleasure to adult genital gratification. When genitality develops, all these partial impulses are repressed and become subject to the primacy of the genitals. The normal individual then has full consciousness that his gentitals co-operate whenever any sexual situation arises and that he wants a heterosexual object with whom to consummate this particular function. All the senses participate in the sexual act. I spoke about the kiss (which is really nothing but a mode of tasting) and the prominence given to it in civilization. The sense of sight too is important in the preliminary stages of mating. One looks at the sexual object and admires her before wishing to mate with her. Some individuals, like the poet, may be able to feed themselves altogether on their eyes, or they may express all sorts of ecstasies about the object through the mouth. Some linger too long on touching, looking, or smelling, and obtain all gratification through a particular sense organ. Such persons belong to the class designated as *perverts* which we shall discuss later. But the average adult is not satisfied with one or two of these partial impulses or components of the instinct. The latter only serve as fore-pleasures to bring about genital union for propagation.

[5] Cf. Brill: "Psychopathology of the New Dances," *New York Medical Journal*, February 1914.

But in order to understand the processes which lead to the end-aim, let us hear what the sexologists say about it. Before Freud, Albert Moll divided the sexual act into two stages, which he called tumescence and contrectation.[6] The former, or tumescent stage, is characterized by feelings in the genitals which crave direct genital gratification. It is a craving for the spasmodic relief of genital tension, resembling the impulse to empty a full bladder. The other stage, contrectation, consists of ideas of central or peripheral origin or of both which strive toward physical or psychic contact with another person. Contrectation thus represents the impulse to obtain both physical and psychical outlets (usually from a person of the opposite sex) through touching, kissing, as well as through other social or esthetic means. Moll differentiates in this manner between the psychic and somatic parts of the sexual instinct. His views can be confirmed by observing idiots in whom masturbation represents a purely "physical act," and immature boys who usually masturbate without assuming any psychic attitude towards another person. On the other hand, we frequently meet with pubescent boys in whom the contrectation impulse, or the psychic component of sex, appears in isolated form. Such boys may be deeply in love without thinking of physical sex. They only think of the psychic attributes of the beloved object.

These stages, while they may not always appear as clearly-cut as Moll formulated them, can nevertheless be clearly discerned. I prefer Havelock Ellis's classification, which modifies Moll's classification by dividing the act into *tumescence*[7] and detumescence.[8] When the sexes come in contact and attraction starts, tumescence begins. The whole body (to speak with Lewin) becomes, as it were, a phallus—although the phallus proper shows this most prominently because it has to deposit the spermatazoa into the female.[9] There is also a definite swell-

[6] Cf. Moll: *Untersuchung über die Libido sexualis*, 1908.

[7] From *tumescere*, "to swell up."

[8] "Analysis of the Sexual Impulse," p. 19, in *Studies in the Psychology of Sex*, F. A. Davis Co., 1908.

[9] Lewin: "The Body as a Phallus," *Psychoanalytic Quarterly*, Vol. II, 1932.

ing of the woman's breasts; they become enlarged and more tense, and the whole glandular system becomes active. Tumescence, with its concomitant physiogolical effects, continues and gradually mounts until the attainment of the end-aim. After that, detumescence occurs: all the tension subsides and the senses gradually return to their normal state both psychically and physiologically. The individual feels relaxed and somewhat depressed and wants to sleep. One of the best hypnotics is coitus, but it should only be prescribed in cases where it can be taken adequately—that is, on the basis of a clear conscience.

The stage of tumescence may continue chronically, as it were, for a long time during the wooing period of modern couples. As a result of ethical and social training, young people in love usually indulge in all the fore-pleasures—in fact, in everything except coitus proper. Such prolonged behavior engenders various neurotic disturbances in those who are constitutionally predisposed to them. The most common neuroses that one encounters as a result of such chronic practices are the various forms of anxieties. In private practice you are often consulted by young women who complain of general nervousness and especially of insomnia. In the greatest majority of such cases there is no organic factor to account for the insomnia, and hence it is altogether due to inadequate sexual outlets. The young man courts his ladylove almost every evening, and they are both in a highly tumescent state by the time they separate. He frequently obtains an ejaculation or he relieves himself later through masturbation. The girl usually indulges in erotic phantasies which invariably keep her awake for hours; and if they continue, they become bound to ideas or feelings when we then have a full-fledged anxiety-hysteria. Such patients, if they have not read psychoanalytic literature, will tell you that they dream prolifically and are often awakened by nightmares. Their dreams are quite characteristic. They are chased by animals, such as bulls or snakes, by bandits with long daggers, or they are held up and robbed. Very often the dreamers are awakened with palpitation and respiratory oppression. More about this when we discuss interpretation of dreams.

Anxiety states of this nature can be readily cured by stopping the inadequate sexual stimulations. This is more difficult than you realize, but if the patient is sensible and is made to realize the nature of the situation, it can be done. Usually it is the woman who is the first victim of anxiety; although now and then, if the man is of the neurotic type, he succumbs to it first. In the beginning of my private practice, before I was thoroughly convinced of the correctness of Freud's concepts, I did a lot of experimenting when such a woman consulted me. I soon discovered that she was keeping company, and that there were nightly excitements without any adequate outlet followed by prolific phantasy formations. I would then act like the average "pill pusher"; I would give a sedative and order the lady to go to the country or away from home for a few weeks. The patient's letters would tell me that the anxiety soon disappeared. But now and then I would be informed that the insomnia had returned. Invariably, I would find that the patient had been visited by her fiancé over the week end. After a number of such convictions, I gave up this "respectable treatment" of sedatives and change of scenery. Instead, I talked freely to the patient about her inadequate erotic excitement and settled the situation by the direct psychoanalytic approach.

Let us now return to the diagram used last week. You will note that the autoerotic phase of psychosexual development is also marked with the term "Œdipus complex." I have already mentioned that Freud, in using this term, referred to Sophocles's *Œdipus Tyrannus*, which is an elaboration of the classical Greek legend, and I take for granted that you all know this Œdipus myth. Freud talked about the Œdipus complex for the first time in his *Interpretation of Dreams*.[10] By it, he meant the early family situation or the child's first adjustment to his microcosm. As you know, it is during the first four or five years of life that the child lays the foundation, so to say, for the later adjustment to his macrocosm—to the great outer

[11] Cf. Freud's *Basic Writings*, l.c., p. 307.

[191

world in which he is destined to live. During this early period —that is, during the oral, anal, and phallic phases of ego development—the child lives altogether in his own little world, surrounded by his parents (or parental substitutes) and necessarily dependent upon them for all his needs. But the child—particularly the little boy—soon shows a dislike for his father, and a distinct preference for his mother. This is a perfectly natural feeling. The child, as I told you, is in an anaclitic relation to the mother. Everything good comes from her, and since the child is born with all the attributes that later appear in the adult, he soon shows a feeling of possession, of mastery over his mother.

On the other hand, there is no logical reason, as far as the child is concerned, why there should be a father in the house. The child looks upon him as a big, growling beast of whom everybody is afraid. This impression is further strengthened by the fact that it is the father who usually disciplines him as he grows older. Remember—we were not born to be obedient and orderly. The Good Book tells us that "the imagination of the human heart is evil from the beginning," which means that the child is born without the equipment that would make him fit for civilization. Children have to be trained and their impulses curbed, and it is well known that the father is the most active force in this situation. Naturally, the child prefers to be with his loving and indulgent mother, and the more his cravings increase, the more he needs her and wants her for himself. Animal-like, he wants to sleep with her, to cuddle up against her, and obtain the love and security which he craves. In primitive society, and among anthropoids, the mother constantly stays with the child until he is independent. The Australian Bushwoman, according to Roheim, sleeps on the little boy until he is four or five, in order to protect him. Recently I read a book on South America by Harry Franck[11] in which the author describes a scene in a large city. An Indian and his wife had been hired to remove debris from a demolished house, and they were carrying it from one side of the street to the opposite side. The author was struck by the fact that the wife,

[11] *Vagabonding Through the Andes.*

192]

who worked with her Indian husband the whole day long carrying bricks and wood, at the same time carried a young child on her back. She could have left the child on one side just across the way where she could easily have kept her eye on it, but, the author tells us, such a thing never happens. The more or less civilized Indians keep the child with them all the time even up to the age of about five. That is what the child wants because evidently that is best for him.

We see the same situation among animals. But in our society, the father always interferes with this primitive relationship. He sleeps with the mother in one room, while the little child has to remain in another. I cannot stress too much the fact that the little child draws conclusions as well or even better than the adult. Like the animal, he is not inhibited in following conclusions which we, hidebound by rules of logic and decorum, are prevented from putting into operation. The child is still more or less controlled by what some call vague intuition, but he reasons properly with the experiences at his disposal. He perceives well enough that it is the father who deprives him of his mother. Consequently he resents this intruder, and the older the boy gets, the less he wants his father.

The demands upon the mother however increase as he grows older. I have already mentioned that the child's first pleasurable sensation in the genitals usually occurs while he is being bathed. He begins to get bodily sensations from the mother and craves further contact with her. Sleeping with mother up to a relatively mature age is still quite common even today. Every once in a while I see men who tell me that they slept with their mothers until they were thirteen or fourteen. I reported the case of a man who slept with his mother until she died; he was then forty and suffered a nervous breakdown soon after. Another patient slept with his mother every time he did not feel well. When I saw him, he was twenty-eight years old, and naturally maladjusted to sex. In another case, a woman was sent to me by a trained nurse because her little boy of eleven, with whom she slept, had begun to "act like a man." He had erections and strove to be in contact with her body. When I asked her why she slept with the boy, she replied: "My husband died when the boy was a few weeks old. I am a widow, and I am afraid to sleep alone." Well, you cannot do anything with such people. I tried to make this woman understand the dangers involved, but she refused to change her mode of living. You see dozens of such cases if you investigate the lives of grown-ups.

It is only natural, as the boy grows up, that his mother libido will become connected with his genital system. Usually however adults take a hostile attitude when the little boy shows any tendency to touch or play with his genitals. They will threaten him with some such remark as "If you do it again, we will cut it off," or "You must not do that." One mother told me she said: "If you do it again, it will fall off." Such things constitute what we designate as the *castration threat*. It need not be the classical threat of "cutting it off." I have found in many cases that it consisted merely of a vigorous act such as slapping the hand or pulling the hand away from the genitals. Somehow the child realizes the significance of the gesture. He recognizes its importance and reacts very vehemently to it. But as I have already said, no threat can stop the desire for repetition of a sexual pleasure. The boy continues to crave these contact pleasures from his mother. The castration threat does not have its effect until the little boy accidentally happens to see the genitals of his mother or sister or of some other little girl. When that occurs, he realizes for the first time that there are human beings who really have no penis. The threat that he might lose his own penis then becomes a reality, and under the shock of this discovery, the little boy gives up the desire to get contact pleasure from his penis—particularly the desire to get it from the mother.

It is remarkable how many men one meets who attributed male genitals to women even after they were already mature adults. Such men have usually been brought up in guarded fashion and do not have sisters. I once talked to such a man, an intelligent person who had been educated in Italy. I asked him how he could maintain this belief in the face of the numerous statues he had seen all over Italy. I reminded him of the Piazza Signorelli in Florence where daily I used to see little

194]

boys playing with the bronze penis of one of the statues: the urchins would shine it and laugh over it. That group of sculpture also contained a statue of Venus or some other female divinity without a penis. This man replied that he imagined the penis had not been put on the statues, although it belonged there, simply out of regard for women.

Many boys entertain the same belief, and it is a great shock to them when they miss the penis for the first time. It is this discovery which convinces them that the threat of castration, which they hitherto doubted, actually can become a reality. They then repress the mother image which is thereafter kept submerged by incest barriers. The Œdipus complex thus vanishes and the rivalry between father and son no longer has reason for existing. The little boy then makes peace with his father. Having always admired him and considered him omnipotent and omniscient, he now adjusts himself to the father by identifying himself with him. This identification is a sort of "assimilation," or an introjection of the father into himself. All the fears, prohibitions, or commands which hitherto came from the father are now incorporated into the boy's mind and, as I said above, constitute what we call one's conscience or super-ego. It is as if the little boy thought: "I am now as big and strong as father, or even bigger and stronger than he." It is this standard of measurement which is responsible for all our progress. Every normal boy always tries to outdo his father; sons who just obey, never amount to much. Progress consists of not following in your father's footsteps. History shows that this is true.

Many years ago, in the Vanderbilt Clinic, I investigated the unconscious reasons for the selection of vocations.[12] I started with my colleagues, asking them why they had become doctors. At first they said they did not know. But soon they began to talk, and in every case it developed that they had tried to outdo their father or some father substitute. One of them for instance said that his father, who had been a veterinarian, wanted him to follow in his footsteps. He went through school

[12] Cf. Brill: "The Psychopathology of the Selection of Vocations," *Medical Record*, February 1918.

and then said to himself: "If I am going to be a veterinary surgeon, why should I not be a real surgeon?" He then went to college, and although he did not become a surgeon, he did end up as a neurologist. At any rate, he went ahead of his father.

In other words, the adjustment to one's father is an assimilation on the basis of that empathy which I have previously described. You notice this empathy more frankly in adults after they have actually lost the father. They then try to do all the things the father would have wanted them to do. One of my friends, a doctor, suddenly began to carry a cane. I had never seen him carry a cane before, and I asked him about it. "That was my father's cane," he explained, and since then he has always carried a cane. Another man I knew became interested in some charity or other simply because it had been his father's interest. Quite often we notice the same behavior toward teachers and other parental substitutes.

The father is thus disposed of through identification, and the mother through repression. Henceforth the boy no longer craves maternal affection—although a certain amount of affectionate relationship to the mother unconsciously continues. The disappearance of the Œdipus complex usually takes place by the age of four or five when the boy obtains more and more libido from persons and things in the outer world, and if he is brought up properly, the autoerotic period comes to a close at the beginning of the school age. As I shall show later, the adjustment of the girl follows a different path.

The next period of development is the phase of *narcism*, which appears when the child is five or a little older. During this period, the various components and partial impulses of the sexual instinct, having been partly repressed and sublimated, are being collected together for object-finding, but the first object which the boy finds is himself. The term "narcism" (or narcissism) was borrowed by Freud from the myth of Narcissus, the beautiful boy who fell in love with his own reflected image. During this period of development the boy is, as it were, in love with himself, and everything revolves about himself. Narcism is really egotism erotically tinged. The boy is very much interested in himself, in his own body. You will often observe that at this age of five or six, the normal boy will no longer talk about himself in the third person. Instead of saying, "Charlie wants this," he now says, "*I* want this." In other words, his ego has become developed. When you work with defectives, you find that they never reach this level of development. They usually refer to themselves in the third person and rarely reach the stage where they can talk about themselves as "I."

The narcistic phase, although a short one, is nevertheless of great importance psychiatrically, as you will hear later. In the normal course of development, narcism is soon followed by the *latency period*, which, as I have already told you, corresponds mostly with the school age. During this period the early infantile sexual manifestations, which have been partially repressed and sublimated, are now consolidated into one stream to be subjected to the primacy of the genitals. In the narcistic phase, the little boy often forms very good friendships with other little boys; in other words, the first object-finding is homosexual. But gradually the normal boy begins to center most of his interest in girls, and thus he goes from homosexuality to heterosexuality. This process manifests itself first in feelings of rejection and resistance to the little girls. But these resistances are soon replaced by cravings and phantasies of a heterosexual nature.

Those are the evolutions, then, through which the little boy passes. The situation in the girl, as I said before, is somewhat different. During the first few years of life—that is, through the oral, anal-sadistic, and the beginning of the clitoric phase —her evolution is the same as the boy's. The little girl, like the boy, must have food, protection and love, and hence she too, is in an anaclitic relation to the mother. Soon, however, something happens which shows her that she is different from the boy. There seems to be a law in nature that opposite sexes attract each other and that the same sexes are rivals. The little girl soon gravitates toward her father and he toward her. The father has by this time been somewhat disappointed in the lady whom he has married. She is a nice enough wife, but she cer-

[197

tainly is not what he thought of her before marriage! When his little daughter arrives, he sees in her a repetition of the erstwhile love object. She resembles the woman he loved before; and in addition she looks a little bit like himself. You will find that being in love is really a narcistic situation. When a man loves a woman to the point of being crazy about her, it is because he has surrendered his whole narcism to her. That is why the young man who is madly in love would actually give his life without hesitation for the love object; he has projected his narcism altogether on that person. That usually happens only once in a lifetime. Normally every person thinks of himself first.

In any case, when the father looks at his little daughter he feels that she is going to grow up into something unusual—into his ideal conception of a woman. Like all human beings, he is swayed by the omnipotence of thought, and he says to himself: "She is going to be the kind of woman I think a woman should be." He is thus compensated for that part of the love object he had lost. He begins to love the little girl and shows it. He spoils her, is indulgent with her faults, and shows her special favors. The little girl of course soon finds that her mother is a rival for her father's attention. In this way, the antagonism between the two begins to function. Observant parents see these things so often that there can be no question of exaggeration in what I say.

As the girl grows older, a new development takes place which is characteristic only of women. The little girl, usually at the age of two or three, discovers that other children have what she does not have—a penis. She is puzzled by this phenomenon and wonders why this is so. As one little girl said to her mother when she saw her little brother naked for the first time, "Why haven't I a tassel like Johnnie?" The mother then explains the difference between the sexes, but that does not allay the little girl's resentment. She soon develops what we call the "penis-envy," which is analogous to the castration complex in the boy.

The essential difference in the evolution of the sexes is thus as follows: At the time when the little boy begins to feel narcistic and superior, the little girl begins to feel that she is inferior. She strives at first to ignore her penis-envy by rejecting the whole idea that she has no penis. She strives to act like a boy in every way, but gradually she is forced to accept her feminine position. Some however become hoydenish, compete in boyish athletic games, and insist on behaving like boys. But since that cannot continue, many of them become hysterical with the onset of puberty, when they are forced to recognize that they are in fact girls. You will find that there is hardly a young girl who does not at some time wish that she were a boy. When you ask them why, they usually answer: "Because a boy can do everything." But analysis shows that they envy the boy because he can take his penis out and "stand against a tree." What they really mean is that they would like to have a penis, like the boy.

The penis-envy, which produces the feeling of inferiority in the girl, also affects her relations to her mother. For when she feels inferior because she is bereft of something, anyone else who is in the same situation is also considered inferior. It is no consolation for the little girl when her enlightened mother explains that she herself is a girl and consequently has no penis. The child simply puts her mother into the same inferior category and blames her besides for not having given her a penis like her brother's. This reproach of the mother for not having made them into men invariably appears in the analysis of women. But, as I said, the average girl gradually accepts her feminine role by the time she reaches puberty when she has more or less developed her secondary sex characteristics and when the boys begin to be attracted by her. Her deferred narcism then comes to the surface. She now realizes that she possesses some alluring premiums, and she then begins to take note of her looks and to cultivate her charms.

Those who refuse to resign themselves to their femininity either develop a neurosis which shows this struggle in disguised form, or—what is rare—they openly insist on being men, on acting and dressing like men. History shows that such *transvestites* have played a part in life. One woman, a Dr. Walker (who died only a few years ago), actually got Congress to pass

[199

an act allowing her to wear men's clothes. I knew another woman who walked around in riding breeches most of the time. Occasionally, she would even stuff a handkerchief in the genital region to simulate a natural bulge. In another case, the woman was so anxious to be a man that she refused to urinate in the usual way. She would always sit facing the wall, so that she could urinate like a man.

Modern life and education tend to encourage masculinity in women. Girls are often given athletics and other activities usually more appropriate to boys. Athletics, to be sure, are good for all young people, but it should be borne in mind that girls should be brought up to be women, just as boys should be brought up to be men. Their education must be based on the natural scheme of life. A person of one sex who strives to become like the other sex invariably develops into a misfit or a psychotic. I have in mind such an unhappy yet talented woman who merged into a neurotic tantrum, during which she attempted suicide, because she could not do as well in broadjumping as the men with whom she competed. Her physician could not convince her that her feminine structure was not as well adapted for such forms of athletics as that of men. Girls who are allowed to live in the phantasy of being men have a terrible time when puberty and menstruation begin. It is wiser to bring girls up to understand that they are just as important —just as supreme—as boys but that they are destined to pursue different paths of development in the scheme of nature.

There is another important result which comes from this difference in the development of the sexes. The boy's narcistic phase, as I said, occurs at the age of four or five when the Œdipus complex comes to an end with the repression of the mother and the incorporation of the father into himself. This introjection of the parental image, and especially the father image, gives rise to the development of the super-ego. At this time, you recall, all the prohibitions and commands which the father previously hurled at him from the outside are now on the inside and act as his conscience. The father no longer has to remind him what to do and what not to do. The severe super-ego, which was set up as the heir of the Œdipus complex, tells him what is right and what is wrong. The super-ego in other words is made up of the earliest precipitates of the parents, reinforced later by our ethics, our religion, and our morals.

In the girl however this development does not follow the same path. The penis-envy causes the girl to give up her mother attachment and enter into the Œdipus situation where she remains for an indefinite period. She only gives it up late in life and then incompletely. Hence, the super-ego formation is not as strong and as independent as in the boy and this in turn exerts a definite effect on the development of the feminine character. The feminine super-ego is usually not as rigid as in men, and this has given rise from time immemorial to the idea that women are not as reliable, not as good witnesses as men. I once heard an elderly judge say that he hardly ever believes a woman and hence argued against women on juries, because, as he said, they are too emotional and unreliable.

One need not agree with the judge and yet admit that there is something to what he said. He simply did not understand feminine biology. Women are as truthful and as reliable in their labors as men are in theirs; but women do not have to be as severe or as strict as men. Their labors run in different directions. You see that clearly in the whole animal kingdom. In our society, in olden times, the males always fought to the death, whereas the females had only to exchange masters. Genghis Khan never took any prisoners: he killed all the men, but the women he adopted. This same consideration is seen in modern times when women are tried for some offense. It is very difficult to find a jury of men who will convict such a woman. They usually identify her with a mother, a sister, or some other feminine image.

In other words, women are different because of biontic differences. They were destined to occupy themselves with the offspring; they consequently developed what we call a maternal feeling, and that surely must have a different psychogenesis than the male super-ego. It is therefore not to be conceived as an inferiority or fault if women are biontically and environmentally differently constructed. On the contrary, a

[201

rigid, aggressive, and highly moral woman inspires us with suspicions that she might be unfit for her feminine role. We expect women to be feminine—which is quite different from masculine. That is the normal thing.

QUESTIONS AND ANSWERS

Question : Does this penis manipulation in the phallic stage serve the purpose of localizing the libido, and what should be our attitude towards the child?

Answer : As I told you, the penis is a predestined erogenous zone, and hence you might call such acts a preparation for its future function. But we live in a civilization which cannot encourage genital activity in early life. We must strive to bring up the child to be in harmony with his cultural environment and not to come into conflicts with it later. This is the main problem for parents, educators, and doctors. As a physican, I may not be as concerned about society as about the future of the individual. As willing as we would be to keep the child comfortable, we must not forget that if we encourage him in anything that would later cause him to collide with the society in which he lives, he will get into trouble. That really accounts for the parental reaction to such childish behavior. Our efforts should be to guide him in such a way that his later adjustment will be easy. It is sometimes best to ignore such autoerotic activities in a child, but guide him towards normal object libido in the form of games and friendships. To be sure, we must never become excited over slight deviations from the accepted sexual standards, for experience teaches that there is hardly a person whose sexual sanctum would not shock someone. The average child properly guided will go through the normal sexual evolution. As to the adult, as long as his sexual practices do not conflict with society, I see no reason for excitement or indignation. Let me illustrate what I mean by the following case:

A distinguished professor wanted to spend his sabbatical year in New York so as to be analyzed by me. His reason for desiring treatment was that throughout his married life he

could have coitus only if his wife's genitals were hairless. His
wife was compliant from the beginning, and everything had
gone along satisfactorily for over twenty years of their married life. "Well, professor," I asked, "are you contemplating
a new marriage or perhaps a love affair? Otherwise, it would
hardly pay you to give a year's time and considerable money
for something which may not come to pass." He replied that
no, he did not contemplate anything new, but that he was
always aware of the fact that his sexual need deviated from
the average. I admitted that, but I advised him not to be
analyzed because he was not in conflict with anyone. It was
not a question of right or wrong since he and his wife had
solved the problem for over twenty years. I thought I knew
why he was that way, and I might have been able to change
him—but as long as his sexual behavior did no harm to anyone,
and as long as he and his wife were well adjusted to it, I thought
it was best to let things alone.

I take the same attitude toward some perversions—in particular, toward homosexuality. I was a consultant to the Department of Correction during Mayor Mitchell's term of
office, and for many years I have lectured to the New York
detectives. I have always advised the detectives not to bother
the well-behaved homosexuals. In former years, you know, the
detective bureau wasted much time and effort to trap homos
just because they were "degenerates," as the police called
them. I never could see any valid reason for this, as long as
the homos kept their sex to themselves and molested no one.
On the other hand, I have always warned homos that, like
heterosexuals, they cannot behave obnoxiously with impunity.
If the homosexuals behave themselves and restrict themselves
to certain spheres and to their own kind, I see no reason for
persecuting them. They are not homos by choice; some can be
cured, but ninety-nine per cent of them do not wish to be
cured. When they consult us, it is usually because they are in
some trouble—generally, when they are being blackmailed.

I take the same attitude toward other perverts who really
do not wish to be changed. Thus, I saw an exhibitionist who
had been arrested in Central Park. I asked him why he had to

[203

do it there. "But I get the thrill when I do it there," he replied. "In that case," I said, "you have to take the consequences and go to prison." And, as a matter of fact, he is in prison now. On the other hand, I saw no objection in the case of a voyeur who would get his outlet by looking at pictures of show girls displayed in front of playhouses.

Question : Do you consider modern women feminine?

Answer : I certainly do. Women can no more get away from their fundamental femininity than we can from our masculinity. They may cut their hair and wear trousers, but they are still female and attractive. As Goethe put it: *"Das Ewig-Weibliche zieht uns hinan."*—"The eternal feminine always attracts us." The eternal feminine always exists, and you cannot get away from human nature. For that reason, I cannot see any hope for all those changes which reformers try to make on the basis that the female is the same as the male. *Ça n'existe pas!*

LECTURE VIII

So FAR, I have traced the evolution of the sexual instinct as it develops in the average human being from childhood to adult life. The child's sexuality, as you remember, is not centralized as in the adult. The child at first gets pleasure from erogenous zones some of which are predestined for adult sexual function and some of which are not; in Freud's term, the child is "polymorphous-perverse"—that is, if judged by standards of civilized adults. For the child derives pleasurable outlets from the partial impulses of the sexual instinct—such as aggression, exhibitionism, touching, tasting, looking, hearing, and smelling —in the frankest, most primitive manner. Later these impulses are partially repressed and sublimated, and the rest are subjected to the primacy of the genitals. The amount that goes through in pure and sublimated form is used in mating and in the struggle for existence. In brief, in the normal course of events the child goes through the autoerotic, the narcistic, and the latency periods until the age of puberty when he attains genitality and finds an object, normally of the opposite sex.

It sometimes happens that the individual does not go through these stages in the usual manner. Some accident or trauma occurs in one or another of the pregenital organizations, leaving a weakness, or what we call a point of *fixation*. Because of such a *locus minoris resistentiae*, as well as of other accidental factors, this point of fixation later attracts an excessive amount of libido, and the result of such a libidinal regression is either a perversion or the negative of it—namely, a neurotic symptom. I have mentioned that perverts are those in whom a partial impulse or component of the sexual instinct has been raised to the whole sexual aim. In some cases—and these claim our greatest interest—instead of a perversion, the abnormal flow of libido is repressed and then comes up in the form of a neurosis. Here, instead of being a "peeper," one may be troubled with bad vision or painful eyes. The neurotic symptom invariably expresses in disguised form that fragment of pregenitality in which the fixation occurred.

Thus the compulsion neuroses represent fixations in the anal-sadistic phase, whereas homosexuality and paranoia, as we shall show, are based on fixations in the narcistic phase. Without discussing in detail the question of the origin and predisposition of the various neuroses,[1] I shall merely state here that hysterical symptoms show themselves in early childhood, compulsion neuroses in the second period of childhood (from 6 to 8), and the paranoias and schizophrenias after puberty. It is interesting to note that the predisposing fixations of the latter neuroses—which are characterized by grandiose delusions, turning from actual reality, and incapacity to form transferences—are found in the stage of libido-development prior to the establishment of object-finding, that is, in the autoerotic and narcistic phases. Paranoia and schizophrenia, although they manifest themselves late in life, are nevertheless based on very early inhibitions and fixations.[2]

But in order to understand how such faulty processes occur, let us go back for a moment to the early development of the libido. The average child, as you know, learns to control his natural impulses by means of the training which parents impose upon him. The child's natural expression of these impulses arouses feelings of antipathy in adults because the latter have themselves been forced to control and repress them. As I have said, the only way to keep under control those natural impulses which continuously strive for expression is by the formation of dams which constantly oppose them. Such dams or re-action-formations are: sympathy, shame, disgust, and morality, which can be seen wherever there is civilization. In some places they are more pronounced than in others. In this country, for example, our public urinals are very much hidden, whereas in older European countries, which have already made a more sensible adjustment to such matters, they are more or less in evidence. In Paris, Brussels, or Vienna, you can see comfort stations everywhere.

In New York, they are not only hidden but are very far apart. Only the other day a cultured European—who was a stranger in our city and who seemingly suffered from "Anglo-

[1] Those interested are referred to Freud's paper, *Die Disposition zur Zwangsneurose*, originally published in the 4th Series of the *Sammlungen zur Neurosenlehre*, Heller (Wien, 1918); English translation in Vol. II of the *Collected Papers*, Hogarth Press, London.
[2] Brill: *Freud's Contribution to Psychiatry*, p. 140, W. W. Norton.

Saxon prudery"—told me a joke which, though not new to me, nevertheless was quite apropos. It was about a stranger who came to New York from some small town. While he was walking the streets, his bladder became full and he vainly looked for a place to empty it. Much distressed, he stopped

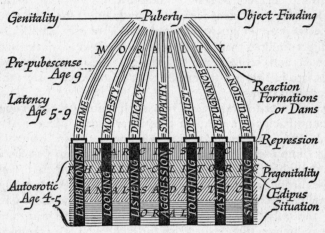

The above diagram gives a schematic outline of the psychosexual evolution as given by Freud in his *Three Contributions to the Theory of Sex*. The partial impulses and components of the sexual instinct are followed through from the autoerotic and narcisstic periods into the latency period and puberty. An effort is made to show the reaction formations or dams that are formed by civilization to hold down the primitive impulses. It must be emphasized, however, that this is just a scheme.

near a group of autos, but immediately a chauffeur yelled at him: "Hey! What the hell's the matter with you?" Then he went up against the wall of a building, but this time a policeman threatened to arrest him. In his despair, he noticed a doctor's sign and rang the bell. He was ushered into the office of an elderly doctor who looked up benignly and asked: "What can I do for you?" "Doctor," said the stranger, "I cannot empty my bladder." The physician handed him a basin and said: "Well, just try." The man tried and succeeded only too well. "You are doing fine," said the doctor, nodding encouragingly. "Yes, doctor," replied the provincial, "—if they let me."

This story expresses the situation as it exists in our big cities. The country gentleman in question naturally had no idea that he could have repaired for this act to our best hotels or to a corner saloon. Such a joke, told in Italy or China, would miss the point and would be misunderstood, but you all laughed, because·you had probably found yourselves more than once in a similar situation. Moreover, you know what trials and tribulations our children have to go through before they can empty their bladders with impunity. Thus I recall when I was a medical student and an assistant in a hospital during the summer, a young girl of about 17 or 18 was brought in one evening because she could not urinate. My instructor explained that the neck of the bladder was paralyzed by the pressure of the retained urine. The girl had been on a day's picnic with other young people, and she was too bashful to leave the group and relieve herself. As a result of her rigid childhood training, this poor girl had to undergo all the indignities of being catheterized.

That can happen only in a civilization which teaches that the mere admission of a natural need constitutes an act of immodesty. We are taught to hide—nay, to ignore—natural wants. In sensitive people such behavior often produces untold difficulties. Thus I have spoken about the fuss made in the nursery over the child's anal activities. The child of course is in every respect a helpless creature, altogether dependent on his mother or nurse, who can do whatever they want with him. But there are two things which they cannot control altogether. They cannot make him eat, and they cannot make him move his bowels. The child soon realizes this and makes good use of these powers. He cannot utilize eating so well as a weapon, for hunger is a need which comes quite frequently, but bowel movements can be retained for a long time. The child thus finds that his anal activities are especially effective in annoying or controlling the adult tyrants.

Thus no child wants to go to bed in the evening when his

mother thinks it is time to sleep. But he has to be trained to a certain regularity in habits of sleeping, eating, and in bladder and bowel functioning. The child however sees no reason for this regularity. He frequently tries to postpone going to bed by refusing to move his bowels. The mother then tries to bribe or intimidate him into giving up his feces, and her eagerness to grasp it causes him to think that feces is something of great value. In bestowing it on his mother he imagines that he is giving her a valuable present. Naturally, when he is angry at the mother, he simply refuses to give it. Such nursery struggles in neurotic families often result in so-called anal-erotic characters.

This is especially true of those in whom this struggle was continued into the latency period or even later. I have in mind a patient who suffered from periodic attacks of rage during which she wept, cried, and shouted at her servants, her relatives, and especially at her husband. She had been brought up in one of those very nice families where training of the anal-urethal functions is started meticulously very early in life and is more or less continued into puberty. She consciously recalled how she could "get her mother's and nurse's goat" by refusing to move her bowels at the proper time or place. Up to the maturescent age, she used this weapon to her advantage. Between the ages of six and ten, she would occasionally defecate or urinate in some inappropriate place—as in her brother's room—and this invariably upset the household. When she grew older, she found that she really could not always control her bowels; she met with accidents not only at home but also on visits, for which she was severely punished. At the age of about fourteen however these functions were thoroughly controlled, and she developed into a very spotless and very moral young lady.

Before proceeding with this interesting case, let me recall what Freud tells us about the anal-erotic character.[3] In his classical paper on the subject,[4] Freud describes persons who are

[3] Cf. Brill: *Psychoanalysis, Its Theories and Practical Application*, 3rd edition, chapter on "Anal-Eroticism and Character," p. 390.
[4] *Sammlung Kleiner Schriften zur Neurosenlehre*, 2nd Series, p. 132.

later reacting to an enhanced pregenital anal-sadism, as very *orderly*, *economical*, and *obstinate*. These qualities are usually carried to extremes. A person of this type may be so orderly that he will be unable to tolerate the slightest disarrangement on a friend's desk. A slight film of dust or a barely perceptible spot may cause an outburst of anger. He will call down his secretary if the latter's trousers are not well creased or his shoes not polished to a sparkle. He himself usually looks spotless and manikin-like. He is extremely scrupulous and severe about everything in others. As a business man, he has the reputation of being very economical—often of being miserly and exacting to the last penny. Once an anal character makes up his mind, he remains obstinately set, and nothing can change him. He is usually very revengeful; he never forgets an injury —even if it is something, say, that was inflicted upon him in early youth by a father or by an older brother. As a writer or speaker, he is very critical and sarcastic and will rarely give credit without nullifying it in the next sentence. No matter how well-bred, he has a tendency toward foul-mouthedness and toward excrementitious wit. He rarely enjoys a joke dealing with object-libidinal situations. He notices something filthy in everyone and in everything.

The cases that I reported [5] show these characteristics clearly, but I have naturally seen many other varieties. Some of these cases sublimate their anal-eroticism in various useful though symbolic vocations and develop into well-adjusted personalities. But even they sometimes merge into a neurosis, and their anal-erotic traits then manifest themselves in disguised form. Thus the lady mentioned above was ordinarily a very refined person and quite generous with money, but when she got into an attack, everything changed. It was during one of these attacks that she became my patient. At our first consultation she repeatedly worried about my fee and was full of rage and anxiety against her husband and children. She exaggerated her husband's illness into imminent death and was sure that she was ruining her children because she felt no love for them. She turned her rage on herself and thought that she was about to

[5] Brill, l.c.

die of some horrible disease such as syphilis or that she was going insane. She imagined that everything about her person was bad and hopeless. Some of the psychiatrists who had seen her before me diagnosed her case as manic-depression and others as involutional melancholia despite the fact that she showed no symptoms of real depression and no signs of menopause.

Now this woman was thirty-five years old, married, and the mother of four healthy children. Her husband, it seems, had no love for her; since their marriage, he had lived on her money and had done nothing useful himself. Analysis showed that she married him to spite her father, of whom he was in every way the opposite, and even though he had infected her with gonorrhea a few months before their marriage. She claimed that she had disliked him ever since then, and yet she married him and refused to get a divorce as her friends and parents had repeatedly urged her to do.

Ordinarily she took good care of her children through trusted and capable servants, but whenever an attack came on she hated the sight of them. Her symptoms alternated between anxiety about herself (usually fear of death or insanity) or hatred and rage against others. During her attacks, she seemed to take a fiendish delight in telling everybody that her husband had infected her with gonorrhea and that he was sexually perverted. She went into minute details about her intimate sexual experiences with him and claimed that he forced her to do various perverse acts. She dwelt on these activities in such a way as to impress everybody with disgust, but she admitted to me that not only was she a willing partner, but that she herself had often initiated these experiences. I might add that she had had a varied sexual career before and after marriage, and ordinarily considered herself a *femme du monde*. During an attack however, she acted like a squeamish old maid or like a pure virgin and could not find adequate words to express the horror and disgust which her former experiences inspired in her.

Analysis showed that ordinarily she controlled her anal-sadistic character through strong reaction-formations (such as meticulous cleanliness about her person, stylish dressing, and showy charities), but that she regressed to it from time to time at some crucial period of her life. Her attacks repeated compulsively her early struggles with her parents, especially with her father. Thus in her early childhood, whenever she soiled herself or was very unruly, her father spanked her. This spanking developed her masochistically, so that from the age of five spanking gave her pleasure. She recalled that she often misbehaved to provoke it and that the last spanking she received at the age of nine was for soiling herself and defecating in her mother's bedroom. In her attacks, her husband was the father-substitute; and whenever she told virtual strangers about their intimate sexual behavior, he would naturally become enraged, and beat her—so severely, on two occasions, as to fracture her arms.

Analysis showed that her desire to speak about her intimate sexual activities was an unconscious repetition of her former habit of soiling herself. By dilating on her intimacies with her husband, she wished to show that she had done something which was very naughty and which merited condign punishment. When she was beaten for it by her husband, she felt more or less relieved. Such episodes usually produced a definite improvement in her mental state: they acted like a shock-therapy. She then proudly exhibited her arm immobilized in a plaster cast and treated it with the typical *belle indifférence* of hysterics. On a few occasions she reacted to her husband's maltreatment as if she had atoned for her sins. To use Alexander's term, she felt that she had "bribed" the super-ego and that she was now purged of her sins.

It is interesting to note that although rich and ordinarily generous, she always acted like the proverbial miser during her attacks. At these times she was also forever worrying about her bowel movements. She regularly spoke about the frequency, consistency, and size of her feces—not only to me, but also to her family and friends. If you will read the literature on anal-eroticism, you will note that feces and money (especially gold) have always been associated. Misers invariably suffer from chronic constipation; they hate to give up anything.

In sum, the adjustment to the anal-erotic organization follows the same path as the other pregenital phases. Everything being equal, it passes away in the usual manner, leaving only slight reaction-formations. If it has been accentuated to the extent of causing a fixation, the result may be a compulsion neurosis or a psychosis which resembles the manic-depressive types—as illustrated in the case mentioned above and in other cases reported elsewhere.[6] I feel that there are many cases of this type, which because of their seeming periodicity are diagnosed as manic-depressives. It is my opinion however, that in contrast to the ordinary manic-depressions, which according to Abraham show a constitutional enhancement of the oral zone, these cases show an additional or preponderant enhancement of the anal-sadistic phase. Not one of these so-called depressives which came to my notice showed any psycho-motor retardation in the classical sense. Instead of the classical depression they all showed attacks of rage and the type of anxiety which one observes in children who, having held back their bladder and bowel contents as long as possible, then begin to fret, fidget, and cry—or actually, as it were, explode.

It is difficult to leave this topic without mentioning a few additional cases of this type, where the symptoms, although appearing periodically, nevertheless were nothing but exaggerations of a compulsion neurosis which had existed for a long time before. Thus, a woman of sixty had numerous attacks before I saw her, which were diagnosed as manic-depressive attacks. They were neither manic nor depressive in the Kraepelinian sense, but they usually lasted from two to three months. During the attacks, her symptoms were characterized by an almost constant querulousness and by an obsessive preoccupation with names and numbers. She continually tried to recall the address, the street number, or the name of someone

---

[6] Cf. Brill: "The Application of Psychoanalysis to Psychiatry," *Journal of Nervous and Mental Disease*, December 1928; also *Freud's Contribution to Psychiatry*, p. 158, W. W. Norton.

she had once known, especially in early life, and became enraged because she was unable to do so. Her children often took great pains to find those names and addresses for her, but that did not help, for she still doubted them. Examination showed that even between the attacks she suffered from a compulsion neurosis which she was however able to control and keep to herself. The attacks occurred when her regular life was disturbed by some new burden. To be sure, she had many other obsessions and phobias.

Another case concerns a man who was ordinarily recognized by his friends as an æsthete in every sense of the word. He merged into periodic attacks during which he was depressed and agitated because of being troubled by bad taste in his mouth and by peculiar odors. Oral surgeons and nose and throat specialists finally found nothing more to account for his symptoms; yet the latter nevertheless persisted for periods lasting from five to twelve weeks. He too had a compulsive mode of thinking ever since childhood on the usual anal-sadistic foundation. Briefly, up to the age of thirty-six, this man had the habit of sticking his finger into his rectum, then smelling and tasting it. At the age of about twenty-two, something happened which started a struggle against this habit, but it was not until years later that his first attack appeared. Lack of time forbids further discussion of this case. I cite it merely to illustrate the type of cases which I consider anal-sadistic neuroses but which are variously diagnosed by psychiatrists.

Let us now turn to the component of aggression, which is at the basis of compulsion neuroses, and trace its evolution in the child, in the normal adult, and in the neurotic. Aggression is naturally very strong in all male animals. Everything in life — self-preservation and preservation of the species — depends on it. A weak animal cannot survive very long, and a human weakling is extremely impeded in his course of life. But if we allowed free play to our aggression, we would have murders every minute, and since the whole fabric of our civilization is built on the precept "Thou shalt not kill," we had to devise means to suppress aggression. The best that modern man can do when he is angry is to curse. Instead of killing, he can say:

"I wish he were dead." He thus expresses a wish that is based on the infantile omnipotence of thought. He really does not believe his wish will produce that death, but the phantasy is in itself a mild relief. All cursing is nothing but a substitute for aggressive wishes.

During the pregenital period, the child is "without pity"; he is in our sense cruel, destructive, and with remorse. To make him fit for civilization, he must be repeatedly curbed until a reaction-formation or a dam is formed within him which henceforth opposes this natural aggression. This particular dam, we said, is sympathy. Philology must have been aware of this very important psychic structure, for the word sympathy means "to suffer with" or "to feel with." Through continuous correction and curbing by his environment, the child finally learns to sympathize with human beings and also with animals. Thus, I recall a little boy who received a stuffed rabbit as a gift. This toy would squeal when squeezed, and naturally the boy loved to hear this sound. He was not strong enough to exert sufficient pressure to produce the squeak, but he soon discovered that the same thing could be achieved by throwing the rabbit on the floor. He then continually threw it out of his crib and vociferously demanded that someone pick it up for him. This continued for some time, much to the annoyance of the grown-ups. But they wished to please "His Majesty, the Child," and so humored him in this pastime.

Months later, when he was able to walk, the little boy applied this experience to the very mild house dog. Whenever he saw this toy spaniel lying on a chair, he would go over and throw it to the floor. His mother, who was very fond of her dog, warned him repeatedly not to do this, but he kept it up whenever he thought he was not being watched. One day his mother lost her composure, and when the little boy shoved the dog off the chair, she ran over and knocked him down too. "Whenever you knock down Fluffie," she said, "I will knock you down." Of course the child was bewildered and felt terrible. But the mother unconsciously, as it were, forced him to sympathize or feel with the dog's sufferings, or better, she caused him to "empathize" himself with the dog. Observation showed that he never molested the animal again; on the contrary, he soon learned to like it.

This reaction-formation against the child's aggression is an accepted institution of modern society and is brought about in many ways. If you watch children playing in the streets, you will often see incidents like the one I witnessed many years ago. Four or five little fellows were striking and abusing another small chap, who simply stood there and cried while the others alternately hit him, seemingly without any display of anger. The tormentors apparently saw no reason why they should not abuse this little fellow, and they kept it up until presently a bigger boy of about eight happened to come over. "Get out!" he yelled as soon as he took in the situation. "Hit a fellow your size!" The "gang," including the victim, all ran away. In primitive life, such a weaker victim might have been torn to pieces. But in our society we cannot allow a person to be abused simply because he is weaker, and hence we continually stress the idea of fair play. The bigger boy, in other words, already possessed that dam of sympathy which we impose on all our children, and he "suffered with" this little victim—he could empathize himself with him.

Sympathy, then—like all the other dams of civilization—is developed at the age of three, four, or five as a reaction-formation against aggression. Once this dam has been established, one can no longer be cruel and destructive in the primitive sense. A person who does not possess the capacity for sympathy cannot develop into a civilized human being, and he is consequently a danger to the community. Extreme cases of this type represent what some psychiatrists used to call "moral idiocy (or imbecility)." Such people can commit any crime for no other reason than that it pleases them to do so. They do not seem to have the ability to distinguish right from wrong. The famous Leopold and Loeb case some years ago—in which two wealthy college students murdered a small boy simply as an "experiment"—is an example of this. A person of that type is one in whom the dam of sympathy has never been formed.

Of course, a certain part of aggression escapes repression and then participates in the hunger and mating struggles. Another part of it is sublimated or transformed to higher aims. Schools, particularly in Anglo-Saxon countries, have always emphasized athletics in an attempt to teach young people how to give vent to aggression in a regulated manner without actually resorting to primitive ways. Our great interest in prize fights is perhaps the most direct by-path for vicarious aggression. If you go to boxing bouts, as I sometimes do, you will realize the truth of this statement. Everybody is delighted when there is blood or when someone is knocked senseless. On the other hand, if there is a lag in the fighting—if there is no slugging and no blood—the fans become restless and "razz" the combatants. They stamp their feet and often shout "Give us back our money!" or "Throw the bums out!" I remember the Dempsey-Carpentier fight, which grossed about a million and a half dollars. It cost fifty-five dollars for a ringside seat, and the place was jammed. The bout lasted only about four minutes, and you would have thought that the fans would have been disappointed over spending so much money for such a brief period of fighting. But, on the contrary, everyone was extremely happy. I returned to New York in one of those busses which transported the fans back from Boyle's Thirty Acres in Jersey City to Times Square. All the way home they talked with enthusiasm about the way in which Carpentier had been knocked cold by Mr. Dempsey. You could easily see that it was a wonderful vicarious outlet for their pent-up aggression.

The other sports have the same mechanisms, except that they are not as directly sadistic. They are all simply a means of giving vent to aggression. One identifies himself with the favorite fighter, player, or team, and in this way gets a vicarious outlet. In ordinary life, if someone accidentally steps on your toes and says "Excuse me," you have to control yourself and say that you don't mind it, even though you really do not feel that way. But at prize fights or football games you can be frank; you can hurl abusive language at the scapegoats or the referee, and thus obtain some sort of substitutive outlet. I often think, in fact, how terrible it would be if we abolished prize fighting and the other aggressive sports. It would probably be unsafe to walk the streets even in broad daylight.

The normal person, then, ordinarily forms a dam of sympathy against aggression, relying on certain substitutive outlets for that part of it which is carried through. Sometimes however, as we said, this dam is not properly formed. It is either not strong enough or it is too strong. If the innate aggression is not sufficiently repressed and sublimated by the time the individual attains genitality, he may crave genital outlet through aggression alone. He is not satisfied with just a little teasing or toying with his ladylove, preparatory to attaining the end-aim; instead, the aggression in itself forms the full outlet. In such cases, we deal with the perversion of *sadism*. A perversion, remember, is a deviation from the aim, insofar as a partial impulse or component of sex is substituted for the whole aim—that is, coitus. The true sadist is one who does not want or does not need genital outlet in the characteristic form of copulation. All he wants is to use aggression on the love object, and that alone furnishes him the required aim. Thus such a man once told me that female genitals disgusted him. What he wanted was to handcuff women and then perpetrate all sorts of aggressive acts upon them. That alone constituted his outlet.

The term "sadism" was coined by Krafft-Ebing after the Marquis de Sade, a French littérateur who wrote playlets and other works describing this perversion. De Sade himself was accused of torturing women and was tried for it; but it was a satirical tract against Napoleon I which finally landed him in the Bicêtre. At Sade's time the Bicêtre was simply a prison for political offenders. But de Sade concocted all sorts of fantastic stories about people being diabolically tortured there, wrote these tales on pieces of paper, and threw them out of the window. The people were horrified by the stories he spread, and when the Revolution started, the first thing they did was to storm the Bicêtre. If you are interested, there is an excellent life of de Sade by an Englishman named Geoffrey Gorer.

Masochism, the opposite of sadism, was also named by

[219

Krafft-Ebing after a littérateur—the Austrian writer, Sacher-Masoch. The latter, whose works you will find in many bookstores, made his heroes and heroines desire to be humiliated and tortured as an end-aim. Sadism or masochism, as Freud showed, have their normal roots, and in various proportions exist in normals as well as in neurotics. Those terms incidentally were found rather clumsy by later psychiatrists, and so they adopted, instead, Schrenk-Notzing's term, *algolagnia*, which means "pleasure in pain." Sadism was thus designated as *active algolagnia*, and masochism as *passive algolagnia*. These terms, though not popularly used, are scientifically preferable.

Although a certain amount of exaggerated activity or passivity is found in some normals, it is a perversion only when seen in pure form. I see such cases occasionally in my office and sometimes after they have conflicted with the law, when I am asked to give an expert opinion about them. There are different forms of sadistic perversions. In the old days there were the "braid-snitchers," who cut off one or both braids from women, but I have not seen this type since the ladies gave up wearing long hair. Nowadays we have the "pinchers" or "pin-prickers," who ply their perversions in crowded places where it is hard to detect them. One of these individuals invented a device which he kept in his sleeve; it was so arranged that when he brushed up against a woman and slightly extended his arm, she was pricked with a pin. The woman's scream was enough to bring about an orgasm. Such perverts are known to the police but are only rarely caught by them. Occasionally I also see sadists of the "Jack the Ripper" type, who represent the overt or symbolic lust-murderers, and also, rarely, the necrophiliac.[7]

I could discuss perversions for a long time, but here we are mainly interested in their negatives or the neuroses. Of this form, the most characteristic, as I already said, is the compulsion neurosis. The compulsive neurotic is constantly afraid that he is going to do something harmful to himself or to some-

[7] Those interested may read my papers on "Tobacco and the Individual," l.c. and "Necrophilia," *Journal of Criminal Psychopathology*, Vol. II, No. 4 (April 1941).

one else. He is terrified at the idea and then develops all kinds of defense reactions—sometimes regular ceremonials—against it. Such behavior manifests itself in morbid doubts, phobias, and obsessions. These neuroses were called *psychasthenias* by the French, and by the Germans, *Zwangsneurosen*. The latter is in my opinion a much better term since it stresses the characteristic element of compulsion, whereas the indefinite French term, *psychasthenia*, simply means mental weakness, which as a rule does not exist in such patients. On the contrary, most compulsive neurotics are mentally above the average.

Let me cite an illustrative case: A very prominent business man, the president of a large corporation, once consulted me because an elevator girl in his building had been killed while in the line of duty. It was definitely established that she died through her own negligence. My patient did not know her, and he first heard of the accident when someone asked him to contribute to a fund for the girl's family. The idea suddenly occurred to him that he was responsible for her death. He knew well that he had nothing to do with it; yet for almost two months he struggled with this obsessive idea and finally had to consult me. He started by saying: "Now, doctor, please don't think I am crazy. I am not crazy; I am the president of the X—corporation and a member of this and that organization—" And he then related the story which had obsessed him for so many weeks.

Of course, he had nothing to do with this woman's death. The incident simply fitted in with his compulsive neurotic background; as soon as he heard of the girl's death, it somehow took possession of him. When people are dominated by certain feelings—by certain cathexes—they unconsciously grasp at anything which harmonizes with the unconscious feeling. To be sure, this patient was a typical anal-sadistic character who was ordinarily able to sublimate his aggressive tendencies; yet on five previous occasions he had similar obsessive attacks which were mostly centered on morbid jealousy. At the same time, during the intervals, he was dominated by what he called superstitions, which in reality consisted of obsessive ceremonials. It would take too long a time to describe some of these ceremonials, so instead I shall cite one from another patient. The latter had a hard time taking a bath because the only way he could get into the tub was not to splash the water at all. If the water splashed even the tiniest bit, he had to empty the tub and start in all over again. It sometimes took hours before he was finally in the tub; so that he took a bath only once in a while and was always afraid to start it.

He had no idea why he had to be so careful. But one day I casually asked him what would happen in case he did splash the water. "It would make a noise," he replied; "someone might be annoyed by it." After further questioning, he added that he thought the noise might wake up his father—who had been dead for the past fifteen or twenty years! To be sure, ever since the patient's early boyhood, as far back as he could recall, his mother used to warn him not to make any noise when his father took his nap before dinner, for if his father was awakened, he would spank him. The little boy then struggled between the desire to annoy his father and the fear that the father would hurt him in turn. This feeling was generalized and later displaced to many activities of his life.

But in order to show you a fragment of the development of an obsession in a person predisposed to it by constitution and environment, let me cite the following case: A lawyer was brought to me many years ago by his family physician because the patient suffered from a typical compulsion neurosis. His law partners had originally urged him to see his physician because of his peculiar behavior in the office. Whenever he lost a case, he insisted that he was at fault, and on a few occasions he even suggested that the firm should compensate the client. On the other hand, whenever he won a case he felt that he may not have been fair to the defendant, and he would then wonder whether the ruling of the court should be reversed. His partners finally got tired of this behavior and insisted that he consult a psychiatrist. The latter, who believed in the old methods of treating neurasthenics, thought that the patient needed a good rest and fresh air and suggested that he take a long leave of absence from the office and settle down on a farm.

The patient followed this advice. He gave up his practice

and bought a farm which was well-equipped in every way and staffed by competent foremen and laborers. All the new owner had to do was to pay the bills and live the life of a country gentleman. For a while everything went well; he had no clients to cope with and no cases to try. But one day he happened to see one of his trucks being loaded with barrels of cucumbers which were to be sold for pickles in the New York market. He noticed that the barrels were covered with pieces of sacking which were tacked all around. It suddenly occurred to him that one of these tacks (which were at least three-quarters of an inch long) might get into the barrel and work its way, ultimately, into a pickle, and that someone would then eat it and die. The thought so terrified him that he ordered the foreman to stop the cucumbers from going to the market. He became even more upset when the foreman told him that a dozen or more barrels had already been sold at the market. The idea that someone might be killed in the manner just described obsessed him to such a degree that he started to trace all the cucumbers previously sold. He obtained a directory of all the pickle factories within a radius of a few hundred miles and wrote to each one, warning them that something dire might happen if anyone ate one of his former cucumbers. And since this seemed the only way of shipping his apples and potatoes to the market, he henceforth would not allow these products to be sold lest someone should be killed.

The climax of this obsession came one day when he happened to be at the railroad station and saw a carload of timber which he had sold to be cut up for railroad ties. He noticed that one piece was a little rotten in the middle. Immediately the thought occurred to him that if this piece should be used as a tie on the Twentieth Century Express tracks, it would cause a wreck in which hundreds of people would be killed. He became so alarmed at this idea that he got in touch with the buyer of the wood and paid him a bonus to get his lumber back.

It was at that point that he came to see me. When he told me about the incident of the lumber, I pointed out that all railroad ties are very carefully inspected before being used and that in any case they never have hundreds of people on this train. But he insisted that they *might;* he just had to have mass murder. Similarly, I tried to reason the thing out with him when he told me about the tacks and the cucumbers. "Look here," I said; "suppose one of those tacks, which were almost an inch long, did get into a cucumber. Suppose the tack remained undetected through all those various processes before the cucumber became a pickle. Let us say that the pickle finally is ready to be eaten. The diner does not usually swallow it whole; as a rule, he cuts it up in pieces, and he is surely bound to find the tack." "Yes," he replied, "an American might do that; but a Dutchman might swallow the pickle whole!" In other words, he could not get away from his sadistic phantasy: somebody had to be killed.[8]

Let us now look at the history of this patient. He came from New England stock. His father was an army officer, and his mother a former schoolteacher. Soon after his birth, his father was transferred to an old-time Western military post. When he was less than two years old his mother became ill—probably neurotically—and was forced to return East. The boy was then brought up mostly by army orderlies. Although he grew up into a healthy youngster, he received very little cultural training or education until he reached his pre-pubescent age. His father, who was an expert on firearms, made small guns for him and taught him to shoot when he was very young. The patient recalled vividly that at the age of about five he shot his first animal on the prairie—a trophy which was preserved and which he still possessed.

That sort of free life continued up to the age of about eight. At long intervals, his mother would appear for a while, but her poor health soon made it necessary for her to return East for treatment. At the age of about eight, his father was transferred back East, and the boy for the first time came under the regular care of his refined mother. She took him in hand and began to make a good Christian out of the little heathen. She taught him herself for a while, paying special attention to his religious training and later sent him to school. Having seen so

[8] This case was reported in my book *Freud's Contribution to Psychiatry*, p. 142, W. W. Norton (New York, 1943).

little of him for many years, she was naturally very attached to him now, and as this was quite different from his father's rough and ready behavior, he reciprocated her love and made every effort to please her. He still went out shooting whenever he had the opportunity. But one fall day when he was about ten, he shot a squirrel and saw it convulse as it died. He had had many similar experiences before, and they had never affected him, but this time the animal's death made such a deep impression upon him that he resolved never to shoot again—and he never did.

We shall see later why there was such a deep reaction to an act which hitherto had made no impression on him. Thereafter his whole character seemed to change; instead of his former aggressive behavior, he now tried hard to be a good Christian as his mother wanted him to be. She was in the habit of reading Bible stories with him or of discussing with him the things he learned in Sunday School. He recalled that following such discussions he often felt much sorrow for himself. In brief, analysis showed that his father identification, which rested on a rather poor foundation because of his mother's absence during the anal-sadistic and phallic phases of his autoerotic age, now became markedly disturbed. In his endeavor to repress his prolonged anal-sadistic organization, the reaction-formation to it had to be correspondingly exaggerated. The dam of sympathy had to be so heavy in order to hold down his former sadistic aggression.

This was well shown later by his general adjustment to life. He was a good student and soon caught up in all his school subjects, but he was a very poor mixer. He was very rigid and punctilious in preparing his home work. He sometimes stayed awake until the early hours of the morning in order to finish his home work as completely and neatly as possible. He had been destined to go to West Point, but his revulsion against shooting made him abandon the thought of an army career. He gave all kinds of excuses to his father for not following the original plan. When he was occasionally invited to join shooting parties, he either refused to go or managed to separate himself from the rest of the party, shoot in the air, and then ex-

[225

plain his lack of quarry on the grounds of bad luck. His father died when he was about to enter college, and three years later, when the World War I broke out, he found himself in a quandary. His patriotism impelled him to volunteer, but his resolution not to shoot was equally strong. Through influence, he succeeded in being appointed an adjutant to a general, in which post he did not have to do any shooting. After the war, he finished college and eventually took up the study of law.

As has already been shown, his sexual life never developed normally. As a boy he heard all kinds of obscene expressions from the soldiers in the army posts and saw a lot of things which intrigued and fascinated him. At a very early age he had a few homosexual experiences with grown-ups, but he insisted that sex never played much of a part in his life. Except for some mutual masturbation at the age of five or six, he never masturbated. Under his mother's training, he suppressed everything verging on the sensual and became very rigid and fanatical. Physically he grew up into a handsome and clean-cut fellow, but he was extremely timid and reserved. The girls attracted him, but he never had any amours. His object-finding was very weak. He made several futile attempts to adjust to women, but ultimately he came to have no use for the opposite sex at all.

According to the patient, his first phobia occurred when he was about seventeen. One morning, as he was about to put on a newly laundered shirt, he removed the pins and threw them out of the window. He heard some children playing in the street below, and suddenly the thought came to him that one of the children might pick up those pins, swallow one, and die. That was his first obsessive phobia. Investigation showed, however, that ever since early boyhood he was dominated by rigid rules and regulations imposed upon him by his father, by the rough orderlies, and by the all-pervasive army atmosphere. He had strong compunctions whenever his ordinary routine was in any way disturbed, regardless of whether anyone knew it or not. Without going into further details, we can say that the patient was dominated by obsessive thinking since his early life, and that at the age of seven or eight he already had a flourishing compulsion neurosis. His manner of eating, of drinking, and of bowel movements became more and more complex and difficult because these things could only be achieved through all sorts of defense-reactions and ceremonials. All his symptoms could easily be recognized as direct descendants of the first ego-organizations—the oral and, especially, the anal-sadistic ones.

We have already shown that as a result of his mother's absence, the development of his Œdipus complex was more or less inhibited. Moreover, the reaction-formation to the infantile aggression—that is, the dam of sympathy which is ordinarily formed at the age of four—never developed in him at that time. On the contrary, his infantile aggressiveness was in every way encouraged; there was no real attempt made to control it or to force it into repression and partial sublimation. In other words, most of his infantile partial impulses and components of sex did not pass through the cultural evolution of the average child. Most of them remained on a more or less infantile level. His aggression increased little by little with age, and had it continued without restraint he might have developed into an overt sadist. But the memory of his mother from the first years of his life, as well as her reappearance at his pubescent age, undoubtedly thwarted his abnormal development. But whereas his mother stopped him from attaining his sexual aim through aggression and thus prevented him from becoming a pervert, her influence could not close the breach already there; her influence was not strong enough to abrogate the fixation already present and thus to stop the overflow of libido to it at puberty. But his mother did succeed in fortifying his superego or conscience so that he became a neurotic instead of an avowed sadist. In the neurosis, he did in a negative way what he would have done openly as a pervert—that is, he was forever struggling with phobias that he might kill and hurt.

That is what Freud meant when he said: "The neurosis is the negative of the perversion." Had the patient been brought up in a civilized community, he might have been very sensitive —but, in all probability, normal. As it was, he was finally able to force his enhanced anal-sadism into civilized, or controlled paths. The dam which had to be constructed against the aggression that had developed almost unhindered until pubescence, naturally could not be as strong as if it had been erected during the first three or four years of life. Of course in such cases we must always presuppose a certain constitutional predisposition, and that was also present in this case. This patient was always very sensitive. He was also much burdened by heredity: his mother died in a mental hospital, and a sister was very neurotic, probably schizophrenic. In other words, as a result of an innate constitution and of fate, this patient brought along into adult life a fragment of his infantile sexuality with which he was unable to cope properly. The neurosis occurred when he attained genitality to a certain degree and was in quest of a love object which he was incapable of finding.

In daily life, whenever you see anybody whose reactions to life are extremely exaggerated—too much modesty, too much sympathy—you can always suspect the reverse of it in the unconscious. One has a right to think that such a person has to have an exaggerated sense of pity in order to hold down an equal amount of lurking cruelty which might otherwise break through. I have in mind a woman who was an ardent voluntary worker for a society against the abuse of animals. She was a married woman with children, but she was at least as interested in this work as in her home life. She walked the streets every day and spent hours watching to see how drivers treated their horses. At that time there were still many horse-powered vehicles in the streets. She would go on ferry boats and examine all the horses carefully. If a halter was too tight or if a horse showed an abrasion, she would report it to the society and see to it that it was corrected, and often she would make sure that the driver was punished. She carried out these daily duties particularly in winter time when the horses were likely to fall if not properly shod.

On the surface, this was a very laudable occupation. She undoubtedly achieved good results. But when I studied her, a different picture was presented. I found that she had always been abnormally fond of animals. When she was a young girl, she was extremely attached to her dog. At the same time however, she was very sadistic to this pet. She used to beat him so much that on a number of occasions her parents deprived her of the animal. She would then become terribly excited and emotional; she would cry and beg until finally the dog would be given back to her. Her conduct of course showed that she had a powerful ambivalence of love and hatred for her dog. Later in life she tried hard to sublimate these feelings and succeeded to some extent. In other words, there was an unconscious background for her *zoophilia*—as there always is for such exaggerated behaviors, but this in no way marred her good work.

There are also cases in which the unconscious aggression develops neither into a compulsion neurosis (as in our pickle-phobic patient) nor into a trait of character in which the repression is held down by a strong sublimation (as in our horse-loving friend). The following case was, one might say, midway between the two:

X, a single man of thirty-nine, came to me because he felt "nervous" and because he found it hard to mix with people. He lived on a farm, but he had a substantial income and had gone to the country only because his old family physician thought it would benefit him to live "next to nature." After a short time, his neighbors discovered that X was extremely fond of animals. He used to pick up sick or stray dogs and cats and nurse them back to health, and the boys in the neighborhood soon found that he would give them rewards whenever they brought such maimed animals to him. X often suspected that the boys purposely injured a cat or dog in order to win the dime or quarter reward; nevertheless, he was unable to reject such sick animals once they were brought to him. He had a wired enclosure for his cats and another for his dogs. Here they were regularly attended by him and his help and not seldom by a veterinarian. His fondness for animals became so well known that a man once brought a blind pony to him and said: "Unless you buy this pony, I'll have to have it shot." X immediately paid for it and had the animal examined by an ophthalmologist, who diagnosed double cataracts. In due time the pony was made to undergo an operation, and the cataracts were removed. But the post-operative behavior of the pony was such that the anticipated results failed to appear.

I could enumerate many other interesting activities of a similar nature, but these will suffice to show the type of man X was. He had been living on this farm with an old maid relative for over four years when he finally found his way into my office. His was a long and very interesting story, but lack of time enables me to give only this brief summary: X was markedly burdened by heredity. His father was a chronic alcoholic, and his mother a weak sort of neurotic who died of tuberculosis at the age of forty-four. An older sister died in infancy, so that X was an only child. His father was a brutal individual who maltreated his wife, his child, and often the house dog. X was only seven or eight when his mother died, and since then he had been subjected to a very brutal bringing-up. While his mother was still alive, he developed all sorts of fears—especially of dogs—which continued until he was about twenty-five. When he got to college, his classmates discovered this phobia and soon began to torture him with it. They would get some dog—especially a bull-dog—and throw it into his room through the window, locking the door from the outside so that he could not escape. He passed many terrible hours in this way. But gradually the phobia disappeared, and the fear was then replaced by an exaggerated fondness for dogs and other animals.

Clinically, he was a schizoid-manic type of personality with moderate emotional fluctuations and showing peculiar character traits. He was a highly cultured person but very masochistic. Tears came to his eyes at every interview, being evoked by the most trifling of associations. After he had been with me for five or six months, he told me the following story, which he found very hard to bring to the surface. He said: "Doctor, I am ashamed to tell this, but I have a very nasty habit which I cannot resist once it comes up. You know how fond I am of animals and especially ponies. Well, for years while riding in the country, I sometimes become obsessed with the desire to beat my pony. Sometimes, with much effort, I can

230]

control this, but on a number of occasions I simply was unable to." He then told me that on such occasions he would beat the horse until his arm became stiff. He would then feel generally weak and very remorseful. A feeling of love for the horse would overwhelm him, so that he would pet it, feed it sugar, and then lead it back to the farm, a distance sometimes of four or five miles. After the beating he was unable to ride the horse.

These attacks had appeared irregularly for many years. To give you a full analysis of the case is out of the question here. Briefly, the horse was identified with his father and with his mother's dog, which his father used to beat when he was in an alcoholic state. The attacks of beating the pony always represented a definite episode from his past, when he was enraged at his father and wished to kill him. Sometimes the attack was also directed to his mother; the attacks always appeared after a feeling of depression during which he thought of suicide. The pent-up aggression within him and the lack of libidinal outlet brought to the surface the destructive components, which he displaced to the animal as a parental substitute. Unlike the other two cases of repressed aggression—which in the one resulted in a negative of the perversion (compulsive phobias) and in the second, in an exaggerated trait of character—we have here an exaggerated love for animals (masochism) with an occasional failure of the repression coming out in the attacks. If you bear in mind, then, the phases of the psychosexual development as outlined in the diagram, the symptoms will invariably indicate where the difficulty lies. For the affliction is always based on a fixation in some pregenital phase of development, and it invariably shows either a failure of repression or a weak reaction-formation against some of the partial impulses or components of the sexual instinct.

Thus I recall a patient who came to me because of eye trouble. For years this man had had a terrible time getting the proper glasses. He was sent to me by Dr. R, one of our leading ophthalmologists, who had tried for years to help this patient, and had finally come to the conclusion that he was just a neurotic. The patient would wear his new glasses for a short time, and then find that they were no better than the previous pair. He complained of pain in his eyes and of blurred vision so that at times he could hardly see anything through his glasses.

In our very first interviews, I discovered that this man was in the habit of frequenting places where he could peep at women. During the summertime, for instance, he lived near the seashore; there in his room, he fixed up a telescope with the idea that he could look through it and watch women undressing in the distant bathhouses. It never worked—but he occupied himself that way for hours whenever he thought that the light was propitious for it. When in New York during the summer season, he would take up a post at street crossings. He would select places like 33rd Street at the crossing of Sixth Avenue and Broadway, where there is a lot of traffic. In the strong sunlight, the shadows of the women's limbs would be outlined through their white, translucent dresses as they went on and off the street cars or busses. He would stand there for hours just to get a glimpse of that. This behavior was also periodic and lasted for a few weeks at a time. During such attacks he had no eye trouble and needed no glasses. After a few weeks however, he would develop compunctions about his desire to peep. He would begin to struggle against it and would finally give it up. He would then begin to wear his glasses—only to find that they were no good.

In other words, this patient really went through cyclic attacks during which he struggled with a mixoscopic perversion. His case too was a perfect illustration of Freud's statement that the neurosis is the negative of the perversion. When he gave vent to his perversion, he had no eye trouble, but when he tried to suppress it, he immediately developed the negative symptoms of pains and poor vision.

His neurosis, it turned out, was the result of a definite trauma which occurred when he was a little boy. On a number of occasions, out of sexual curiosity, he tried to see his mother and other women exposed. He was caught by his father in the act of peeping through the keyhole to see his mother undress, and was severely punished. He grew up however into a very moral young man—one of those fellows who have no interest whatever in women. He was shy and aloof in their presence and was generally a poor mixer. But while still very young, he had profuse phantasies about sexual looking followed by strong feelings of guilt. These phantasies became more pronounced as he grew older. At about the age of twenty he gravitated between peeping and self-reproach, and as time went on his self-reproach was accompanied by somatic disturbances which centered mainly on the eyes. Appealing to eye specialists for help and not getting any represented his struggle with his father. He was anxious to show his father that he really could not see female genitals—that he was castrated—and at the same time he discredited his father's omnipotence by showing that the ophthalmologists could not make him see.

Whether the reaction to the trauma was constitutionally enhanced in the first place, I cannot say. The patient's history showed no hereditary burdens to speak of. But we know that inquisitiveness, or the desire to investigate everything nearby, is a natural characteristic of all higher animals, and that the sense of sight plays a special part in this regard. The desire to see the sexual organs is a perfectly normal impulse. All animals are equipped with curiosity, for this serves to master their environment. It is a natural expression of self-preservation. The normal child uses this impulse continuously, and ordinarily adults offer no objection to it. On the contrary, they not only tolerate it but strive to develop it. But when the child wants to see his little sister's or his mother's genitals, he immediately gets into trouble. We clamp down on him as soon as he shows such curiosity. The normal child soon learns to control and hide this curiosity and later to sublimate it—that is, to deflect it to aims other than sexual.

I feel, for example, that our admiration of scenery or of paintings is in a great measure due to the repression and control of that primary impulse. When you analyze artists you will not seldom find that an early strong curiosity to see the genitals, which has been deflected to the rest of the body or to the surroundings in general, later gave the impetus for artistic production. But please remember that such thwarting does not necessarily produce artists. The latter are gifted to start with,

[233

but that is a different problem. Nevertheless, I have seen some artists who gravitated between art and perversions. I have in mind a sculptor who, when he had commissions, worked diligently and well and produced fine pieces of art. But as soon as he had no commissions, he would go out into public places—such as subways or movie theatres—and try to touch women. He got into conflict with the law on several occasions, so that his wife was afraid to let him out of her sight when he had no work on hand. This sculptor insisted that at such times he did not know what he was doing, and I believe there was some truth to his claim.

I can also tell you about a well-known pianist who acted in a similar way. As long as he practiced daily for hours, sex meant nothing to him, but once the concert season was over and he stopped practicing, he had strong desires to be a *toucheur*. As I have not analyzed these two cases, I can only speculate that their tactile centers were organically over-developed. From my interviews with them on special occasions, however, I can state that their sexual life was infantile. The married sculptor was definitely a *toucheur* and led a very poor sexual existence with his wife—who was really a mother to him. The pianist was of the "fairy" type and sexually weak all around. As a matter of fact, all perverts show an executive weakness in their erotic life.

Any sense organ may become libidinally overcharged either organically or accidentally and then be the center of a perversion or a neurosis. Many years ago I was visited by a doctor who wished to discuss his strange *vita sexualis* with me. From early childhood he had been fascinated by vocal music and especially by the contralto voice. At the age of 36, he heard a woman sing the Spring Song from *Samson and Delilah*. Although timid by nature, he arranged to meet the singer and soon married her. Not long afterward, during an epidemic, she died. He came to see me a year or so later, when he told me that he obtained as much gratification, simply by listening to records of her singing, as he did when she was alive. I have in mind two cases, one a friend of mine, who fell in love with their future wives before they saw them merely by talking to them on the telephone. The voice was the sole attraction in both cases. But I know of no other case in which the auditory sense acted as the *pars pro toto* to produce full gratification—as in the case of the doctor.

In the normal individual, cultural reactions are formed against all these infantile perversities. Those reactions which civilization erects in every human being—sympathy, morality, disgust, shame—act as dams against the disseminated sexuality of childhood. Exhibitionism, for example, is normal in every child. But once the dam of shame is formed, say, in a little girl, she begins to act quite differently. She might formerly have asked you to come and see her take a bath, but now such behavior is no longer possible. I remember a case of a little girl whose parents I used to visit. She always wanted me to see her have her bath. But one evening she did not invite me, and I said: "Marjorie, can I come and see you take your bath?" The little girl was shocked by my remark, and began to cry. Her mother explained that she no longer wanted strangers in her bathroom. In other words, she had now developed the reaction-formation of shame as a dam against her innate exhibitionism.

Touching, looking, tasting, and smelling, which children enjoy so much, are held down, then, by the dams of civilization. Anyone who cannot be disgusted by anything is not normal; anyone who has no sense of modesty is not normal. Those of you who come in contact with defective children know that they either do not develop these dams at all or only imperfectly. Thus it is very difficult to teach them to control their bladder and bowels. Most idiots simply cannot reach that level. Of course, most defectives never attain genitality or object libido. You know also that some schizophrenics, though formerly quite normal in this respect, very often play with feces and smear it all over their bodies and on the walls. They seem to have lost the reaction-formations of modesty and disgust as a result of the disease.

Bear in mind, then, that all those reaction-formations control the primitive impulses with which we are born. Unless they are formed, the individual will not be normal. In the average person, a certain amount of these early impulses is repressed, and another part is sublimated in the struggle for existence and in mating. If something happens to prevent the natural evolution of the impulse, there results a fixation. The neurotic symptom definitely points to the traumatic region, and all you need is to trace it to the traumatic episode. Of course this is easier said than done. It usually means months, and even years, of hard work with the patient.

QUESTIONS AND ANSWERS

Question: In the neurotic, do you find that the repression comes on rather late?

Answer: If you mean repression as I explained it, I would say that it may occur at any time, but usually it occurs early in life. Every sensitive person who had occasion to repress something disagreeable or incompatible may get symptoms sooner or later. As I explained, a symptom originates as a result of an interaction between predisposition and accidental factors. If the repression fails as a result of something that occurred later, there will be a neurosis. The whole thing depends on many factors. The neurosis may not become active until a later age, but examination will show that it has been there in latent form. Wherever there is a strong conscience—too much sensitiveness —a conflict is sure to arise sooner or later and end in a neurosis. Sometimes the latent conflict shows itself only in character traits and sometimes in symptoms. That depends on the impressions or experiences which the individual has absorbed from his environment—in other words, from his training.

In training children, we must try to avoid extremes. It is best to bring them up so that they will be more or less flexible. They must have a conscience, but not too strong a conscience. They must be able to overlook certain things and not become excited over minor matters. One is best off with a conscience which behaves like Schnitzler's hotelkeeper. A good hotelkeeper, it is said, does not concern himself with what goes on in the various rooms of his hotel as long as it does not disturb the outside. Only when there is too much noise does he interfere.

Question : Is there any explanation for the fact that perversions are limited almost entirely to the male?

Answer : Yes; the sexual life of the female, as I have said, is different from that of the male. The male is aggressive in everything, and hence all his senses actively cooperate. The female however is by nature passive. Although her senses, too, cooperate, they work in an entirely different direction. All she has to do is to give you a sweet look—and you are dead! The male, on the other hand, has to pursue and subdue, using his muscles aggressively. That is why the male has more trouble in the struggle for existence; that is why, for example, he dies earlier than the female. In the lower species of animal, as I have already told you, the male dies soon after he accomplishes his mission of impregnating the female. We are higher animals, and among us the male is needed for a longer period.

There is another point: The female can get away with perversions much better than the male. Her sexual life is not as specialized as it has to be in the male. But that is a large subject in itself, and we do not have time for it. I will only add that women as a class hardly know that such things as perversions exist. Most women are trained by the man so that sexually they become whatever he is. It depends on him whether they develop into normal sexual objects or into the opposite. There is a Spanish proverb which says: "A woman is like a guitar: the beauty of its playing depends on the player." That is certainly true of the female sexual behavior. I have seen numerous women—well-bred and intelligent—who spoke about perversions in a most matter-of-fact manner. They did not know that these activities were considered perverse because their husbands had educated them, as it were, to it.

LECTURE IX

LET us now consider the next phase of psychosexual development which, as I said, was designated by Freud as *narcism*. From the diagram, you can see that it extends from the age of four or five to the age of six. It is during this period that all the autoerotic partial impulses which we have discussed previously are collected or, perhaps better described, are canalized into a channel or stream. This stream then flows from the former autoerotic sources to object libido. At the onset of puberty this libidinal stream becomes subordinated to the primacy of the genitals for object cathexis. To be more precise, we can say that in the process of unifying his sexual instinct, the little boy, like Narcissus of the myth, takes himself —his own body—as the first love object, and as he continues to mature he gradually gravitates to some love object outside of himself. In other words, one's first love object is of the homosexual type and, everything being equal, this gradually changes to cravings for the opposite sex. This half-way phase

238]

of narcism between autoerotism and object love is perhaps indispensable in the course of normal development, but if this course is impeded sufficiently to result in a *fixation*, the individual so affected may develop homosexuality or paranoia.

Narcism as a psychosexual designation was first used by Havelock Ellis and by Näcke in the sense of a sexual perversion. Freud however broadened the term because, as he amply demonstrated, narcism constitutes a phase of development of every normal person.[1] As a matter of fact, a certain amount of pure narcism always remains with us; we always love ourselves more than anybody else. Every language has special expressions for this feeling. The French say *"Chacun pour soi,"* the Italians *"Ognuno per se"* (everybody for himself), and the Germans *"Erst komm ich, dann komm ich, dann komm ich wieder"* (first come I, then I, then I again.) The nearest English equivalent for this acknowledged egotism is "God helps him who helps himself." Here, although the accent is still on egotism, it is more or less mitigated by making the Lord a partner in this transaction. But we must not forget that narcism, in the psychoanalytic sense, is egotism erotically tinged. It is, as we said, characteristic of the pubescent boy who, in quest of a love object, first finds himself.

However, if everything runs normally and the young man finds a heterosexual object, his homosexual tendencies are not altogether abrogated. They are, to be sure, deflected from the sexual aim and withdrawn, as it were, to the ego-instincts. Here they are utilized as erotic contributions to friendships, comradery, and philanthropy in general. This mode of development, let us repeat, represents the normal state of affairs, but to clarify what happens if one later develops homosexuality or paranoia, we will recall what we said about the termination of the Œdipus situation. When the little boy represses his mother image, a result of some castration threat, he then no longer craves any sensual gratification from her but usually retains an affectionate relation for her. This manifests itself

[1] Cf. Freud: "Zur Einführung des Narzismus," *Jahrbuch der Psychoanalyse*, Vol. VI, 1913, English translation in *Collected Papers*, Hogarth Press.

whenever he is in need, especially when there is a threat to his life. During illness or in dangerous situations, as said before, the strongest men yearn for the mother and loudly call for her. The *madonna mia* exclaimed by Italian soldiers when in severe pain was reported as a frequent exclamation in all other armies. Moreover, throughout life the mother unconsciously controls man's behavior toward women. Having thus given up his mother, the rivalry between the son and his father ceases, and he then adjusts himself to his father by way of identification. It is as if the boy would say to himself: "I am now like father. Like him, I am going to get a wife." But the average boy is henceforth unconsciously controlled by the admonitions, commands, and prohibitions formerly imposed on him by the father. He strives unconsciously to imitate his father, but also to outdo him. This is the normal Œdipal evolution.

The later manifest homosexuals however follow a different path. Analysis shows that in their childhood, such individuals pass through a phase of very intense but short-lived attachment to the mother, and after consciously overcoming it, they remain loyal to her and identify themselves with her. Hence in looking for a love object at the age of puberty, they select one on a narcistic basis by their own image. The invert craves a young man resembling himself whom he wishes to love as his own mother loved him. This process of development is also favored by the absence of the father or where there is a weak father and a correspondingly aggressive mother. These factors were found in all the homosexuals whom I have studied. In the absence of the father, the mother is bound to prolong the boy's narcistic phase, and instead of measuring himself by normal masculine standards, the boy then strives to emulate her ways. Such boys often frankly wish to be women and show tendencies towards feminine modes of behavior.[2] However, when he attains genitality and craves genital outlet, he looks for someone like himself, someone with male genitals. It is as if he would say: "I am mother, and I want someone to love just as

[2] The male transvestites who dress in feminine attire but have heterosexual cravings also belong to this class.

240]

my mother loved me." This can only be accomplished on a narcistic basis.

There are other factors which favor such development. For one thing, the homosexual has never gone through the evolution of the castration-complex and hence has never given up the desire of the penis in the feminine sex. The homosexual has never given up the primacy of the penis in the love object and he cannot therefore tolerate the idea of any love object without a penis. Unless one is aware of this mechanism, the homosexual behavior always remains a puzzling mystery. For no one could ever understand why overt homosexuals always looked for feminine qualitites in their love object—a fact well-known from the early Greek times. Homosexuals have always sought love objects of the feminine type; they always desired young boys, or so-called "fairies" because they showed feminine qualities. If you are interested, you may visit one of the homosexual dances or "drags," as they call them. There you will learn that they always give prizes for the "prettiest girl." The "prettiest girl" is naturally some male who can best affect femininity in mimicry, speech, and dress. The question is: if homosexuals really want women, why do they show a sexual horror of real women?

That question was posited to me by a woman many years ago when I was still a medical student. A crowd of us students used to go out every Saturday night to some place of amusement. At that time, New York was wide open. There was the "Haymarket" and many similar rendezvous, about which one can still read in works on old New York, where students of moderate means used to congregate. One Saturday night our leader suggested that we visit a "fairy joint," and so about ten of us went down to the "Black Rabbit" on Bleecker Street. To satisfy the police regulations one had to join the "club" by paying the initiation fee of one dime and signing some fictitious name in the roster at the entrance. Inside, the place did not look different from dozens of other music halls which abounded at that time in New York City. There was an orchestra of three musicians—violin, piano, and drum—and men and women were either dancing or drinking beer at small tables. When we looked closely however, we found that all the "women" were really men dressed as women and affecting feminine behavior. This strange sight was interesting and at the same time repugnant. It was the first time I was face to face with that queer problem. After sitting there for a while, it became rather dull, as well as somewhat disagreeable. Suddenly a real woman—a streetwalker—came in and sat down near us. It was like a breath of air in the hot desert! We called her over to our table, offered her a beer, and were soon engaged in conversation. She happened to make some remarks about the crowd, and so I jokingly asked her how she liked her competitors. She looked back contemptuously. "Competitors?" she said, "I can't understand youse guys. You come in here to see those fellows dressed up like rotten-looking girls. If you want girls, why don't you take us?" Of course, she unwittingly did us an injustice—but there we were, and we had to remain silent.

That question, posed by this *quondam venus vulgivaga*, unconsciously remained in my mind, and it was not answered until I became a Freudian. Very early in my psychoanalytic career, a homosexual patient told me his experiences of the night before. He had been to a dance where he had met a very pretty "girl." "Doctor," he said, "she was so pretty that even a normal man could have fallen in love with her." I said, "Look here. Suppose you had discovered that this pretty girl was really a girl. What would have happened?" He thought for a moment and replied: "I would have been just as horrified as one who suddenly found that the woman he ardently loved had a leg cut off." It then dawned on me that he would have felt like one who is suddenly confronted by a castrated individual. He would have been shocked at the absence of the penis. That answer convinced me of the truth of Freud's assertion, namely that the primacy of the penis is so strong in homosexuals, that its absence is so shocking to them, that any erotic outlet with such a person is absolutely precluded.

Here I wish to state that the average homosexual, contrary to what so many people believe, is not an effeminate "fairy." Nor is the "fairy" necessarily a homosexual. Usually he is a dysglandular type, a badly put together individual, whose stream of libido is rather shallow and disseminated. The "fairy" as we see him is of the polymorphous perverse type and like a child he can lend himself to any sexual activity. If a homosexual gets hold of him, he readily becomes homosexual; if a sadist gets hold of him, he may lend himself to masochistic acts. "Fairies" are just sexual weaklings, but they are not necessarily homosexuals. The true homosexuals (whom I have met by the hundreds) are as a class as virile as the average person. Those I have seen were from the most active walks of life and their general attitude and manner betokened nothing feminine.

I have also learned that even so-called "fairies" if favored by circumstances can lead normal sexual lives. Let me cite one such case: I was once consulted by a "fairy" who, if anyone ever looked the type, he certainly did. But when I asked what his problem was, he said that he was constantly annoyed by homosexuals who tried to "make" him. He wished to know whether I could recommend glandular or some other kind of treatment to change his voice and make him appear more masculine. When I asked him the usual questions for my case record I found, to my amazement, that he was married and had three children.

By vocation at least he was true to type—for as a class the effeminate types usually follow artistic vocations. Briefly, I found that as a little boy, he lived in the same block as his wife Mary. She had always been his friend and protector when boys used to tease and bully him—as often happens to individuals of his make-up. Mary was about his age, but she was quite aggressive and always shielded him against his tormentors. This friendship continued as they grew up, and they finally married. His wife was still the aggressive part of the household; she not only took good care of the family, but she also managed his business while he devoted himself entirely to the artistic part of it. He assured me that he was perfectly contented with his meager heterosexual life and that he never had any homosexual tendencies. From this and similar cases, I am convinced that the "fairy," because of his infantile sexuality, can adjust himself to heterosexuality if favored by opportunity, or to inverted or perverted sexual activities if he happens to stray into those paths. On the other hand, the overt homosexual though strong and aggressive nevertheless craves a feminine object with male genitals.

There are other contributions to homosexuality into which I cannot enter here. If you are interested, I can refer you to some case records on *Homoerotism and Paranoia*.[3] What I told you is not always as schematic as it was depicted—no more so than a case of pneumonia or appendicitis, which in practice is not always as typical as described in a textbook or lecture. Moreover, you must never forget the constitutional factors or the sum of that which is inherited—that is, the genotype. We do not always know what constitution is, but we do know that in such cases you will frequently find some kind of heredity, just as in schizophrenia and in similar mental states.

I may add that homosexuality is a very prevalent sexual deviation. One cannot be definite about matters of this kind, but investigators in big cities abroad have found that from one to three per cent of the male population is homosexual.[4] Many years ago I made a similar investigation here and found that there is no doubt that in New York there are thousands of homosexuals belonging to all strata of society. What is said of male homosexuality is also true of female homosexuality—of Lesbianism. There are thousands of Lesbians in New York who, like the male inverts, have their own meeting places. But women, as I have already indicated, can conceal their sexuality much more effectively than men. If two males live together affectionately, it is soon noticed, but in women such behavior evokes no suspicion of abnormality.

Male inverts, as mentioned above, have a *horror feminae* which as a rule precludes any physical relations with women. On the other hand, I have known quite a number of Lesbians who married, had children, and who evidently gave full satisfaction to their husbands. Two Lesbians married only because

[3] Brill: *Freud's Contribution to Psychiatry*, p. 137, W. W. Norton, New York.
[4] The most instructive and comprehensive work on this subject was written by Magnus Hirschfeld: *Die Homosexualität des Mannes und des Weibes* (Berlin, 1914).

they wanted children, and as soon as this was accomplished, they got rid of their husbands. Some female inverts are thus physically able to lead married lives, whereas the manifest male homosexual can only rarely do so. I have however known many Lesbians who manifested a real horror for any physical contact with men, and I have known a number of inverts who married for convenience and made fairly good husbands. In some, the wives discovered the true situation and did not change the family status. Such inverts are naturally bisexually predisposed. They have not the horror described above and with the help of phantasy can effect weak heterosexual relations.

The homosexual's horror of women of course is only a horror of naked women, who represent, as was shown, castrated persons. In everyday life, however, many homosexuals like to associate with women and are often on very friendly terms with them, and strangely enough some women show a preference for this type of men. Investigation indicates that such women are usually of the sexually repressed type who are continually striving to steer clear of sex; as the average man invariably arouses in them strong defense reactions they unconsciously seek the company of those who are sexually indifferent to them. I have seen such attractions in young women who are still, as it were, in the age of ignorance, and in old maids on the side of menopause. I have also seen several cases in which the woman of this type insisted upon marrying the man despite the fact that he confessed his homosexuality.

The social implications of homosexuality are no less important. Homosexuals were always looked upon with disfavor even among the Greeks of antiquity among whom the *Paidon Eros* was a recognized institution. In modern times it has been considered as a sign of insanity or at least of degeneracy. During the first weeks of my internship in the state hospital, I discovered accidentally that one of the patients was a homosexual. He was an intelligent, professional man, and as far as I could discover was perfectly sane. On investigation, I was surprised to learn that he had been committed to the hospital because he tried to continue a homosexual association with a man who had tired of him. The latter had then sent some of his love-letters to the district attorney, and this resulted in a commitment to the Central Islip Hospital. I was then quite ignorant about such sexual deviations which even inspired me with repulsion, but I felt that it was wrong to keep this man in a mental hospital, and I helped him to return to Germany.

It may interest you to know that this was before we had any laws relating to the deportation of alien mental cases. Soon after I entered Central Islip State Hospital, I was delegated to take a census of all patients there. To everybody's surprise, I found that over sixty per cent of all patients of foreign birth were aliens or non-citizens. I then selected those who were still quite young—some of whom promised to remain burdens on the state for the rest of their lives—and suggested that they be sent back to their native countries. This was done in many cases, and the patient I have just mentioned was one of the deportees. He was happy to go back to Germany, for though he frankly admitted his homosexuality, he was not insane.

A few words about the medico-legal aspects of homosexuality. Like all the other laws relating to sex, they are not only unscientific but unjust. It seems that our law makers were just as evasive or perhaps rather as intimidated by everything relating to sex as the average citizen. In the provision on "Crimes Against Nature" the New York State law states that a person who commits bestiality, *coitus per anum, per os,* or attempts sexual intercourse with a dead body, is guilty of sodomy and is punishable with imprisonment for not more than twenty years. Viewing these acts as psychiatric sexologists, we feel that this provision is unscientific to say the least. It is based on ignorance and revenge rather than on an objective evaluation of facts. Some of the acts mentioned above are nothing but variants of the ordinary sexual acts commonly indulged in during the heat of playing by so-called normals. The term sodomy which comprises all the above mentioned acts was originally applied to the act of pederasty among male homosexuals. Later it was generalized to include all *unnatural* acts, especially zoophilia. However if we take nature as our model and judge by the behavior of animals, we are forced to conclude that none of these acts are really unnatural. With the exception of necrophilia, the most extreme deviation from the normal, all the others are frequently encountered in the intimate lives of otherwise normal people. We call them perversions only when they absolutely dominate the picture, that is, when they are fixed. Occasional indulgence in these acts does not stamp those practicing them as abnormal. Thus pederasty or pedication is as repellant to most homosexuals as to normals; the greatest authorities on homosexuality claim that only about ten to eleven per cent of homosexuals indulge in it. I can confirm this from my own investigations of over five hundred inverts. A prominent lawyer informed me that as the law reads it would hardly be possible to convict a person on sodomy.

The statutes of all the other states are equally confusing. Thus the statute of Minnesota, which is in every way identical with that of New York, makes the penalty ten years. The statutes of most of the States are restricted to the common law understanding of sodomy. Some however give liberal interpretations of it. Indeed a survey of the penal codes of all states shows that there is a definite tendency to say as little as possible about crimes of a sexual nature. As expressed in such a case in Illinois,[5] "The Statute gives no definition of the crime, which the law with due regard for the sentiment of decent humanity, has always treated as one not fit to be named. . . . The records of the courts need not be defiled with details of the *different acts* which may go to constitute it."

To be sure, this was written in 1897 but it has never been changed. In brief, the legal implications of homosexuality and other sexual deviations are still to be put on a scientific or humane basis. More could be said about this very important subject which results from a fixation in narcism, but unfortunately time does not permit us to go further.

Let us now consider the other narcistic fixation which results in paranoia.

Before Freud, we hardly knew anything about the mechanisms of this enigmatic psychosis. The disease, we were told, was characterized by delusions of grandeur and persecution

[5] Houselman v. People, 168 III 172, 48N (1897).

which—once developed—remained so for the rest of the patient's life. It was not until Freud issued his classical paper on the subject in 1911 that we were able to understand it. Freud's great discovery was that *the delusion of persecution represented a defense reaction against a repressed, homosexual wish phantasy*. According to the patient, his persecution comes from an "archconspirator" whom he hates; yet when one examines this more closely, one invariably finds that the archconspirator is someone whom the patient really loved. He is usually a former friend or a substitute for the patient's father. It may be the head of the state. Paranoia shows mechanisms similar to homosexuality except as regards object-finding. Instead of finding an object for genital outlet, the paranoiac sooner or later desexualizes himself; he gives up all genital outlet. In the histories of paranoiacs, one invariably finds that they have always been highly moral with rigid personalities who showed this special constitution from the very beginning of childhood. They were usually devoted sons especially to their mothers, and often enough the parents themselves have always considered them peculiar. The history of some paranoiacs shows that they have made an effort to attain heterosexual object-libido and that they usually failed. They have all suffered shipwreck in this attempt.

To understand the mechanisms of paranoia, especially its characteristic delusions of grandeur, it will be necessary to recall its process of development. Paranoia is based, as was already said, on an impediment or a fixation of a partial impulse of the infantile sexuality which thus prevents it from further participation in the full evolution of the sexual instinct. It will bear repeating that during the narcistic stage all active auto-erotic impulses become collected into one stream which is then subordinated to the primacy of the genitals for object-finding. The developing boy, as was already said, takes first himself, his own body, as the love object, and experience shows that the genitals may represent the main interest in this love object. The boy's first choice is an object with genitals similar to his own, and later this changes to a heterosexual object. Those who remain homosexual could not give up the desire for genitals similar to their own in the love object. The narcistic fixation is sometimes enhanced through a disappointment in a woman or through a failure in social relations with men. These may cause a failure of sublimation and a sexualization of social feelings. Any or all these factors may produce a backward coursing of the libido or a retrogression to homosexuality. On the other hand, those who develop paranoia strongly defend themselves against such a sexualization of social feelings with the result that the libido, having become desexualized, regresses to the ego. This in turn enhances the ego and culminates in grandiose delusions. The paranoiac is never able to give or get object-libido without merging into the difficulties just described.

The type of paranoiac that you encounter in the hospital is, as a rule, of the chronic variety. He belongs to those who have gotten into a conflict in early life and had to be hospitalized. Those that one meets in private practice often present milder pictures. Many of them even have some insight; they realize that they are not normal. Some actually know that they are considered paranoid and are willing, sometimes even anxious, to discuss the situation with us. The classic variety of paranoiacs go through first a persecutory stage and then develop grandiose ideas. The enhancement of the ego is brought about by withdrawing their libido from persons and things of the outer world to their own person. You have also seen such patients who assert that they are the greatest person in the world —even greater than God. In Central Islip I knew paranoiacs who thought themselves God, and in Zurich I had a patient who used to become furious if he was not addressed as "Mr. God." About ten years later on one of my revisits to the hospital, I greeted this patient with "Hello, Mr. God." But he turned to me contemptuously and said "It is not Mr. God. It is *General* God." In ten years he had promoted himself to the highest godhead.

Grandiose ideas are thus most characteristic in paranoia. In other words, the paranoiac either remains, as it were, in the narcistic stage or regresses to it after a homosexual conflict. In studying paranoiacs, one often finds that they had suffered

[249

some trauma in early life—a trauma in which the father played the principal role. The paranoiac either thinks that he does not get enough from the father, or else feels that the latter is too strong a rival. Paranoiacs are not always able to desexualize themselves completely, hence they continually struggle with the homosexual components.

After Freud wrote his classical paper on paranoia, I believe I was the first to write one in English describing these mechanisms. I took the case of R as a paradigm—a patient that I had in Central Islip State Hospital five or six years before. Originally I had no idea that my case contained more material than that of any other paranoiac, but after I heard Freud's views, that case flashed through my mind because it plainly demonstrated all the mechanisms which Freud gave in his classical Schreber case. As I have given a full report of the case history of R,[6] I shall not repeat it here. Let me cite instead the case history of a paranoid patient who showed glaringly the struggle between sexualization and desexualization of his social feelings or a struggle between homosexuality and paranoia.

V., a young man of 23 years, was brought to me by his older brother because he entertained numerous ideas of reference and persecution. He imagined that some people disliked and persecuted him. On a few occasions, he thought that the head of his department tried to shoot him because the latter held his hand in his pocket which showed a bulge as if he had a gun there. There were many other phenomena—auditory and psychosomatic—which left no doubt that we dealt with a paranoid schizophrenic.

After the acute state subsided and the patient regained some insight, he spoke quite freely about his delusions. He was the younger of two children whose father died when the patient was still a child. The mother, who was an active, hard-working woman, died about four years before the onset of the patient's malady. Until his older brother married soon after the mother died, the two brothers slept in the same bed and the patient always showed a strong dependence on his brother. As he had

[6] Brill: *Freud's Contribution to Psychiatry*, p. 106, W. W. Norton, New York.

always been in delicate health, his education was continually interrupted, but at 19 he obtained a position in the factory where he remained until the malady set in. Questioning revealed that the patient's delusion revolved around Mr. X, the head of his department, whom the patient considered the arch-conspirator.

As a matter of fact, Mr. X had always been very friendly to the patient. He was a friend of the family and tried in every way to help the patient establish himself. The patient himself admitted that his chief had been very nice to him until he (patient) "fell in love" with a young woman in the office.[7] He then felt that his chief resented his feeling for this woman and henceforth began to find fault with him and persecute him. Analysis showed that Mr. X was identified with the patient's brother with whom there had been some homosexual playing in early boyhood. As the woman in question was the chief's secretary and much older than the patient, she was really identified with the patient's mother. Throughout his life the patient was very attached to his mother so that there was much contention between him and his brother for her favors. Following the death of the mother and the subsequent marriage of his brother, the patient became depressed and gradually developed the symptoms just described. The imaginary love affair was nothing but a weak effort to imitate his brother, but as this could not bring him any satisfaction, the former rivalry for the mother was unconsciously revived. By the mechanisms of identification and projection, he then blamed Mr. X (his chief) for hating and persecuting him. Instead of saying "I love my brother (or Mr. X) I want him to take me as his sole love object," he utilized the paranoid mechanism of projection and said "No, I don't love him; I hate him because he took my mother away from me." The delusion that X wanted to shoot him was definitely traced to an early repressed pederastic experience with his brother.

In brief, the whole morbid picture represented a mixture of homosexuality and paranoia. The patient never passed through

[7] This amour was typically schizophrenic; the woman in question knew nothing about it.

the Œdipus situation as described above. He did not possess any repressed father image to guide him. He looked up to his brother and was passive to him but could not identify himself with him. On the contrary, analysis showed that he always strove to identify himself with his mother. In other words, there was a fixation in the narcistic stage of development which later, when the patient could not attain a suitable love object, developed into a picture indicative of both homosexuality and paranoia. In the typical paranoiac (Kraepelin's *paranoia originaria*) where there is not as much distortion as in the schizophrenic, the picture is comparatively transparent; *the delusion of persecution is always a reaction to a repressed homosexual wish-phantasy*. Here the situation was more complex, more vague.

Love and hatred, as we see it in paranoia, are very closely related. This emotional ambivalence holds true also in normal, everyday life. In normal relationships however, the love is so strong that it covers up the hatred. A man in love with a woman never sees any of her faults and will strongly resent it if one calls these to his attention. But if such a love comes to an end, the obverse of the picture often appears; the man then magnifies the woman's faults and comes to the conclusion that she was really a terrible person. This ambivalence always existed in this relationship, but as long as the love element was dominant, the disagreeable part was simply covered up. This same is seen in paranoid states, albeit in exaggerated form. V being a praecox, his love and hatred lacked the emotional force that is usually seen in normal amours.[8] The real paranoiac, as was said, displays a cleaner-cut system. The archconspirator may then be the President, the Governor, the Mayor, or some other powerful father-surrogate who spends all his time scheming against the patient. One invariably finds this mechanism in paranoiacs who attempt assassinations of public leaders.

[8] An outline of this case was reported by me in "Sexual Manifestations in Neurotic and Psychotic Symptoms." *Psychiatric Quarterly*, January 1940.

There are many other variants, milder forms of homosexuality and paranoia, which are neither psychotic nor inverted but manifest throughout life a strong struggle with mother fixations. Such patients are never seen in hospitals, but they often consult us in private practice. In some, the mother fixation usually prevents them from marriage while in others it does not, but it produces peculiar marital relations. Among the first we have the eccentric old bachelors. The behavior of such men is characterized by a lack of interest in modern women or by unjust criticism of them. Some of these old bachelors are interested in the higher things of life, in esthetics and art, and rarely marry. They usually live with the old mother as long as she lives. Some seem to get along quite well, while others become neurotic or become psychotic when the mother dies.

I once asked such a bachelor, a man of about fifty-five, why he had never married. "I would have done so," he said, "if I could have found a woman like my mother. All that modern women want is just to jazz around." This fellow was interested in nothing but yachting, and he was always sailing off to Florida or Bermuda or some other health resort. He suffered constantly from stomach-aches and colds. He had so many of the latter, in fact, that he was afraid to go on trains for fear of "all the germs." When his mother was alive, she watched over him and always admonished him to be careful about catching cold. After her death, he incorporated her into himself and then, as it were, heard her voice constantly admonishing him to be careful of his health. That is a typical picture of many old bachelors. They represent essentially a form of narcism, in so far as they cannot give themselves to any female outside of mother. However when she dies, they have to withdraw their libido to their ego and this ends up in a neurosis or psychosis.

The second type of mild mother fixation will be well illustrated by the case of L. This man of 49 brought his wife to me because she suffered from "agoraphobia." This diagnosis was made by the family physician because the patient was often disinclined to leave her home. On questioning, I soon found that we did not deal with a true "agoraphobia." Her fear of

Psychoanalytic Psychiatry

going out alone manifested itself periodically from a few days to a few weeks and was based entirely on conscious mechanisms.

Briefly, the situation was as follows: Mr. L. was an only child strongly attached to his mother. When he married, his mother attempted to extend her domination to her daughter-in-law. The latter rebelled against it and for a time there was a struggle between the mother and wife in which the latter finally came out victorious. L. remained with his wife despite the fact that she severed all relations with his mother. My patient stated that L. was a very good and generous husband, but there was something about his behavior which she could not quite understand. She knew that he married her because she was considered quite pretty. He wished her to dress lavishly because he was fond of frequenting night clubs and sporty resorts where he was well known. She was sure however that he was more interested in showing her off than in pleasing her. After she had lived with him for years she had realized that his behavior towards his friends was peculiar in many ways. Thus soon after marriage L. introduced her to the R's, a couple who, like her husband, moved around in sporty society. He asked her to be friendly with them, especially with Mr. R. The patient did not like this uncouth man and did not conceal her feelings from her husband, but the latter pleaded with her to disregard R's faults because he was his best friend. Wherever the L's went, the R's were there.

Mrs. L. then changed her attitude toward the R's which pleased her husband because R. had now become a junior partner in L's business firm. In due time there developed a sexual affair between R. and Mrs. L. which lasted for over two years. She was sure that her husband did not actually know this but she felt that if he should discover it, he probably would forgive them. But suddenly, as if out of the blue, her husband's attitude to R. changed. A slight disagreement resulted in a violent quarrel and all their relationships were cut. Meanwhile Mrs. L. would have been pleased to stop her amour with R. but the latter threatened to expose her. Realizing how her husband now hated R., she was not so sure that he would forgive her. She had to resort to all sorts of subterfuges to see as little of R. as possible. That accounted for her frequent attacks of fear of going out alone; there was nothing unconscious about it. And when her physician labeled her behavior "agoraphobia" she used it freely as an excuse for her behavior.

The most interesting part of this case is L's subsequent behavior. Within a few months after he broke friendship with R. he became attached to M. and then repeated with minute precision his former behavior, especially in relation to his wife and his new friend. In her own words: "He was crazy to have me act toward M. as I did before to R." This situation was repeated a number of times over a period of years, and although the wife did not enter into sexual amours with every one of his new friends, she became involved in all sorts of complications which made her life very exciting and burdensome.

In brief, we dealt with an attentuated homosexuality based on an unresolved Œdipus complex. L., who was unconsciously fixated on his mother identified his wife with her. In the course of his psychosexual development he attained genitality but had difficulty in finding a heterosexual love object to gratify his needs. Mrs. L. was sure that her husband was never "in love" with her in the popular sense of this term but that she gratified his "show off" feelings. She was a pretty woman and he wished to exhibit her in expensive restaurants, night clubs, and race tracks to gratify his own narcism. Last but not least, he always insisted that she become very friendly with his friend. For years she could not quite understand this and considered it as a "strange quirk" of his character. As a rule, the friends which he selected were married, and whereas Mr. L. showed a strong attachment for his new friend, he was only lukewarm to his friend's wife.

Psychoanalytically speaking, L. constantly strove to reconstruct his early family situation: father, mother, myself, through wife, R. myself; R. the friend representing his father. In other words, L. tried compulsively and repeatedly to be united to his friends through his wife. He unconsciously strove to reconstruct the early family romance, namely to share his wife with his friend as he formerly shared his mother with his father. Such situations in extreme form are designated by sexologists as *troilism,* the *ménage à trois* of the French.

Magnus Hirschfeld calls troilism a disguised homosexuality. It is to be sure an attenuated form of it, insofar as it is an effort to share the mother with the father or father-surrogate on the basis of bisexuality and the more complete Œdipus complex.[9] For it must not be forgotten that in the adjustment to the Œdipus situation, identification with father or mother depends on the relative strength of the two sex predispositions (*Anlagen*). For it is the bisexuality of the individual—a constitutional factor—which participates in the fate of the Œdipus complex. Moreover, in cases like L. one must assume the existence of what Freud calls a more complete Œdipus complex. Here the boy not only shows an ambivalent attitude towards the father and an affectionate feeling for the mother, but he also behaves at the same time like a girl. That is, he evinces an affectionate feminine attitude to the father and a jealous hostility towards his mother. He cannot understand why his father prefers to sleep with his mother rather than with him.[10]

A form of paranoia which always used to puzzle us was what the Germans called *Alkohol Eifersuchtswahn*—or alcoholic delusions of jealousy. In every psychiatric textbook of the last and the beginning of this century, one read that this psychosis was due to alcoholism. I remember well such a patient in the Central Islip Hospital, who insisted that he never drank except for an occasional glass of beer. I did not believe him until his wife assured me that this was true. I was still puzzled because I was taught that the classical case of delusions of jealousy was invariably based on alcoholism. However, after I heard the same from a number of other such patients, I began to doubt the alcoholic factor in this form of paranoia, and I reasoned that the frequent occurrence of alcoholism in this disease was probably an effect rather than a cause.

I explained the jealousy by the relative or absolute impotence which is encountered so often in this disease. For when I asked

[9] Cf. Brill: *Freud's Contribution to Psychiatry*, p. 126, W. W. Norton (New York, 1944).

[10] Cf. Freud: *Das Ich und das Es*. p. 39. International Psychoanalytic Verlag, 1923.

some of these patients how they knew that their wives had other men, they frequently admitted that they had no direct evidence but that they were nevertheless sure of it because they were not sufficiently stimulated by their wives. As one of them expressed it: "If she did not run around with other men, she would be in need of sex and would then be anxious to excite me sexually." In other words, he blamed his wife for his impotence. When I became a Freudian and learned to view everything psychogenetically, the problem of alcoholism assumed an entirely different aspect.

Jealousy is a normal emotional state observed in all animals during the mating period. I have never seen a lover who was not jealous and usually without much cause. Indeed, I feel that jealousy is a phyletic phenomenon or a racial inheritance. From our knowledge of animals and primitive men we have learned that the mating struggle was as inexorable as the struggle for food. It is still more difficult than appears on the surface. The male still has to fight hard to obtain and retain a mate, and although society now tries hard to keep away intruders, once the parties concerned have signed their names on the dotted lines, disturbances from within and without do occur from time to time and manifest themselves in desertions and divorces. Any male worthy of his name is therefore equipped with the pugnacity which we call jealousy and often utilizes it when there is seemingly no real cause for it. In extreme cases, the individual creates rivals through phantasy which often develop into fixed ideas.

I saw such a patient who was married to a former "fat lady" of a well known circus. He insisted that his wife drugged his food so that he could not be awakened and that she went out through the window to meet her lovers during his sleep. She could not have gone out through the door because he locked it and hid the key. I called his attention to the fact that his wife weighed about four hundred fifty pounds and hence could hardly get through the window of their country cottage. Although he admitted this fact, he still maintained that this must have happened dozens of times or he added, "The guy must be strong enough to move the whole wall." To be sure, this patient was insane, but I have heard similar arguments from men who were perfectly rational and who explained the *modus operandi* of the deception on more rational bases.

However, the part played by alcohol in delusions of jealousy is quite clear if we think of the fact that alcohol removes inhibitions and thus reduces the power of sublimation. Under the influence of alcohol, one, as it were, "forgets his troubles" or can realize one's wildest wish-phantasies. In studying such cases we find that the patients invariably wish to run away from heterosexuality. Every chronic alcoholic studied by me either never attained genitality and object-finding or there was some noticeable weakness in his development which sooner or later led to a regression to the oral autoerotic phase. Some gave histories of bad experiences with women, unhappy marriages or love affairs for which they invariably blamed the women. Their excuse for excessive drinking is that they are lonesome and seek companionship in bar rooms or clubs. And, as is known, the homosexual element is glaringly displayed in such gatherings whether they are of the upper or lower strata of society.

I wish I could give you an analysis of a case of jealousy delusional paranoia. Unfortunately this cannot be done here. The classical case of this type of paranoia was described by Freud [11] and later condensed by me.[12] This patient came to me for treatment, but as his jealousy delusions were of such a nature that it was dangerous to let him remain in his home, I sent him to Freud. He was in Vienna for about two and a half years and returned home considerably improved but still under the compulsion to question his wife. Freud then advised that I continue the analysis. After six months of treatment I was able to discharge the patient as cured, and he has been well since. It is in this paper that Freud gives us a deep insight into the phenomenon of jealousy. He tells that there are three forms of jealousy.

(1) The first, or *normal jealousy,* is an emotional state which shows itself mainly in a feeling of grief. The individual is de-

[11] Cf. Freud: "Über einige neurotische Mechanismen bei Eifersucht, Paranoia, und Homosexualität," *International Zeitschrift fur Psychoanalyse und Imago,* 1922.

[12] Cf. Brill: *Freud's Contribution to Psychiatry,* p. 111, W. W. Norton (New York, 1944).

jected and anxious, fearing lest he should lose the love object. He acts like one who suffers from a trauma to his narcism; his vanity is extremely hurt. He disparages himself for losing the woman, and at the same time he feels hostile to his rival. Even this form of jealousy is not under full control of the ego; the jealousy is not, as a rule, proportional to the actual situation.

(2) *Projection jealousy* which is found in both men and women is due to displacement of one's actual unfaithfulness, or a tendency in that direction, to one's partner. Conventional society, especially in Anglo-Saxon countries, permits some coquetry to married persons especially at social gatherings. A married man may indulge in mild banter with his dinner partner. Indirectly he can even talk sex to her through suggestive jokes which invariably conceal thoughts ordinarily tabooed. The jealous paranoiac cannot countenance such behavior. He does not believe that one can go so far and then stop. He represses his own infidelity and magnifies any indication of friendly feelings by his wife towards other men into sexual acts.

(3) The most severe form is *delusional jealousy* which, like projection jealousy, is due to repressed impulses to infidelity, but here the objects of the phantasies are of the same sex. Freud states that delusional jealousy is an acidulated homosexuality and belongs to the classical forms of paranoia. The delusion represents an effort to defend oneself against strong homosexual tendencies, and in the male it is expressed in the formula "I do not love him; she loves him." Every case that I had the opportunity to study showed that the delusions were first directed to the type of men that the patient himself admired and loved. Thus one of my patients indulged in phantasies that his wife had affairs with great financiers, soldiers, and professional men. Another patient who started in the same way later generalized his jealousy and then suspected any men who happened to come into contact with his wife. In brief, one can say that jealousy is an outward manifestation of the struggle to find a love object. Normal jealousy is therefore logically determined and short-lived. Once the man attains full gratification over a greater or lesser period of time, his jealousy subsides.

In pathological jealousy we invariably find some weakness (fixation) which precludes full attainment of the love object. The jealousy then represents the outward projection of the repressed homosexuality which was either initiated by an early homosexual trauma, or by constitutional and environmental factors. The paranoiac, as we said above, desexualizes himself by withdrawing his libido back to his ego. The schizophrenic by virtue of his genotype cannot go this full length, and hence his struggle represents a conglomerate of desire and rejection of homo- or heterosexual objects. In the psychotics of jealousy delusions, the question debated, as shown by the symptoms, is shall it be a homo- or a heterosexual object. The constitutional factor sometimes permits for a time an apparently normal heterosexual adjustment, and the struggle does not manifest itself until later. Thus I saw a man of seventy-six who was pathologically jealous of his sixty-nine year old wife. Following a stroke ten years before, he gradually became impotent and then regressed to an early repressed homosexual experience. By projection he then accused his wife of relations with young men. In the Orient where homosexuality is not tabooed as in Western civilization, elderly men often openly resort to *paidon eros* when for some reason heterosexuality becomes impossible.

There are still other variants of mother fixation which now and then come to our attention. Thus I have seen patients who after having lived complacent married lives for years suddenly began to feel a strong need for other women and somehow managed to get their wives to assist them in their active hunt for new love objects. Those seen by me were individuals of the highest cultural type who consulted me because they could not understand their strange behavior or because they became deeply embroiled in all sorts of difficulties. In all of these cases the wife either acted from the beginning as a real mother-surrogate, or gradually assumed this role. The *modus operandi* in one case, which can serve as a paradigm for the others was as follows: The husband, acting like a petulant child, informed his wife that he was "madly in love" with Miss or Mrs. X. After considerable argumentation, the wife would then try to bring them together by inviting the woman in question to teas and dinners. Soon after attaining his aim, the husband felt remorse and wished to get rid of the woman. This was effected by introducing her to his best friend and encouraging her to have confidence in him. The friend knew all about these affairs and was quite willing to cooperate. This scheme did not always work as premeditated; the woman did not always accede to his suggestion. It was during a commotion created by one of these women who sensed that the patient wished to get rid of her, that I was consulted. The wife acted like a distressed mother who was most anxious to get an errant son out of a quandary. Neither she nor her spouse showed any indication that her part in the situation was in any way anomalous.

In summing up, I wish to stress that the ideal which Freud posits for normality, namely to attain genitality and find the proper love object, frequently encounters many obstacles. I have mentioned here those complications which the psychiatrist is likely to meet quite often in private practice. But the psychiatrist who only describes and classifies, the psychiatrist who is not versed in Freud's psychology does not recognize the underlying problems of such cases. The cases that I have seen have been treated before by at least a few neurologists or psychiatrists of this type. Sooner or later the patients sensed that these doctors did not understand them and then went to somebody else. I do not wish to imply that such patients know the deeper mechanisms of their problems; they do not. But they somehow often sense whether you can read their unconscious. Please do not consider this in the mystical sense. I have no doubt that such a phenomenon actually exists and constantly operates, especially in sensitive neurotic types and between doctors and patients during analysis.

LECTURE X

THE last lecture is always the hardest. So many unfinished topics crowd themselves into the mind that one is at a loss to know which to attack. To be sure, I told you in my first lecture that I did not aim to make psychoanalysts out of you, that the object of this course was to demonstrate to you some of the hidden motives of your patients' struggles. To accomplish this, I made full use of the methods elaborated by Freud and his pupils. For I do not know of any better approach to the knowledge of the psyche.

You have surely noticed that I did not always adhere methodically to the theme under discussion, that I have wandered freely from normal into primitive, from infantile into neurotic fields, seemingly without any regard for the order of things. One of my former students ventured to explain my unorthodox meandering as an effort to crowd too much into a small space. This is true, but I might add that it is hardly possible to delve into psychical disturbances without straying occasionally into unknown territory, sometimes even into some remote phyletic ramification. Indeed the whole Freudian system came into being in this manner. Starting with the psychopathology of hysteria, Freud was led into the realms of dreams, childhood, primitive life (*Totem and Taboo,*) and finally into pre-history (*Moses and Monotheism*).

Throughout our discussions here I often had to drop what I considered interesting thought, for fear that I might wander too far afield. Sometimes however the rules of methodical presentation were abandoned as it were, because something flashed through my mind which I could not stave off, something which I had to show you. After having given this course for so many years, I now realize that I have unconsciously striven to retrace with you the path that I myself have followed in the field of psychiatry, and as I started in 1903 and am still marching on, I could hardly cover this distance in the ten hours at my disposal. I am not apologizing to you for my seeming peculiarity; one is what one is. I am merely voicing my regrets for an apparent negligence. However, in this last hour I shall endeavor to gather up some of the loose ends that are still dangling in front of me.

I devoted my last lecture to the anomalous situations resulting from mother fixations. I was trying to show that they start during the pregenital phase of development and that, if a fragment of the infantile sexuality is carried along into adult life, an incompatibility results which ends in a neurosis. To those that we have already described, I wish to add one more case. I was consulted by a husband and wife together. The husband explained that the object of this visit was to discuss with me the marked disharmony in their married life: they were quarreling almost constantly. But before he could complete the second sentence, they started a living demonstration of the problem. She objected to something he said and cried out, "That's not so," and for the next five minutes I was busy noting "He . . . ," "She . . . ," "He . . . ," "She . . . ," until it became unbearable and I stopped them.[1]

[1] This case history appeared in "Phyletic Manifestations and Reversions," *The Psychiatric Quarterly*, January 1946.

After calming them, I learned that their scuffles, to put it mildly, had been going on since marriage, according to the wife, since they had met. They had been married 24 years and had one child of 22. Both were beyond middle age; the husband gave his age as 53 and the wife as 48. The wife was frank to say that she did not expect much benefit from this visit. She said, "I have been analyzed; I think I know what it all means, but it has not helped me." I retorted that psychoanalysis does not pretend to cure everything, that I would do my best to be of help to them. But the arguments continued; every time one of them made a statement the other interrupted with a strong contradiction. Thus she related that her husband once broke her nose and her leg. He burst out shouting: "She is a liar; I only punched her on the nose. I did not break her leg; I only threw a stool which scratched her leg."

After insisting again that there must be no more interrupting or shouting, I learned that they started fighting soon after they had become acquainted. Yet despite almost constant disagreements for at least eight months, they nevertheless decided to marry. Sex seemed to have played a minor part in their marital existence. For the first two years she did not want any children and hence there was hardly any sexual life between them. She then went through a very distressful pregnancy, and even before the child was born, she vowed that she would never have another child. I asked about their subsequent sexual life and she said, "How can you have relations with a man you hate?"

In brief, throughout their 24 years of marriage, they alternated between quarreling and not talking to each other. They frequently separated and remained apart from a few days to a few months, but for some reason they always returned to each other. They had consulted physicians and lawyers who, after recommending various medical and social remedies, finally advised a separation or divorce. When I asked him why this was not done, he said: "I thought of it dozens of times, and I left her many times, but I always went back. There is something about her that I like." When I discussed this matter with her, she maintained that she hated him, and when I asked why she stayed with him when she was financially able to live without him, she could not explain it.

Following the first visit I arranged to see them separately, and I then obtained enough information to explain some of the unconscious factors of this strange case. The wife claimed that she experienced no pleasure in sex and hence invariably objected to it. Coitus took place only rarely, usually after long arguments and sometimes after real fighting. For the last ten years there was hardly any sex between them; the husband admitted that he resorted to prostitution. She insisted that she was a perfectly normal woman, but that as she disliked her husband, she had no use for sex.

The information obtained from about ten interviews with each of them convinced me that we dealt with a glaring anal-sadistic situation, that both husband and wife showed pronounced anal-erotic character traits. That was the only way one could explain why despite the hostility that raged between them continuously for almost a generation, they still could not live without each other. I doubt whether their peculiar behavior can be conveyed in reading. Delicacy keeps me from reporting the strong expletives they hurled at each other during their wranglings in my presence. Their arguments were replete with expressions associated with the behind and its emanations.

I naturally tried to discover some of the deeper mechanisms of this strange behavior. Most of the information that I obtained during their visits to my office came from the husband. One day when he talked about his early life he became very emotional and said: "I must tell you about my mother. She is dead but I cannot say, 'May she rest in peace.' She was the most selfish beast you can imagine. It is too bad that I have to speak of her this way but that's the truth. My father died when I was ten years old, and she dragged me out of school when I was not yet eleven and made me go to work. She had plenty of money, but she was the meanest tightwad you ever saw. She treated me, her only child, like a dog. She refused to buy me clothes and never gave me anything but spankings."

He went on depicting his dead mother in the vilest terms and ended up, "She is dead and I hope she sizzles in hell; I detest her." As I listened to him, I reflected that his anal-sadistic character was the result of a typical constitution and fate. For judging by her behavior, his mother must have been an anal-sadistic character, and his environment could not have been more favorable for the development of his anal-erotic character traits. Yet although he hated her, he was unconsciously guided by her throughout his life. Whatever he accomplished was negatively or positively influenced by his mother fixation. Thus his dominant idea throughout life was to acquire money, a characteristic of his mother which he claimed to have hated. He chose a woman seemingly of a higher cultural level but she turned out to be just as anal-sadistic as his mother. One could truly say of them, "Birds of a feather flock together."

His anal-erotism was just as patent in his outward relations with people. He admitted that he was generally disliked because he used expressions for which he was often forced to apologize. No matter how hard he tried to control himself, he invariably reverted to exclamations which alluded to the posterior region. Listening to them, it was both repulsive and fascinating. It was somewhat fascinating because their whole behavior in action and speech perfectly demonstrated those theories of Freud which I found difficult to accept when I first heard them. I recalled when I first read Freud's paper on anal-erotism and character. As Ernest Jones and I were taking leave of Freud in Vienna, I to go back to New York and Jones to London, he gave us each a reprint of this paper. After we settled on the train to Munich, I read and translated it to Jones who at that time could not read it in the original. When I finished, we looked at each other and I remarked, "No wonder people have strong resistances against Freud's theories."

I said this because the views expressed in this paper were entirely foreign to us, and, as they dealt with tabooed material, they were far from agreeable. However, soon after I returned to New York, Dr. Frederick Peterson referred a case to me for analysis which fully demonstrated those very theories of Freud.[2] As I said above, when I heard this couple hurling vile

[2] Cf. Lecture 8, p. 210.

invectives at each other, I could not help thinking that as repulsive as this sounded to others, they themselves unconsciously
enjoyed living in this fetid atmosphere. When they became excited, they shouted at each other, "You give me a pain in the
a . . ," [3] or they resorted to the very common invitation which
one sometimes hears in our lower national spots in street brawls,
from people who apparently have no inhibitions to invite one
bluntly to kiss the behind. (Even an experienced psychoanalyst,
as you can now observe, speaks as it were with a bit in his
mouth when he wishes to use those tabooed terms.)

I have often wondered why one should invite a human being
to do something to him which he himself considers disgusting.
Judging by the popularity of this request over the centuries of
civilization—it is heard in all corners of the civilized world—
one might surmise that there must be some unconscious hanker-
ing for it. As disagreeable as it sounds now, it may conceal
some forgotten outlets of the hoary ages.

As shown above, we know from other repressed mechanisms
that some present-day abominations have been practiced and
relished in the remote past. Thus the human odor, now so re-
pellent to cultured people, was once as attractive as it still is to
animals,[4] and former gods have degenerated into devils or sa-
tans.[5] It is therefore not so far-fetched to assume that the afore-
mentioned request now thrown as a challenge of contempt at a
despised enemy once contained painful or pleasurable components now fully repressed and only to be awakened through an
outburst of rage. It seems that the inviter considers the invitee
emotionally so low and weak as to order him to revive for him
these long repressed and disgusting outlets, or mnemically expressed, the rage ecphoriates deeply buried engrams which were
utilized on similar occasions by our animal forebears.

As a matter of fact, we do not have to seek long for these
hidden feelings. We know that the anus is the source and origin

[3] This widely used exclamation ordinarily ends with the word "neck,"
which is merely a displacement from below to above, but they always
ended it with the letter "a."

[4] Brill: "The Sense of Smell in the Neuroses and Psychoses," l.c.

[5] Alexandra David-Neel: *Magic and Mystery in Tibet*, p. 49, Claude
Kendall, (New York, 1932).

of our most important erogenous zones, both the penis and vagina emanated from it, and that it still remains the excretory-expulsive organ par excellence. Moreover, when we come down to ontogeny, we know that the child enjoys his anal functions and even uses them as a mode of defense and spite against grown-ups. The anal opening is also still used as a substitute for the vagina by some people who wish to avoid pregnancy, by some homosexuals (pederasty), and by masturbators of both sexes. Last but not least in the form of regression, the anal region is the seat of neurotic symptoms such as *pruritus ani*, hemorrhoids, and ceremonial constipation. In brief, there is no doubt that the anal zone still retains its old erogenity as well as its defensive character.

However, before venturing still deeper into phylogeny, let us consider another type of neurotic disturbance associated with the anal zone. I have in mind cases which resemble more a perversion than an ordinary neurosis insofar as the libido, though slightly distorted, nevertheless evinces itself almost in its pristine form.

Of the numerous cases of this type, I will cite the following: E. F., a young man of 24, was diagnosed by a number of psychiatrists here and abroad as a psychopath. I fully agreed with this diagnosis for want of a better classification. Without going into the details of the case, the patient had always been a problem. He did not steal, he did not run after women; in fact he did nothing against the moral code, yet he was a problem to his father. Since early childhood he was playful and mischievous; he was always a poor student, never made the grades, and when put to work he could not hold any position for more than a very brief time. He was a typical only child of a very eccentric, probably psychotic mother. The father on the other hand was a highly regarded citizen who was very successful in his vocation.

I soon found that the patient had been a typical *pseudologia phantastica*. In early childhood, he could not distinguish reality from phantasy, and as he grew up, he continued to magnify and distort everything. For years he told stories of hobnobbing with celebrated people; whenever he visited me he volunteered that

he had just come from a luncheon with a famous actress, a
Duchess, or some other celebrated person, and as he was a member of a very nice family, I did not at first doubt his statements.
However as time went on, I became convinced that there was
no truth whatever to his boastful stories, that he was just a
childish "show off," which I considered as a reaction to a feeling of inferiority.

He was sexually moronic: he showed no signs of sexual ma-
turity in the sense of striving for an object. He was never erotically attracted to women, but he liked to be seen with pretty
and well-dressed women in restaurants and theatres. He himself
was always well groomed; he could not resist buying flashy
clothes and jewelry, a habit that caused many disturbances between him and his father. The patient's great desire was to shine
in society in which he was encouraged by his mother. The latter was well known in American circles abroad, as she was in
the habit of spending every spring and summer in fashionable
resorts and spas in France and Germany.

I soon concluded that the patient was no case for analytic
therapy, but, as he was quite willing to come to me, I assisted
his father in his effort to adjust the patient to useful activity.
One day I had an interview with his mother's secretary and
companion, an intelligent, worldly woman who had been with
the family for many years. She casually asked me whether I had
heard of the scandal in which the patient was involved last summer in a certain watering place abroad. She did not know the
details of the situation but she was sure that it was of a sexual
nature. She admonished me not to ask the mother about it, but
she felt that the patient himself would talk about it if I broached
the subject indirectly. It was not difficult to elicit the following facts.

Since his early age the patient was inquisitive about the ne-
cessities of nature, particularly defecation; he had a strong, obsessive desire to observe these functions in both men and
women. During the summer vacations abroad he usually occupied the same room with his mother. As far back as he could
recall, he often saw or heard her urinate when she thought he
was asleep, and as he grew older, he frequently lay awake for

hours hoping especially to see her defecate. At home where the opportunities for such lurking was precluded by his father's presence, he indulged in phantasies of seeing his mother and others perform this act. Following pubescence the curiosity to see those acts changed into a strong impulse to stop people from performing them. During the last three vacations abroad, he actually put his desires into operation in the following manner: knowing that the guests in this spa were in the habit of walking after drinking from the various mineral springs and that they often repaired to the woods to relieve themselves, he followed them closely in order to thwart them. Such pursuits made him increasingly excited, sometimes to the point of ejaculation, and this was especially marked when his prey manifested discomfort through his pursuit. On many occasions his intrusion was resented and sometimes he was threatened if he persisted, but that only increased his excitement.

But as he had no opportunity to do the same to women, he finally decided to follow an elderly woman into the *chalet de nécessité*. When he carried out this plan, he was recognized, and the resulting disturbance forced his mother to leave the hotel. He denied any wrong-doing, pleading that he made a mistake, which, though believed by his mother, was not accepted by the management of the hotel. Briefly, the patient suffered from an active and passive algolagnia based on coprophilia which was mostly confined to phantasy. The active algolagnia manifested itself in his effort to prevent others from performing the act while the role of the passive element evinced itself in identifying himself with his victims. This perverse behavior had its origin in his early childhood when his mother made use of spanking and bribing in teaching him to control his natural needs. He distinctly recalled that, in his strong effort to hold back his feces as a resistance to his mother or her substitute, he experienced both pleasure and pain.

Let us now return to the phyletic outcroppings which now produce crude and unseemly actions. As mentioned previously, the pleasure which is ontogenetically inherent in the anus came originally from the cloaca, which still exists in pure form in birds,[6] and which underwent complicated changes in its phyletic course of evolution. Some of its original functions were diverted into separate channels, and some—defecation and flatus —continued in the anus and were endowed with disgust in the course of civilization. Yet notwithstanding these complex transformations, some of the abandoned feelings unconsciously strive to assert themselves, and the popular invitation to kiss or suck the posterior seems to be a distorted expression, an echo as it were, of these long discarded pleasures.

That similar phyletic excrescences are occasionally encountered physiologically is well known. A good example is the vermiform appendix which once had a useful function but in the course of evolution gradually sank into disusage. If it is now accidentally stimulated to action, its effort to function is not only deleterious to the organism but often causes fatal results. Similar situations sometimes occur in branchial cysts or fistulae.

Moreover every individual cell has its individual little psyche, and hence every organ, which is only an aggregation of cells, starts with what Bleuler calls a "psychoid,"[7] that is especially adapted to the cooperative needs of the whole organism. To be sure, the psychoid of the cloaca underwent many modifications before it attained its new form in the duckbill, and still more specialization in man, but, notwithstanding all these changes, its phyletic engrams now and then become ecphoriated in symptoms, dreams, myths, and under strong affect also in normal life.[8] To be more specific we must bear in mind that all higher animal formations began with the *gastrula*, a cup-shaped body made up of two layers which on further evolution developed a true gut with an anterior and posterior opening or a mouth and anus.[9] Beginning with the cloaca in the four-legged land animals that evolved from those vertebrates which emerged from the water and henceforth, there was a gradual evolution of the

[6] W. Bölsche: *Das Liebesleben in der Natur*, Vol. II, p. 194, Dietrich, (Jena, 1922).

[7] Cf. E. Bleuler: *Die Psychoide*. Julius Springer, (Berlin, 1925).

[8] Cf. Brill: "The Universality of Symbols," *Psychoanalytic Review*, January 1943.

[9] Cf. Ernst Haeckel: *Natürliche Schöpfungs-Geschichte*, p. 300, (Berlin, 1898).

copulative organs, which became increasingly more specified from the amphibians, to the reptiles and birds, culminating in the cloacal mammals. Thus the ornithorhynchus, not only forms the gateway between three great animal families but is also the first mammal to show a rudimentary penis, a pipe for the passage of semen only and which, like the vagina, evolved directly from the anus.

Bearing in mind all the long and gradual evolution of the pre-destined erogenous zones of *homo sapiens*, it should not be hard to understand why the anal functions now endowed with aversion, are nevertheless also sometimes pleasurable. This, as we said before, is quite evident in the child, and, whereas grown-ups react outwardly with disgust to these anal functions, some of the lower strata of society seem to enjoy them. This is readily confirmed by some of the customs and proverbs of primitives and modern peoples. The Egyptians and Romans revered among their deities also a *Deus Crepitus* and the French and Italians who are quite frank about their instinctive activities possess many proverbs about *l'art de peter*. Thus Zola in his "La Terre" describes a contest of wind-breaking by peasants, and who would now think that in serious minded old England, it was once the duty of a vassal to do before his king every New Year *unum saltum, unum sufflatum, et unum bumbulum*.[10] To be sure, our cultured present day citizens conceal everything relating to the anal activities, but during analysis some freely admit great interest and pleasure in the anal functions while others show the same through marked reaction formations.[11] Thus many people tarry in water closets as long as possible; some privately admit that they like to read and contemplate there and some even refer to it as the library, all of which confirms the old Latin saying, *Suus cuique crepitus bene olet*.

I could add many additional cases to confirm the fact that it is not too daring to assume that the invitation to kiss or suck one's posterior is a phyletic return of distorted wishes. But as it is only brought to the surface during brawls it may also ex-

[10] Camden, "Brittania," edition of London, 1753, Vol. I, page 444.
[11] Brill: *Freud's Contribution to Psychiatry*, page 142, W. W. Norton (New York, 1944).

press a very old defense reaction which harks back to a time when man was still on the level of his relative, the *mephitis mephitica* or the common skunk. After studying quite a number of patients whose anal-sadism was extremely accentuated, I do not think that this is a groundless conjecture.

Admitting that these assumptions seem hard to accept, they are however amply confirmed by the numerous expressions not seldom heard in the less cultivated classes of our society. Let me cite one such example: my next-door summer neighbors, a very staid and religious family, had often complained to me of their ill-mannered neighbors from across the street. They wondered whether the frequent and noisy outbursts between the husband and wife, which were very annoying, could be stopped. I was slightly acquainted with the head of this vociferous family who was a trainer of prize fighters and who claimed to cure neurotics by exercise, boxing, and wrestling in his gymnasium. I tried to philosophize with my good neighbors about environment and culture in order to help them endure what they could not cure. A fight just then started across the street and as the quarreling between husband and wife rose *in crescendo*, the termagantish wife yelled repeatedly, "I s . . . on you!" My poor neighbors were very embarrassed. I, on the other hand, was very interested because I had never heard this expression before.

It was a good illustration of an outburst of rage which can be often seen and heard in vulgar crowds where control and repression hardly exist. To dispel my kind neighbors' disconcertion, I raised my voice and gave them a dissertation on anal-erotism, and when my neighbors argued that such behavior connoted a very low state of culture, I readily agreed, but I reminded them that even cultured people, when angry, often speak of "raising a stink," or say "it stinks," and that when one talks of a low character, one often calls him a skunk.

I am also thinking of the diarrheas which are regularly associated with attacks of anxiety. It is well known that in such states, the sphincters often relax and sometimes cannot be controlled. Many a soldier suffered more severely from such mishaps than from shrapnel. During school examinations some

[273

students are forced to leave the room and have to be accompanied to the lavatory by an instructor. In such cases one usually thinks that the student wants to cheat, but I have known it to happen to some of the best students where there was no need for cheating. One must not forget the popular expression: "He was so frightened that he defecated in his pants." (I did not use the right word but you all know what I mean.) May not the relaxation of the sphincters represent another ecphoriation of old defensive engrams?

However, let us now leave the nebulous period of man's coming of age and return to the couple whose peculiar behavior stimulated our excursion into phylogeny. After I had listened to his tirade against his mother, I decided to lay bare some of his unconscious behavior to his wife, and I explained to him how he displaced the hatred for his mother to his wife and how his ambivalence to his mother prevented him from leaving his wife despite his conscious dislike for her. I added that I was sure that his wife's behavior was based on similar unconscious determinants but as I did not expect them to come to me for prolonged analysis, I thought that it might improve their relations if he knew that his wife suffered for the sins of his mother. He seemed much impressed by my statements and said: "Doctor, I feel terrible about it and I assure you that I will behave differently in the future."

About a week later he reported that his new attitude seemed very puzzling to his wife. She could not adapt herself to his sudden change and for the last few days she accused him of conspiring against her with two male acquaintances. To atone for his past, he unknowingly over-compensated for it by taking her to nice restaurants and amusements which he had not done for years. One evening they met some acquaintances, and two of the men complimented her on her looks. All this confused her; she could not grasp it and reacted to it with suspicion. She wished to know what he was up to; did he conspire with these men to get her embroiled with them and then divorce her? When he tried to pacify her, he again lost his self-control and the fight between them started *da capo*. In brief, she was so thoroughly conditioned to their pregenital anal-sadism, that she could no longer assimilate any direct object libidinal advances. His changed attitude and the compliments of the men which would have pleased any normal woman, she immediately repressed and distorted into delusions of persecution. Unfortunately this was the last time I heard from this interesting couple. I say unfortunately because there was so much more that one could have learned from this case.

Discussing the evolution and neurotic manifestations of the sadistic components leads us to one of the most fascinating of Freud's theories, namely the death instinct. In his *Beyond the Pleasure Principle* and somewhat later in *The Ego and the Id*,[12] Freud postulated life and death instincts in place of his former sexual and ego instincts. The life or erotic instinct, according to Freud, comprises the inhibited and the uninhibited sexual impulses as well as the instinct of self-preservation, while the death instinct represents the sadistic or destructive components. The function of the life instinct or *Eros* is to produce life by uniting single, living particles or germ cells, while the task of the death instinct is to cause the living organic matter to revert to its former lifeless or inorganic state. The life instinct is by far the more striking and lends itself more readily to investigation. However both instincts strive to reconstruct a disturbed state, which started with the origin of life. They are both active in every living organic matter; the life or erotic instinct naturally predominates. The destructive function of the death instinct however is neutralized by the muscular system. Throughout life the individual exerts his aggression or destructiveness on the outer world, preferably on other living beings.

If we consider the average span of life we can see that childhood is full of energy, full of aggression; the child grasps at everything within reach and if possible, annihilates it by direct destruction or assimilation. Through the self-preservative instinct the child obtains nutrition and in turn new growth through cell multiplication, and when this process becomes retarded or ceases at the age of puberty, the erotic instinct, fus-

[12] Cf. Freud: *Beyond the Pleasure Principle* and *The Ego and the* Id. International Psychoanalytic Publications, London.

ing with the aggressive components produces new life through union with a mating partner. However, as age advances, the death instinct gains the upper hand; the aggressive impulses recede, and the pace of life gradually ebbs away; all action slows up, and the aged man then yearns for peace and calm in a quiet retreat in the country. Mother earth thus draws him back into her bosom.

The two instincts show various fluctuations, now one and now the other predominates; this is especially the case in the neurotics where there sometimes results a complete and sometimes partial separation of the two instincts. The classic example of a seemingly purposeful mixture of the two is the fusion of sadistic and erotic components as ordinarily observed in the sexual behavior of man. On the other hand, the perversion of sadism represents an almost complete separation of the two instincts; this is especially seen in cases of necrophilia.[13] Freud conjectures that the epileptic attack represents a product of marked separation of the two instincts; the same seems true of the various forms of fainting spells. I have case records of female patients whose fainting spells represented a distinct flight from erotic situations. Thus a young woman of 28 fainted frequently while reading novels or witnessing plays or movies. Analysis showed that such collapses invariably occurred at a critical sexual situation, usually a coitus phantasy which the patient could not complete. In male patients this symptom is rare and invariably occurs at the end of an erotic realization. Many neurotics however fear that coitus might hurt them; some are actually afraid that it might kill them, and even so-called normals often assert that the sexual act is debilitating. To be sure, this energetic act is followed by some physiological fatigue which has long ago given rise to the popular view that coitus is harmful. This post-coital depression which, as will be shown later, is an echo of the erstwhile death instinct, manifests itself in modern man in strong feelings of reproach even where there is only the slightest cause for it. Modern human beings have been deeply impressed with the evil of sex but they regu-

[13] Brill: "Necrophilia," l.c.

276

larly forget everything when Eros beckons; later however they feel and act like Goethe's Dr. Faust and Marguerite.

The struggle between the erotic and sadistic instincts is clearly observed throughout life. Thus impotence is conducive to feelings of depression and ideas of suicide. I have known some men who actually attempted to kill themselves because of impotence. This is especially the case in masochistic individuals who turn their sadism on themselves; they react unconsciously to the aggressive influence of a brutal father. On the other hand, the sexually potent man is full of life, he is proud of his sexual prowess and boasts of it; this is especially observed in young men at the beginning of their erotic life. But it is in the psychoses where the struggle between the erotic and destructive instincts is glaringly seen; this is especially the case in involutional melancholias of women. As previously stated, in this malady which Freud designates as the *narcistic neurosis*, the Ego is tortured by the Super-ego and submits to it. The patients invariably complain of many psychosomatic symptoms which are referable to the genitals; their insides are hopelessly diseased; they are entirely destroyed. In the milder forms the patients often express delusions of poverty; they imagine that they are very poor and act like veritable misers.

Investigation indicates that such depression is sometimes preceded by a short erotic episode, as shown by the following case: Mrs. N., aged fifty, had been a childless widow for seventeen years, and except for a short flirtation a few years after her husband's death, she lived a sexually continent life. About five months before she consulted me, she spent a summer vacation with a distant relative, Mrs. G., a widow like herself. As they were both very fond of music they attended regularly the concerts given there by prominent artists and in due time, they both fell in love with the conductor of the orchestra. The whole episode lasted only a few weeks as the hero left, and Mrs. N. never heard from him again. When the two friends later exchanged confidences they discovered to their great chagrin that this man had carried on a secret affair with each of them.

G. got over the experience in a short time, but N. became increasingly depressed over it and gradually developed the clinical picture of involutional melancholia. She accused herself of sexual indiscretions, and although she insisted that she had no coitus with the musician, she could not be convinced by a specialist that she had no venereal diseases. Now and then she became agitated and somewhat confused; she thought that people knew about her "immoralities," and that her friend, the musician, was near by. In brief, as a result of a short sexual experience, there was a sudden flare-up of the erotic instinct, and when it rapidly flickered out, the destructive instinct took possession of her, and she then felt utterly ruined and ready to die. In other words, the insignificant amour aroused in this elderly woman a strong desire to fulfill her hitherto dormant maternity; she was sure that the man wanted to marry her, and she even hoped for a child. There was absolutely no basis for these feelings; they represented the last gasps of maternity so often observed in childless women approaching the menopause.

However the struggle between these two instincts also exists during the menopause of women who had borne children and who are not psychotic; all women show indications of this struggle. They complain of nervousness, they invariably fear that they will lose their feminine attraction, and paradoxical as it may seem, even those who had used contraceptives for decades and went through abortions, bewail the fact that they will no longer be able to bear children. This reaction to menopause which is merely exaggerated in psychotic women clearly expresses the biontic importance of childbearing in the vital economy of women. The delusion of poverty which signifies a loss of libido and the feeling that the inner organs are effete express the reaction of the women of today to their vanishing maternity, and permit the conjecture that this behavior represents an ecphoriation of dim phyletic engrams, harking back to times when the animal died soon after it completed its biontic mission.

I dare say that all emotional depressions in women, be they of the menopause or of the manic depressive variety, are based

278]

on actual or temporary frustration of maternity. Thus many young women become depressed when they are about to be married, when, as one of the patients' mothers put it, "She has everything in the world to live for." All such cases studied by me disclosed that the depression was preceded by a long period of courtship with marked erotic excitement but without any adequate outlet, so that the forthcoming marriage could be looked upon as an anticlimax to an over-satiation rather than an anticipated realization of a maternal fulfillment. The patients behaved as if they had exhausted their erotic functions and were ready to die like their distantly related insect and fish sisters who perish soon after they have performed their maternal task. The same situation seems to prevail in these puerpural psychoses where the patient repeats that she has no maternal feeling for the newborn child and that she cannot tolerate the husband. But unlike the menopause psychotics, the puerpural as well as the depressive patients of the manic-depressive variety suffer from a temporary maternal exhaustion which usually disappears in time.

In view of these findings I wish to stress the following points: first, that the thanatic or sadistic instinct takes possession of women when their life or erotic instinct is temporarily or permanently checked, and secondly that the reaction which they evince to this change is *mutatis mutandis* of the same nature as that observed in the lower species of animals which die soon after they have actually completed their maternal task. The day-flies die soon after mating, after the female drops her fertilized eggs into the river, and Williamson [14] tells us that soon after the salmon's milt flowed from him in a mist containing millions of organisms which strive to bore into the eggs deposited by the female, he is killed by a vegetable fungus.

In other words, the life instinct having fulfilled its function to unite and multiply, the death instinct takes possession of the organism and leads it back to the inorganic. For the character of the instincts, perhaps of all organic life, is, according to Freud, *an urge innate in living organic matter toward the re-*

[14] Cf. Henry Williamson: *Salar the Salmon.* Little Brown & Co., p. 283, 1938.

instatement of an earlier state, which this living organic matter had to give up under the influence of external disturbing forces.[15] But what seems to be a very simple process in the lower organisms is expressed in a rather distorted manner in the menopause psychotic. This is not only due to the physiologic evolution of the reproductive centers from the lower species to man, but also to the sexual trends of Western civilization in historical times. We must not forget that our modern women find it difficult to give free expression to any phase of sex; as I have mentioned previously they have to express in symbols what was formerly expressed frankly without any shame and distortion. The barren Rachel said to Jacob, "Give me children else I die," and Magnus Hirschfeld in his *Die Weltreise eines Sexualforschers* [16] tells us that in Bombay he was besieged by women from morning till night; they did not seek advice as to how to prevent pregnancy but rather how to insure conception. It is modern prudishness and sex repression which cause our women to express their grief for the loss of maternity in depressive delusions and other hidden mechanisms.

The close relationship between life and death has always been known and described by those who are interested in nature. Havelock Ellis, than whom there are few greater authorities on sex, states: "Over a large part of nature, as has been truly said, but a thin veil divides love from death." In Constantine Weyer's book *A Man Scans His Past*, the hero describes his wife's behavior during coitus in the following words: "She evinces this yearning for annihilation even during our embraces. I had noticed how she closed her eyes, certainly forgetting my existence, forgetting her own existence too, more possessed by a desire for annihilation than by an exaltation of life. I remember the great lesson the forest vouchsafed me, that ceaseless reiteration of the truth that life is by nature a sublime and tragic mixture of pain and pleasure, or if you prefer it, of love and death." This quotation from a layman not only con-

---

[15] Cf. Brill: *Freud's Contribution to Psychiatry*, p. 223. W. W. Norton (New York, 1944).

[16] English title: *Men and Women*, G. P. Putnam, New York.

firms Freud's speculative theory but also our view that in the very beginning of her maternal fulfillment, during the act of conception, the human female reproduces, or mnemically speaking, ecphoriates experiences of that phyletic period when the coital act was the beginning of the end, when it, so to speak, ushered in death.

I have often heard from men that during coitus, especially during the orgasm, some women utter such exclamations as "Oh, I am dying," or "You are killing me," or "Kill me," which they cannot explain in cold blood. May we not conceive these mystical exclamations as mnemic expressions of situations which actually existed in, say Paleozoic times, and which we still observe in some organisms? I believe that we are justified to assume this. Moreover the thin veil between life and death can be clearly observed in some psychotic disturbances as well as in the life of sensitive individuals who have left records of their feelings. Elsewhere I have reported some cases which glaringly demonstrate that before the erotic components become subordinated to the primacy of the genitals, that is, prior to object-finding, the individual is largely dominated by sadistic or aggressive impulses.[17] As a matter of fact our whole social existence is considerably influenced by them; witness for example, the important role played by athletics in our schools and colleges.

Educators have long known that every student must be taught to regulate and sublimate his innate aggression and that it is a sign of good health if he participates in some form of athletics directly or vicariously. Most college students of the neurotic type are rarely interested in athletics; some of them feel physically unfit to participate in games of competition. This is clearly seen in the life history of some of our outstanding poets. One of the most expressive idealizations of death and resignation to it is *Thanatopsis*, which was produced by William Cullen Bryant when he was barely seventeen. Some like Goethe, Byron, Shelley, Keats, and particularly Pope and Swift, have been obsessed by the thanatic instinct in early life.

[17] Brill: "The Death Instinct in Relation to Normal and Abnormal Life" *Medical Leaves*, p. 14, (Chicago, 1937).

The latter two never could stop occupying themselves with the oral-anal-sadistic components. In brief, it seems certain that in order to develop a normal psychosexual life the individual must master his aggression through direct albeit regulated outlets or through sublimation. In other words, to the oft repeated statement, that to be healthy one must attain genitality and find a love object, we must add that the *sine qua non* of such psychosexual development is a mastery of the death instinct by Eros.

I do not think that it is premature to suggest that these principles should be taken into consideration in the education of every child, especially the boy. If for some reasons, physical or mental, the little boy shows abnormal traits in that regard during his autoerotic and narcistic phases of development, means should be taken to correct them. For not all boys so afflicted develop just a neurosis, some may become perverts in which case they are not only burdens to themselves but menaces to society. Every perversion I have studied was instigated by some physical or emotional frustrations during early childhood, which could have been corrected through education.[18]

I have already spoken about Freud's concepts of the neuroses from the point of view of the *Ego Id* and *Super-ego*.[19] Let us now consider the neuroses and psychoses in terms of the life and death instincts. If you recall any of the cases of transference neuroses described above, you will readily admit that these patients evince a struggle between the life and death instincts. The hysterical patients invariably try hard to retrieve through the symptoms what was denied them by civilization. The erotic or life instinct strives hard to assert itself, and it is this factor which accounts for the difficulties in the management of the transference phenomena. The patients seem bent on attaching their floating libido to anyone who comes in contact with them, as shown by their rapid but transient responses

---

[18] The magnitude of this problem can hardly be appreciated by ordinary parents and educators who pay little attention to the early lives of such personages as Caligula or Hitler.

[19] Cf. Lecture IV.

to any form of treatment whether administered by well-trained physicians or by quacks.

On the other hand, the compulsive neurotic shows the struggle between life and death more noticeably. The patient continually battles, as it were, with his father whose love he craves but whose aggressive rivalry he cannot tolerate. Through defense reactions in the form of phobias, doubts, and obsessions he tries to adjust his love and hatred, and although the erotic components are present, they are neither as direct nor as forceful as in hysteria; the hate motif invariably preponderates in every compulsion neurosis.

Schizophrenia is always ushered·in by a severe battle between the life and death instincts in which the life instinct barely maintains itself. The patient usually survives the struggle, but both instincts lose in the affray. To all intents and purposes the patient is dead to his former world, and now lives in a new world which he constructed in his phantasy. Anyone observing the various stages of schizophrenic development cannot fail to see how the patient gradually turns away from reality until he is entirely separated from it.

In the paranoiac, the erotic instinct is desexualized and turned back to the Ego to the extent that the patient sometimes feels even greater than God, but he is in constant conflict with the outer world. The paranoiac is constantly dominated by anal-sadistic or thanatic impulses.

It is however in the manic-depressive forms of psychoses where the struggle between the life and death instincts are most prominently displayed. As shown above, every depression represents either a temporary or permanent victory of the destructive over the erotic impulses. The self-torture of melancholiacs undoubtedly conceals something of the erotic and in this respect resembles the phenomena of compulsion neurosis, but in most cases of melancholia the death instinct colors the whole picture. Moreover, the gratification in both melancholia and compulsion neurosis is based on sadistic tendencies which belong to an outside object which have been turned on one's own person, and in both maladies the patients often succeed in taking revenge on the original object by the

[283

indirect path of self-punishment. But what is most remarkable in melancholia is its tendency to change into mania; this often occurs after an unsuccessful attempt at suicide or vicariously by identification.[20] I am tempted to enter more deeply into the subject, but as I have discussed this elsewhere, I merely wish to state that in the light of the life and death instincts, the manic attacks especially those alternating with depression may be conceived as forms of rebirth.

In summing up I wish to repeat that psychiatry was a barren subject at the turn of this century, and although other investigators, notably Adolf Meyer, have contributed much towards changing its scope and activities, its present status, its present configurations were molded by Freud's psychoanalysis. Freud himself called psychoanalysis, "a child of the twentieth century," because the book with which he introduced it into the world as something new, *The Interpretation of Dreams*, was published in 1900. "He who understands dreams," said the Master, "can also fathom the psychic mechanisms of the neuroses and psychoses." I did not give much time to interpretation of dreams in these lectures because experience has taught me that a smattering of this profound subject is likely to produce more confusion than enlightment. *The Interpretation of Dreams* is Freud's greatest production; its influence on the allied mental sciences, on psychology, sociology, pedagogics, anthropology, and literature can hardly be estimated. It requires more than ten hours to master the subject of dreams. I strove however to impress upon you the principle of *psychogenesis* which was first utilized by Breuer in his case of Anna O.[21] and later perfected by Freud in his analysis of dreams. Every dream, no matter how senseless it sounds, has a definite meaning when analyzed by the methods of free associations and interpretation. And as the dream is a phenomenon of normal psychic activity, one is justified in concluding that psychoanalysis is not only useful in the investigation of psychopathology but also of normal mental processes.

[20] Brill: *Freud's Contribution to Psychiatry*, p. 173, W. W. Norton (New York, 1944).

[21] Breuer and Freud: *Studies in Hysteria*, p. 14, Translated by A. A. Brill, (New York, 1936).

I have given examples of mild psychopathological acts designated commonly as slips or mistakes in everyday life to show that there is no line of demarcation between normal and abnormal psychic expressions. The common jokes which are utilized in every civilized corner of this earth to convey, in a hidden and distorted manner, ideas which are ordinarily tabooed show the same construction as dreams and the most phantastic neurotic or psychotic symptoms. The same is true of myths of antiquity as well as of those which originate in our own times.[22] In brief, I cannot emphasize too much that there are direct paths from the most sensible to the most grotesque mental productions and that the psychotic distortions can always be traced back to logical concatenations of the patient's pre-psychotic life.

The reason why great psychiatrists like Kraepelin, Wernicke, and others could do nothing better than describe and classify symptoms, is that they considered the psychotic person as something *sui generis*, as a being entirely different from the normal; they paid no attention to the unconscious forces, to the *vis a tergo* of human behavior. Nowadays it would seem strange to ignore the love or sex life of patients to which the older psychiatrists gave no thought; indeed they deliberately steered clear of anything savoring of sex. I recall a patient who was examined by Kraepelin and other prominent psychiatrists; none of them investigated her marital life which she tried hard to bring to their attention. Kraepelin diagnosed the case in 1914, as a manic-depressive psychosis and told her there was nothing that he could do but put her to bed and give her medication until her depression subsided. I saw the patient a few months later, and whereas I agreed with Kraepelin's diagnosis in a general way, I still wondered why her former short moods increased in frequency and severity since her marriage, which as far as one could judge by questioning the patient, was perfectly good. I soon found however that the patient led a very inadequate sexual life, that despite years of marriage she could still be called a virgin. It was this sexual inadequacy which

[22] Brill: "The Universality of Symbols," the *Psychoanalytic Review*, January 1943.

added anxiety to the pre-existing moods and thus produced a picture of anxious depression. There were a few other psychoneurotic symptoms which had existed since the patient's childhood and formed part of the morbid picture.

I saw the patient regularly and taught her how to adjust her sexual life by giving her advice which she could have gotten from any physician versed in the rudiments of sex. The anxiety soon disappeared, and when the other symptoms were removed by analysis, there remained only her innate syntonic personality which has served her in good stead as a useful public spirited citizen now for about thirty years. Yet Kraepelin was a great psychiatrist to whom we are greatly indebted. The time has long passed since neurologists and antiquated psychiatrists made sport of Freud's sexual theories; some of them now question their patients about sex and dreams: that is all they can do, just question, for they know very little about these vital problems. Some of them now place their last refuge in little inexpensive machines which transiently electrocute these enigmatic and annoying patients, while others go them one better: they gouge out a part of the patient's brain and thus make an apathetic, partially decapitated being out of an intact personality.[23]

I have stressed the sexual factor in the neuroses, which I consider one of Freud's greatest contributions to psychopathology, with the hope that, even if your psychoanalytic studies proceed no further than this course of lectures, you will retain your interest in this most important part of biology. A knowledge of sex must be presupposed in every seriousminded psychiatrist, for besides its role in the neuroses, sex also plays a leading part in our normal everyday life. As a matter of fact, sex became a problem with the very beginning of civilization, and the more man progressed culturally, the more difficulties he encountered in his sexual adjustment. I need not repeat that sexual dichotomies are at the bottom of all neuroses. It is significant that the word sex stems from *secare*, to cut, which also gives origin to the word, segment, a part of a circle.

[23] Jellife: "Some Notes on Parathyroid Disfunction," *Medical Record*, December 1942.

This theme runs through the creation legends of the Jews, the Greeks, the Hindus, the Persians, and even of some of the primitives. And as I have already called your attention to some paleopsychological vestiges still discernible in present day life, I feel that it is worthwhile to examine another phenomenon of this nature, namely sex dichotomies as we meet them in mythology and in the neuroses.

The principal sagas of creation assume that originally the human being was hermaphroditic or bisexual. Thus in Plato's *Symposium*, Aristophanes explains the nature of love and sex by stating that in the beginning instead of two sexes there was a third one which possessed everything that was common to both. It was however a double being, with two heads, four arms, four legs, four ears, four eyes, and the genitals of both sexes. These androgynes, filled with pride, attempted to scale the heavens, and the gods, fearing their might, wished to kill them all. Zeus however decided to punish their temerity but not to destroy them. He thereupon cut each androgyne asunder "just as one cuts fruit for pickling." Aristophanes goes on to tell how after this double being was cut in two, Apollo twisted each head around towards the severed portion and sewed the skin together and molded them into separate beings. But after they had thus been parted, each yearned for the other half, and when they met they threw their arms around each other and clung together craving to grow together into one. Their desire for unity was such that they remained in this position until they died of disease or starvation. But Zeus taking pity on them turned their genitals, which hitherto hung from their back, to the front so that when they clung together they could now reproduce themselves through genital union, instead of reproducing themselves "in the earth like cicadas."

This Greek myth is repeated with some modification by others. Thus Ovid (*Metamorphoses*) states that Hermaphrodite the son of Aphrodite and Hermes was courted by the nymph, Salamacis when he was only fifteen, and although he repulsed her, she succeeded in embracing him. She then prayed to the gods to unite him to her forever, and this resulted in a being half male and half female.

[287]

Similar myths are also found among the Hindus, Persians, and Jews. The Rabbis indulged in much speculation on the passages in Genesis "He called *their* name *Adam*," and "And God created man in his own image, male and female created he *them*." Many notable Rabbis interpreted these passages to mean that the first being was double—Adam and Lilith, who were then cut asunder. Through all these myths, there prevails an intense desire for reunion of the separate beings.

A myth like a fairy tale is a condensation or fusion of prehistoric events through which, as it were, eternity speaks. The Greek myth previously cited, richer in detail than similar creation myths, lends itself more readily to analysis, or rather speculation, than the others. The most interesting part of it is the androgyne, which naturally brings to mind hermaphrodism as it is seen in almost all classes of the animal kingdom. We know that bisexuality exists side by side with gonochorism or sex differentiation in the lower animal species, and not seldom also in the highest animal kingdoms. To be sure, physical hermaphrodism was long known to many investigators, and since Freud much light has also been thrown on psychic hermaphrodism.[24] Every human being shows some psychic attributes of the other sex and some male inverts feel that they have "a female brain in a male body." A translation of the mythical androgyne and his fate directed by Zeus into present-day biology readily suggests—distortions aside—the whole human phylogeny. Thus his mode of locomotion by means of eight extremities and his reproduction in the earth like cicadas readily suggests the insect world. His bisexuality recalls some fish, amphibia, mollusks, and other animals of the hermaphroditic type. The location of the genitals posteriorly in the androgyne suggests the earliest mode of copulation which undoubtedly was that of prehistoric man. Turning the genitals anteriorly to make possible genital union suggests the most important advance in phyletic evolution of man. Face-to-face coitus started when man assumed an erect posture, when the sense of sight took the place of the sense of smell. Instead of nuzzling her like the bull, stallion, and other mammals, man

[24] Cf. *Freud's Basic Writings* l.c. p. 554.

then looked upon the love object and said, "She is charming, she is beautiful." The abrogation of the sense of smell thus marks the beginning of the mechanism of "displacement from below to above," as well as the development of our esthetic sense, which is also only a displacement from below to above.

But to continue with our speculation about the striving for unity of the severed androgyne, it would be necessary to follow the stages of development of the lower forms of life, from the protozoa to the highest metazoa for which the average psychiatrist has neither the education nor the time. I ventured into these speculations because it seems the dichotomies which we find in the neuroses suggest atavistic regressions to early forms of development.

Only about a week ago I saw a young man who claimed to have a body odor which isolated him from his fellow beings. It was simple enough to diagnose him as a schizophrenic with hallucinations of smell, but if we consider this symptom as "a negative of the perversion" in the sense of our previous discussion, we would say that he struggled with a failure in the repression of the oldest sense or that he strove to impress his fellow being through his bodily odor in the same manner as those mammals from which he is now separated by the longest gap of cultural evolution. But such anomalies or mutations, if you prefer, are not seldom met in psychiatry. Dr. Henry Raphael Gold had recently called my attention to a patient at Bellevue Hospital who utilized spitting in the manner of the big cats. She was at least of average intelligence but during her primitive outbursts she frequently resorted to snarling and spitting like a veritable tigress. She warned me not to stand too near lest she suddenly sprayed me with her spit; she said that she entertained a high regard for me but feared she could not control herself. This behaviour too seemed to connote some phyletic regression which the many psychiatrists who had studied her made no attempt to explain; they were mainly interested in diagnosing the case. Such strange behavior even in psychotics must hark back to something deeply buried, to something that could be construed as mnemic in Bleuler's sense, and justifies the assumption that ontogeny is not only an embryonic repetition of phylogeny, but that it also continues in distorted ways some of the most primitive subhuman traits of the species. The case of the lightning calculator reported by me, as well as some peculiar manifestations among so-called normals seem to favor such assumption.[25]

Only recently I heard that high society now dances *a posteriore*, instead of face to face; the male is behind the female, holding her tightly around the breasts. Whoever originated this form of dancing must have been instigated to it by special motives, probably unconscious ones, but the fact that the other ladies and gentlemen enthusiastically adopted it indicates that it awakened dormant tendencies, in a manner similar to those of the starling reported before.[26] For dancing is nothing but conventionalized motion pleasure.[27]

An instinctual outlet cannot be annihilated; at best it can only be controlled and modified, but now and then it reasserts itself in its original form. Most of our popular jokes have always revolved around sex; the theme naturally depended on some particular situation of the times. Thus in the beginning of the monastic systems, when licentiousness was struggling with mysticism, nuns and monks were the objects of smutty jokes and witty stories. Giovanni Boccaccio, "the greatest of modern story tellers," makes them the heroes and heroines of his *Decameron*, and his two most popular stories, *Il diavolo nel inferno* and *Non vi voglio coda*, which became Italian proverbs, revolve around a monk and a priest respectively. As was said earlier, through wit civilized man expresses in devious words what he cannot do frankly, and as monks and nuns renounced all sex and repaired to the desert to be freed from temptation, it was only natural that they should be lampooned by those who suffered from sex burdens. It is strange however that a similar joke should have come to light within recent years, which in setting and content resembles Boccaccio's stories. Wherever I heard it, I am quite sure that it evoked the same

[25] Brill: *Some Peculiar Manifestations of Memory*, l.c.
[26] Brill: Lecture III.
[27] Brill: "The Psychopathology of the New Dances," l.c.

reaction as Boccaccio's in the fourteenth century. As a matter of interest it runs as follows:

There was a flourishing monastery in the African desert headed by a miracle-working abbot. Because of the extreme heat and isolation a broad-brimmed hat was all that the monks were in the habit of wearing. Everything went well until the nuns, emulating the monks, decided to leave the cities and move their convents to the desert. One hot morning the miracle-working abbot walking alone espied two strange forms in the distance, and as they came nearer, he discerned to his dismay two nuns walking towards him. In his dilemma, he quickly put his large straw hat in front of him and stood as if petrified. But when the two nuns suddenly recognized the saintly abbot, they fell on their knees and one grasped his right hand and the other his left hand and kissed it. But true to his reputation the hat remained where he had placed it; that was the miracle.

I heard this joke first at a dinner party of physicians, and subsequently in equally cultured but different circles, and each time there was explosive laughter. Having been forced to substitute jokes for those given by Freud which could not be translated into English, I got into the habit of analyzing every good joke I hear. There was no doubt about the quality of the wit in this story; it registered one thousand on the "laughmeter" whenever it was told. The reaction was very hearty the moment the nuns grasped the abbot's hands, and this explosion increased with the mention of the miracle. Without going into a deep analysis of this delightful story, we can say that we deal here with tendency wit, the intention of which is to render prominent sexual or hostile facts through speech. This story strives to expose people who ordinarily shy away from everything sexual—people who by comparison make ordinary mortals feel unchaste and inferior. The naïveté of the nuns in the story and the miracle of the pendant hat make us laugh in the same manner as young men rejoice at the discomfiture of their fathers and teachers to whom we ordinarily look for guidance. The story is not only sexually exhibitionistic but it also serves a hostile tendency, as if to say, "the more you try to run away from sex the more it catches up with you." And as one of my students remarked, "It only demonstrates that even a saintly abbot cannot remain sexually indifferent when women kiss his hands."

Fundamentally however, this joke is a good illustration of the urge towards the reinstatement of a bygone time before civilization had made inroads on mortal man. Sexual taboos appeared with the dawn of civilization and reached their greatest height with the development of the monastic system which enjoins upon its members to abjure their whole erotic life. It was easy enough for Moses to command in the name of Jehovah not to commit adultery and for Jesus even to surpass it with his dictum: "Whosoever looketh on a woman to lust after her, hath committed adultery with her already in his heart," but the average individual can hardly live up to such ideals; at best his efforts produce a breach in his personality which he finds hard to control. Like the mythical androgyne he seeks forever to become united to his other, perhaps better, half, and it is this inexorable struggle for union which constitutes the play of forces in life and in the neuroses.

INDEX

i]

Index

[ii

Index

Index

v]

Index

Index

Index

Index

[x

Index

Index

A NOTE ON THE TYPE IN WHICH
THIS BOOK IS SET

This book was set on the Linotype in Janson, a recutting made direct from the type cast from matrices made by Anton Janson some time between 1660 and 1687.

Of Janson's origin nothing is known. He may have been a relative of Justus Janson, a printer of Danish birth who practised in Leipzig from 1614 to 1635. Some time between 1657 and 1668 Anton Janson, a punch-cutter and type-founder, bought from the Leipzig printer Johann Erich Hahn the type-foundry which had formerly been a part of the printing house of M. Friedrich Lankisch. Janson's types were first shown in a specimen sheet issued at Leipzig about 1675. Janson's successor, and perhaps his son-in-law, Johann Karl Edling, issued a specimen sheet of Janson types in 1689. His heirs sold the Janson matrices in Holland to Wolffgang Dietrich Erhardt, of Leipzig.

The book was composed, printed, and bound by The Kingsport Press, Kingsport, Tennessee. Typography by James Hendrickson.